INTERSCIENCE MONOGRAPHS ON CHEMISTRY

Inorganic Chemistry Section

EDITOR: F. Albert Cotton

VOLUME I

Interscience Monographs on Chemistry

INORGANIC CHEMISTRY SECTION

Edited by F. Albert Cotton
Massachusetts Institute of Technology
Cambridge, Massachusetts

ORGANIC CHEMISTRY SECTION

Edited by George A. Olah
Dow Chemical Company
Sarnia, Ontario, Canada

PHYSICAL CHEMISTRY SECTION

Edited by I. Prigogine
Université Libre
Brussels, Belgium

Magnetism and the Chemical Bond

BY JOHN B. GOODENOUGH

LINCOLN LABORATORY
MASSACHUSETTS INSTITUTE OF TECHNOLOGY
CAMBRIDGE, MASSACHUSETTS

INTERSCIENCE PUBLISHERS

a division of JOHN WILEY & SONS

New York · London · Sydney

Library of Congress Catalog Card Number 62-22257
Printed in the United States of America

In gratitude to my Irene

Editor's Introduction

It seems appropriate to say a few words concerning the genesis of this volume. Several years ago I asked Dr. Goodenough to write an account for "Progress in Inorganic Chemistry" of the current position of research into the magnetic interactions of transition metal ions in their solid compounds, most especially their oxides and mixed oxides. These compounds have been intensively studied in recent years in order to elucidate the relationship between structure, bonding and magnetic properties both because of the intrinsic interest of the subject and because of the extraordinary technological potentialities of such materials. In this work Dr. Goodenough has played a prominent role, and he acceded to my request.

To the surprise of both of us, the "article" had grown to the length of a book when appropriate theoretical preliminaries and a comprehensive coverage of the subject matter *per se* were completed. Under the circumstances, it seemed only logical to issue it as a separate volume.

Moreover, since there exists the distinct possibility that a similar situation may arise in the future, the editor and the publishers have decided formally to initiate, with this volume, a series of monographs on Inorganic Chemistry. This Inorganic Chemistry Section of the Interscience Monographs on Chemistry will be available to all future authors whose "articles" grow, in the course of writing, into books.

F. A. Cotton

Preface

This book was originally intended as a review chapter, and this fact has strongly influenced the organization of the material. For example, there is no formal development of the various physical concepts that are introduced. Rather, emphasis is placed on a physical description of these concepts, and the analytic formalism is only summarized or referenced. Since the number of concepts that must be introduced is quite large, even for the treatment of so limited a topic, it is feared that some of them have been introduced too abruptly, as though arbitrarily invoked to explain some isolated phenomenon. This failing is more apparent than real. The fact is that the existence of several competitive factors gives rise to a rich variety of physical manifestations, and emphasis has been placed on the interpretation of this richness in terms of defined factors that appear to operate in a similar manner over the whole range of crystalline materials, from ionic insulators to metals. The hope is that these interpretations not only support some of the extrapolations that are asserted, but also will provide the chemist with a physical intuition that can be fruitful for the design of materials with specified characteristics.

It is a great pleasure to acknowledge that happy association with the colleagues of my group that is the intangible background from which this book has emerged. I am particularly indebted to my associations with R. J. Arnott, K. Dwight, T. A. Kaplan, N. Menyuk, D. G. Wickham, and A. Wold. Special thanks are also due Mrs. Jean Craig who has patiently typed the various drafts and corrections.

JOHN B. GOODENOUGH

Lincoln Laboratory*
Massachusetts Institute of Technology
Cambridge, Mass.

* Lincoln Laboratory, Massachusetts Institute of Technology, is operated with support from the U.S. Army, Navy, and Air Force.

Contents

Introduction

During the last fifteen years, there have been an increasing number of studies concerned with the origins of atomic moments and of magnetic order in solids. An understanding of these two things should provide important foundation stones on which a theoretical superstructure for inorganic chemistry can be built, because such an understanding requires an adequate description of the atomic outer electrons after the atoms have been brought together to form a solid. The following pages are intended to provide an extensive, though not exhaustive, review for chemists of our knowledge as of 1961 in this rapidly developing field. Although the lack of an established and developed theoretical framework would appear to doom such an undertaking to a catalogue of isolated facts, it is shown that a relatively simple set of physical ideas do emerge from present theory to unify a great diversity of experimental findings into a coherent unit.

Heisenberg's 1928 formulation of a many-body exchange Hamiltonian for the coupling energy of a system of atomic spins has served as a great divide for theoretical studies. On the one hand the expression has been accepted and effectively used to interpret the varieties of magnetic order that have been encountered experimentally; on the other it has inspired many attempts at justification from the first principles of quantum mechanics. Immediate contact was made between the Heisenberg expression and the classical, molecular-field formalism for ferromagnetism introduced by Weiss in 1907, a formalism that was generalized in 1948 by Néel to two-sublattice structures to provide an interpretation of antiferromagnetism and ferrimagnetism. Further generalization to six independent sublattices was made in 1952 by Yafet and Kittel, who first introduced the possibility of noncollinear spin configurations. However, it was not until 1960 that Lyons and Kaplan showed how the many-body problem can, in many instances, be rigorously treated to give the true ground state of a system of 10^{23} spins. It is now possible to formulate a connection between the exchange Hamiltonian, especially if generalized to include exchange and crystalline anisotropies, and the variety of magnetic orderings that have been observed with neutron diffraction. Besides collinear ferromagnetism, antiferromagnetism, and ferrimagnetism, these include antiferromagnetic, ferrimagnetic, and ferromagnetic spirals, canted spins that give rise to parasitic ferromagnetism in antiferromagnets, partial magnetic ordering that results in a sinusoidal variation of the z-component of magnetization but no order in the basal plane, and various triangular-spin configurations. The basic theory of spin configurations that has been derived from the Heisenberg exchange Hamiltonian is outlined in Chapter II, and reference to the literature is given for those cases where extension of the Hamiltonian to include exchange and crystalline anisotropies is necessary. Application of the theory to paramagnetism and the relationship of experimental parameters to the strength of the coupling between near neighbors is also given in this section. Because the strength of this exchange coupling drops off rapidly with interatomic separation, it is only necessary to consider near-neighbor, next-near-neighbor, and next-next-near-neighbor interactions. Thus experimental contact with the fundamental phenomenological parameters of the exchange-Hamiltonian formalism is possible, so that the stage is set for experimental verification or rejection of the theoretical attempts to justify these parameters from first principles.

A theoretical justification from first principles of these coupling parameters and of the magnitudes of the individual atomic moments requires a profound understanding of the nature of the chemical bond in inorganic solids. This problem is therefore of paramount interest for the chemist. In Chapter I are introduced the basic theoretical concepts on which our formal descriptions of the outer electrons are built. First, there is the description of the free atom. With no coupling between atoms, this gives the magnitude of the atomic moment and connection with paramagnetic susceptibilities, which permit measurement of these moments. Then there is the description of the electrons after the atoms have been brought together to form a crystallographic array. Traditionally, such descriptions have proven successful for two limiting cases: $R \approx R_0$ and $R \gg R_0$, where R is the interatomic separation and R_0 is the optimum-bonding separation for the outer electrons in question. For $R \approx R_0$, the outer electrons are collective, belonging to the lattice as a whole. The symmetry of the lattice is introduced through the Bragg scattering conditions for the running electron waves. The principal results of band theory that these conditions provide are summarized. Unfortunately, a rigorous solution of the many-body problem has not been achieved, so that drastic simplifications are introduced into any formalism that would start from first principles. The principal assumptions that become more serious with increasing atomic separation are pointed out. For $R \gg R_0$, the outer electrons are localized. The symmetry of the lattice is introduced in this case through the crystalline electric fields that perturb the atomic states. A summary of the assumptions and results of crystal-field theory for one and two outer $3d$ electrons is also given in Chapter I. Finally, there is an estimate of the interatomic separation R_c at which a collective-electron description of the $3d$ electrons must change to a localized-electron description. It is shown that for transition-metal compounds the interatomic spacing is frequently great enough for a localized description to suffice, but that in many cases (especially in metals and alloys) a collective-electron description that avoids the drastic simplifications of conventional band theory is required. It is also pointed out that the anisotropy of the $3d$ wave functions may permit the simultaneous existence of localized and collective $3d$ states.

For transition-metal atoms, the coupling between atomic moments is due to the interactions of the outer d electrons on neighboring atoms. This is in contrast to the couplings of the $4f$-electron atomic moments of the rare-earth atoms, which interact primarily through intermediary electrons either of a conduction band or of an intermediate anion. The problem of $4f$-electron coupling is of lesser significance for chemical bonding, and it is omitted from the present discussion. Discussions of magnetostriction and crystalline anisotropy, though relevant, are also considered of secondary importance for the chemical bond and are omitted.

In Chapter III the basic physical ideas inherent in these theories are applied to the transition metals and their compounds and alloys. These applications are separated into three main categories: materials with $R > R_c$, those with $R \approx R_c$, and those with $R < R_c$. Materials of the first category have atomic moments that follow from crystal-field theory and magnetic couplings that can be described by the sum of various superexchange contributions. The physical bases for the superexchange mechanisms are discussed, and the results of the formalism are presented without derivation. This leads to the tabulation of a few coupling rules that are immediately applicable to the experimental findings. The existence of electron-ordering transformations below the melting point permit some dramatic correlations of crystallographic structure with magnetic order. For $R \approx R_c$, the crystal-field splittings are large compared to the band-width of the collective-electron states, which is sufficiently narrow that for high T the atomic moments approach a localized-electron value. At lower temperatures crystallographic transformations that make $R < R_c$ are common. Spin-pairing in homopolar, $R < R_c$ bonds tends to quench any contribution to the atomic moments from these collective electrons. Interpretation of the atomic moments and the magnetic couplings between them is found possible for the case of $R < R_c$ near-neighbor-directed $3d$ electrons provided the superexchange rules for $R > R_c$ electrons are extrapolated to apply to the electron-spin correlations within the collective-electron states. Inability to introduce these correlations into the theoretical formalism plagues a rigorous description of the collective electrons, but investigation of magnetic order and atomic moments now appears to provide a direct indication of the nature of the spin correlations that stabilize the chemical bond. Thus the physical mechanisms responsible for stabilizing the spins of localized electrons into an ordered array appear to be identical to those responsible for electron-correlation stabilizations of narrow-band collective electrons. This fact at once provides both a fact that must be included in any rigorous formalism and a common theme for the interpretation of the atomic moments and magnetic order found in transition metals and their compounds and alloys. It is for this reason that considerable space is given to a variety of specific compounds that illustrate the application of these concepts to complex as well as to simple situations.

CHAPTER I

Descriptions of Outer Electrons: General

Of the many aspects of magnetism that are encountered in inorganic solids, this volume is concerned only with the magnitudes of the individual atomic, or ionic, moments and the cooperative couplings between them. After a brief review of the origins of the atomic moments of the free atoms, consideration is given to the influence of chemical bonding on the magnitude of these moments and on the strength and character of their interactions. This requires a description of the electrons that are outside of closed shells, and measurements of atomic moments and their ordering provide an important check for these descriptions.

I. Description of the Free Atom

A. THE HYDROGEN ATOM

Any description of the free atom begins with the Schroedinger wave equation for a single electron in the field of a positive point charge $+Ze$:

$$\nabla^2 \psi + \frac{2\mu_r}{\hbar^2} \left(E + \frac{Ze^2}{r} \right) \psi = 0 \tag{1}$$

$\mu_r = mM/(m + M)$ is the reduced mass of the electron and nucleus, $-e$ is the charge on an electron, and $h = 2\pi\hbar$ is Planck's constant. For bound states, i.e. $E < 0$, this equation has the well-known solution (194)

$$\psi_{nlm_l} = f(\rho)P_l^{|m_l|}(\cos\theta)\exp\left[im_l\phi\right] \tag{2}$$

where the radial part of the wave function contains the Laguerre polynomials

$$f(\rho) = Ce^{-\rho}(2\rho)^l L_{n+l}^{2l+1}(2\rho) \qquad \rho = \frac{Z}{n}\left(\frac{r}{a_H}\right)$$

and the integers n, l, m_l are known as the principal, angular-momentum, and magnetic quantum numbers, respectively. The integer m_l has $2l + 1$ possible values (from $-l$ to $+l$) and the integer l is confined to the interval $0 \leq l \leq n - 1$. Related to the Uncertainty Principle is the Bohr expression for the product of the momentum and radius of a classically orbiting electron:

$$pr = n\hbar \tag{3}$$

For an equilibrium classical orbit, the attractive electrostatic force must equal the centrifugal force, or

$$\frac{Ze^2}{r^2} = \frac{p^2}{mr} \tag{4}$$

Combination of equations 3 and 4 gives the classical Bohr orbits

$$r_n(\text{Bohr}) = n^2(a_H/Z) \qquad a_H = \hbar^2/me^2 = 0.53 \text{ A} \tag{5}$$

The reciprocal of the Bohr radius is just the quantum-mechanical mean reciprocal radius of an electron with quantum number n:

$$\langle r_n^{-1} \rangle = \int r_n^{-1} |\psi|^2 \, d\tau = [r_n(\text{Bohr})]^{-1} \tag{5'}$$

The mean radius of the electron is

$$\langle r_{nl} \rangle = \int r_{nl} |\psi|^2 \, d\tau = r_n(\text{Bohr})[(3n - l)(3n - l + 1)/4n^2] \tag{5''}$$

Comparison of the eigenvalues of equation 1 with the energies of the Bohr theory reveals that the n of equation 2 is the same as that of equation 3 and gives

$$E_n = -\frac{2\mu_r e^4}{\hbar^2}\left(\frac{Z}{n}\right)^2 = R_\infty \left(\frac{M}{m + M}\right) hc \left(\frac{Z}{n}\right)^2 \tag{6}$$

where $R_\infty = 2\pi^2 me^4/ch^3 = 109737.303 \text{ cm}^{-1}$ is the Rydberg constant for infinite mass. The radial dependencies of the wave functions are plotted in Figure 1, and the angular dependencies are indicated in Figure 2. In equation 1 both the electron spin and the relativistic corrections are neglected, and the energies of the stable states are independent of l. Spin-orbit interactions must be introduced as a perturbation in any consideration of multiplet structure.

B. EXTRAPOLATION TO THE MANY-BODY PROBLEM

The mathematical difficulties associated with the many-body problem are so great that any conclusions about multielectron atoms are extrapolations from the single-electron problem. In the case of alkali metals, there is a single electron outside of a closed shell. The closed-shell electrons have a spherically symmetric distribution, and equation 1 is appropriate provided the integer Z is replaced by a nonintegral number $Z_{\text{eff}} = (Z - \sigma)$ in order to reflect screening of the nuclear charge by the closed-shell electrons. The screening parameter σ is greater the smaller the penetration of the electrons into the closed-shell electron core. From Figure 1 it is seen that Z_{eff} must decrease with increasing angular momentum l of the outer electron. Hence the energy of the stationary states of the outer electron E_{nl} depends now on both n and l, states with smaller l being more stable than states with higher l and the same n. If there is more than one electron outside a closed shell, it is customary to consider only a single electron moving in the average potential created by all of the other electrons (spherical approximation), and E_{nl} depends upon l through Z_{eff} in the same way as for the alkali metals. However, electron correlations that minimize the electrostatic interactions between outer electrons must then be considered as a perturbation.

C. ELECTRON SPIN AND THE PAULI EXCLUSION PRINCIPLE

Electron correlations are intimately associated with two assumptions: (1) a fourth quantum number, the electron-spin quantum number s, and (2) the Pauli exclusion principle. In order to account for spectral data, it is necessary to postulate that electrons spin about their own axis to create a magnetic moment (625). Whereas the magnetic moment associated with the angular momentum may have $(2l + 1)$ components m_l in the direction of an external magnetic field $\mathbf{H}$, the spin moment may have only two components corresponding to $s = m_s = \pm 1/2$. Classically the magnitude of the moment $\boldsymbol{\mu}_\alpha$ associated with an angular momentum $\mathbf{p}_\alpha$ is

$$\boldsymbol{\mu}_\alpha = -\frac{e}{2mc}\mathbf{p}_\alpha = -\mu_B \mathbf{p}_\alpha/\hbar \tag{7}$$

where $\mu_B = e\hbar/2mc = 9.27 \times 10^{-21}$ erg/oe is called the Bohr magneton.

$\left[\right.$ An elliptic circuit of area $A = (1/2) \int_0^{2\pi} r^2\, d\alpha$ carrying a current i has a magnetic moment $\mu = iA$. An electron moving in a planar

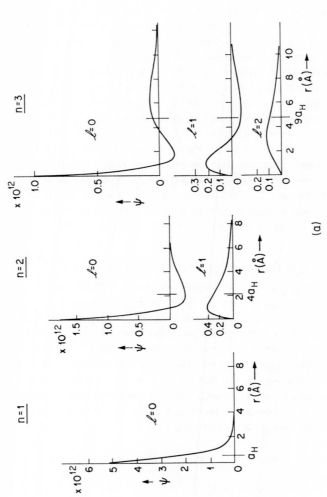

Fig. 1. Radial dependence of hydrogen eigenfunctions. (From *Atomic Spectra and Atomic Structure*, by Gerhard Herzberg, trans. by J. W. T. Spinks, reprinted through permission by Dover Publications, Inc., New York 14, N. Y.) (a) Normalized, radial part of hydrogen eigenfunctions for $n = 1, 2, 3$. Abscissae give distance from nucleus. (b; see facing page) Probability density distribution of the hydrogen electron for $n = 1, 2, 3$; $r^2 \psi \psi^* \, dr$ gives the probability of finding the electron in the spherical shell of thickness dr at a distance r from the nucleus.

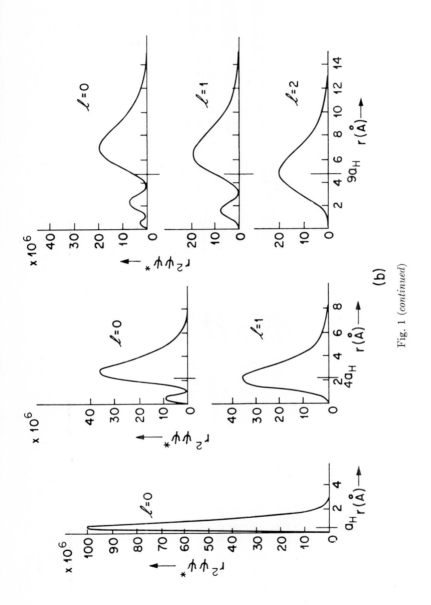

Fig. 1 (*continued*)

orbit of area A is equivalent to a current $i = -e/cT$, where $-e/c$ is the charge of the electron in emu and T is the period.   The angular momentum of the electron of mass m is $p_\alpha = mr^2\dot\alpha$, so that

$$A = \frac{1}{2}\int_0^T (p_\alpha/m)\,dT = p_\alpha T/2m. \Big]$$

Whereas solution of the angular part of equation 1 gives $p_l = \hbar[l(l+1)]^{1/2}$, it is necessary to assume that $p_s = 2\hbar[s(s+1)]^{1/2}$.

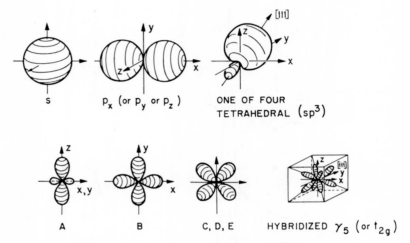

s p_x (or p_y or p_z)   ONE OF FOUR
                                           TETRAHEDRAL (sp^3)

A   B   C, D, E   HYBRIDIZED γ_5 (or t_{2g})

Fig. 2.   Angular dependence of hydrogen eigenfunctions for $s(l = 0)$, $p(l = 1)$ and $d(l = 2)$.   The functions A, B, C, D, E are defined by Equation 63, and γ_5 contains C, D, E.

[This assumption comes out of the Dirac relativistic wave equation for the electron.   In this theory both positive and negative energy states are allowed, so that the energy difference between the two spin states of an electron of mass m moving with velocity c is assumed to be $\Delta E = 2mc^2 = \hbar\omega$.   If the electron has no orbital angular momentum, $\omega s\hbar = mc^2$ where $s\hbar$ is the spin angular momentum.   Therefore $s = 1/2$ rather than an integer, so that $p_s = 2\hbar[s(s+1)]^{1/2}$.]

In order to understand the building up of the periodic system, it is necessary to introduce an additional assumption, the Pauli exclusion principle (503), which states: *In one and the same atom, no two electrons can have the same set of values for the four quantum numbers n, l, m_l, m_s*

(*or* n, l, j, m_j). [The quantum number j is the total quantum number and is given by the vector sum of the orbital and angular momenta, and m_j is the component of j along a prescribed direction.] The quantum mechanical formulation of this principle is: *The total eigenfunction of an atom with several electrons must be antisymmetric in all its electrons.*

D. RUSSELL-SAUNDERS COUPLING, SPECTROSCOPIC NOTATION, AND MULTIPLICITY

In this volume, principal consideration is given to the lighter elements, so that the Russell-Saunders (549) vector model of the atom is used. In this model a multielectron atom is assumed to have the quantum numbers n, $L = \sum_i l_i$, M_L, $S = \sum_i s_i$, (or $n, L, J = |\mathbf{L} + \mathbf{S}|$, M_J). This implies stronger $l_i\text{-}l_j$ and $s_i\text{-}s_j$ coupling than $l_i\text{-}s_i$ coupling. It follows from Pauli's principle that for a closed shell $\sum_i l_i = \sum_i s_i = 0$, and the quantum numbers for the atom are determined by the electrons outside of closed shells. The indicated additions are always vector additions such that different possible values of their vector sum have integral differences. It follows that the total angular momentum J has the possible values $(L + S)$, $(L + S - 1)$, $(L + S - 2)$, . . . , $|L - S|$ so that the multiplicity of terms corresponding to a given J is either $(2S + 1)$ or $(2L + 1)$, whichever is smaller. The degeneracy of these multiplets is removed by the interaction of the magnetic moment associated with the angular momentum with that associated with the spin. These spin-orbit interactions are relatively weak and therefore enter the theory as perturbation terms. This means that the energy differences between multiplet levels (different J, same L and S) are small compared to those between levels having different L and/or S values. Information about the state of the atom is summarized by the notation $^{2S+1}L_J$, where $L = 0, 1, 2, 3, . . .$ is given by the spectral notation $S, P, D, F, ...$ Information about the individual electrons is given by the notation nl^q so that the ground state, or deepest term, of Na, for example, may be indicated as $1s^2 2s^2 2p^6 3s^1\ ^2S_{1/2}$, or in abbreviated form as $3s^1\ ^2S_{1/2}$, electrons in closed shells being omitted.

E. FACTORS DETERMINING THE GROUND STATE

In order to interpret magnetic susceptibility data, it is necessary to know the ground state of an atom with more than one electron

outside of a closed shell. If there were no electron correlations and
no spin-orbit interactions, all terms for equivalent electrons (those
having the same n, l) would have the same energy. However, the
electron correlations and spin-orbit interactions are important. Electron correlations determine the magnitude of the quantum number J,
and spin-orbit coupling gives rise to multiplets associated with a
given J. There are two rules that operate. The first, Hund's (289)
rule, states: *Of the terms given by equivalent electrons, those with greatest
$(2S + 1)$ lie deepest, and of those the lowest is that with greatest L.*
The second rule (123) states: *Multiplets formed from equivalent electrons are regular when less than half the shell is occupied, but inverted
when more than half the shell is occupied.* If the components in a
multiplet term lie energetically in the same order as their J values
(smallest J value lowest) the term is called *regular* and, in the con-
verse case, *inverted*. There is no ambiguity to the rule since the
ground state of a half filled shell ($L = 0$) is a singlet.

Hund's rule is a consequence of the Pauli principle plus electrostatic interactions between the electrons. Since any dual occupation
of a spatial orbital must involve large electrostatic electron-electron
repulsions, the energy of the multielectron state is lowered if such
dual occupations can be minimized. From Pauli's principle, this
dual occupation is minimized if equivalent electrons have as many
like spins as possible. Given several possible terms with the same
$(2S + 1)$, electrons that orbit in the same sense (l_i have the same
sign) collide less frequently than electrons orbiting oppositely.
Therefore of the terms with maximum $(2S + 1)$, minimum electrostatic electron-electron repulsion is achieved in the term with greatest L.

The multiplet formation is due to spin-orbit interactions of the
form (628)

$$W_J = \lambda \mathbf{L} \cdot \mathbf{S} = \tfrac{1}{2}\lambda[J(J + 1) - L(L + 1) - S(S + 1)] \qquad (8)$$

where the multiplet is regular or inverted according as $\lambda > 0$ or
$\lambda < 0$. [This interaction follows from the theory of relativity, which
states that in a coordinate system moving with a velocity $\mathbf{v}$ relative to
another system, there is an extra magnetic-field strength equal to
$\mathbf{H} = -(\mathbf{v} \times \mathbf{E})$ if $\mathbf{E}$ is the electronic-field strength in the other system
(multiplication constants for proper units neglected). The spin of
the moving electron is subject to this field so that the energy is

$W = -\boldsymbol{\mu} \cdot \mathbf{H} \sim \boldsymbol{\mu} \cdot (\mathbf{v} \times \mathbf{E}) = \boldsymbol{\mu} \cdot (\mathbf{p} \times \mathbf{r}) E/mcr$ for a spherically symmetric field $\mathbf{E} = E\mathbf{r}/r$. Since $\mathbf{L} = -(\mathbf{p} \times \mathbf{r})$ and $\boldsymbol{\mu} = -\mathbf{S}\mu_B$, equation 8 follows immediately.] For the transition metals of the iron group, the spin-orbit parameter λ is of the order of 100 to 1000 cm^{-1}. Goudsmit (231) has shown that λ reverses sign on going from a less than half to a more than half filled shell. The physical origin of this sign reversal lies in the fact that an electron spin interacts more strongly with its own orbital momentum. From Hund's rule it follows that if a shell is less than half filled, the individual electrons have their spins parallel to the net spin; if the shell is more than half filled, the individual electrons responsible for a multiplet have their spins antiparallel to the net spin.

F. THE MAGNETIC SUSCEPTIBILITY OF FREE ATOMS

The magnetic susceptibility is

$$\chi_m = N\langle \mu_{\shortparallel} \rangle / H, \tag{9}$$

where $\langle \mu_{\shortparallel} \rangle$ is the average atomic-moment component parallel to an applied field $\mathbf{H}$ for a unit volume containing N atoms. In general there are two contributions to $\langle \mu_{\shortparallel} \rangle$, one arising from the existence of a permanent atomic moment that is aligned in the direction of $\mathbf{H}$ and one from an atomic moment that is induced by $\mathbf{H}$, but by Lenz's law is directed opposite to $\mathbf{H}$. [In the case of molecules and solids, field-induced contributions to the susceptibility that are directed parallel to $\mathbf{H}$ also exist (see eqs. 55, 55′, and 58).] The former is the *paramagnetic* contribution, and the latter the *diamagnetic* contribution.

The diamagnetic contribution follows from Larmor's theorem (389) which states: (For a proof of this theorem, see reference (628), p. 22.) *For an atom in a magnetic field, the motion of the electrons is, to a first approximation in* $\mathbf{H}$, *the same as a motion in the absence of* $\mathbf{H}$ *except for the superposition of a common precession of angular frequency* $\omega_L = eH/2mc = H\mu_B/\hbar$. The angular momentum of an atom is, from equation 7:

$$\mathbf{p}_\alpha = \sum_i m\rho_i^2 \dot{\boldsymbol{\phi}}_i = -\frac{2mc}{e} \boldsymbol{\mu}_\alpha \tag{10}$$

where ρ_i, z_i, ϕ_i are cylindrical coordinates with the z axis parallel to $\mathbf{H}$. If the field is applied slowly, the motion in the rotating reference system is the same as the original motion in the rest system before application of the field, and from Larmor's theorem $\dot{\boldsymbol{\phi}}_i =$

$\dot{\phi}_i^0(t) + He/2mc$ is the angular frequency parallel to $\mathbf{H}$. If there is no permanent magnetic moment, $\sum_i m\rho_i^2 \dot{\phi}_i^0(t) = 0$, and equation 10 gives for the diamagnetic moment induced by the field $\mathbf{H}$:

$$\langle \mu_{\parallel} \rangle_d = -\frac{He^2}{4mc^2} \langle \sum_i \rho_i^2 \rangle = -\frac{He^2}{6mc^2} \langle \sum_i r_i^2 \rangle \tag{11}$$

since $\rho_i^2 = x_i^2 + y_i^2$ and $r_i^2 = x_i^2 + y_i^2 + z_i^2$. If the atoms are all alike in size, there is no difference between the statistical mean $\langle \sum_i r_i^2 \rangle$ over a large number of atoms and the time average $\sum_i \overline{r_i^2}$ for a single molecule, and the diamagnetic contribution to equation 9 is

$$\chi_{md} = -\frac{Ne^2}{6mc^2} \sum_i \overline{r_i^2} \tag{12}$$

where $r_i \sim 1$ A is the distance of a classical electron from the nucleus.

Given a permanent atomic moment, derivation of the paramagnetic contribution assumes that the energy of separation of the lowest from the first excited electronic levels in the atom or ion are either small or large compared to kT. Van Vleck (628) has shown that the matrix elements between levels of large ($\gg kT$) separation, the high-frequency elements, contribute a temperature-independent term that is to be added to equation 12, and that the low-frequency elements are responsible for a temperature-dependent term that corresponds to the classical Langevin (388)–Debye (145) expression for paramagnetism. Both the angular momentum and the spin contribute to the permanent magnetic moment. When the separation of the multiplet components is large compared to kT, $\mathbf{L}$ and $\mathbf{S}$ precess rapidly about $\mathbf{J}$, and the low-frequency part of the permanent moment is only μ_J of Figure 3. By geometry (Fig. 3),

$$\mu_J = \mu_L \cos(\mathbf{L},\mathbf{J}) + \mu_S \cos(\mathbf{S},\mathbf{J})$$

and from equation 7 $\mu_L = -\mu_B[L(L+1)]^{1/2}$, $\mu_S = -2\mu_B[S(S+1)]^{1/2}$. It follows from the law of cosines that

$$\mu_J^2 = J(J+1)g^2\mu_B^2$$

$$g = 1 + \frac{J(J+1) + S(S+1) - L(L+1)}{2J(J+1)} \tag{13}$$

The spectroscopic splitting factor g, also referred to as the Landé (386) g factor, falls within the limits of $1 \leq g \leq 2$, where $g = 1$ corresponds to $S = 0$, and $g = 2$ to a spin-only ($L = 0$) magnetic moment. Now what is needed for equation 9 is the component of $\boldsymbol{\mu}_J$ in the direction of $\mathbf{H}$, $\mu_{J\parallel} = \mu_J \cos(\mathbf{H},\mathbf{J}) = M_J\mu_J/[J(J + 1)]^{1/2}$, averaged over the $(2J + 1)$ degenerate M_J levels associated with a given $\mathbf{J}$. That is, each of the possible M_J levels corresponding to

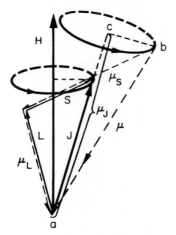

Fig. 3. Addition of magnetic moments in an atom with large L-S coupling. Vector magnitudes:

$$L = \hbar[L(L + 1)]^{1/2} \quad \text{and} \quad \mu_L = -\mu_B[L(L + 1)]^{1/2}$$
$$S = \hbar[S(S + 1)]^{1/2} \quad \text{and} \quad \mu_S = -2\mu_B[S(S + 1)]^{1/2}$$
$$J = \hbar[J(J + 1)]^{1/2} \quad \text{and} \quad \mu_J = -g\mu_B[J(J + 1)]^{1/2}$$

a given $\mathbf{J}$ must be properly weighted by the Boltzmann factor. For the state M_J, the energy due to the magnetic field is, from equation 13,

$$E_m = -\mu_{J\parallel}H = -M_J g\mu_B H$$

and

$$\langle \mu_{J\parallel} \rangle = \frac{\sum_{M_J} \mu_{J\parallel} \exp(-E_m/kT)}{\sum_{M_J} \exp(-E_m/kT)} = g\mu_B x \frac{d}{dx}\left(\ln \sum_{M_J} x^{M_J}\right)$$

where $x = \exp(g\mu_B H/kT)$. It can be verified that algebraic manipulation gives

$$\langle \mu_{J\parallel} \rangle = Jg\mu_B B_J(Jg\mu_B H/kT) \tag{14}$$

where the Brillouin function $B_J(y)$ is defined as

$$B_J(y) = \frac{J + (1/2)}{J} \coth\left(\frac{J + (1/2)}{J} y\right) - \frac{1}{2J} \coth\left(\frac{1}{2J} y\right) \tag{15}$$

Expansion of equation 15 for the case $y \ll 1$ gives

$$B_J(y) \approx J(J+1)y/3J^2 \qquad y \ll 1$$

or on substitution into equation 9

$$\chi_{mp}^{(1)} \approx \frac{Ng^2\mu_B^2 J(J+1)}{3kT} = \frac{N\mu_J^2}{3kT} \tag{16}$$

which is the classical Langevin-Debye result. There is also a second-order contribution to the paramagnetic susceptibility that is independent of temperature. It is due to the component b-c in Figure 3 and has the form (628)

$$\chi_{mp}^{(2)} = \frac{N\mu_B^2}{6(2J+1)} \left\{ \frac{F(J+1)}{E_{J+1} - E_J} - \frac{F(J)}{E_J - E_{J-1}} \right\} \tag{17}$$

where

$$F(J) = J^{-1}[(S+L+1)^2 - J^2][J^2 - (S-L)^2]$$

Usually the ground state is a minimum or a maximum of J, depending on whether the multiplet is regular or inverted, and the second or first term, respectively, of equation 17 vanishes.

In summary, the magnetic susceptibility for an atom with multiplet separation $\Delta \gg kT \gg E_m$ is

$$\chi_m(\text{atomic}) = \chi_{mp}^{(1)} + \chi_{mp}^{(2)} + \chi_{md} \approx N\left(\frac{\mu_J^2}{3kT} + \alpha\right) \qquad \Delta \gg kT \tag{18}$$

where $\alpha = \alpha_p - \alpha_d$ follows from equations 17 and 12, respectively. If a permanent atomic moment exists, the diamagnetic term is relatively small and only enters as a correction term.

In the cases where the multiplet separation is $\Delta \ll kT$, $\mathbf{L}$ and $\mathbf{S}$ precess slowly about $\mathbf{J}$, so that $\boldsymbol{\mu}_L$ and $\boldsymbol{\mu}_S$ precess about $\mathbf{H}$, and there is no distinction between $\mu_{\|}$ and the complete moment vector $-\mu_B(\mathbf{L} + 2\mathbf{S})$. This means

$$\langle \mu_{\|}^2 \rangle = (4\mathbf{S}^2 + \mathbf{L}^2 + 4\langle \mathbf{L} \cdot \mathbf{S} \rangle)\mu_B^2$$

where $\mathbf{S}^2$ and $\mathbf{L}^2$ correspond to $S(S+1)$ and $L(L+1)$. With multiplet separation $\ll kT$, the temperature factor may be disregarded in the statistical averages, and it can be shown (628) that in both strong and weak fields $\langle \mathbf{L} \cdot \mathbf{S} \rangle = 0$ and the form of the paramagnetic contribution is simply the classical Langevin-Debye result. Therefore equation 9 reduces to

$$\chi_m(\text{atomic}) = N \left(\frac{\mu_B^2}{3kT} [4S(S+1) + L(L+1)] - \alpha_d \right)$$

$$\Delta \ll kT \quad (18')$$

The intermediate case with multiplet separation $\approx kT$ applies to Eu and Sm, but is generally a special case. This case violates the Curie law

$$\chi_m = C/T \tag{19}$$

where C is a constant. However, most atoms obey the Curie law (α_p is usually small also), so that measurements of χ_m vs. T^{-1} give straight lines with slope C from which information about the permanent atomic moment can be obtained. In fact, the effective atomic moment as given by the Curie law is

$$\mu_{\text{eff}} = \begin{cases} g[J(J+1)]^{1/2}\mu_B & \text{for } \Delta \gg kT \\ [4S(S+1) + L(L+1)]^{1/2}\mu_B & \text{for } \Delta \ll kT \end{cases}$$

$$= \left[\frac{3k}{N} C \right]^{1/2} = [8C_{\text{mol}}]^{1/2}\mu_B \tag{20}$$

where C_{mol} is obtained from a plot of molar susceptibility vs. temperature. In the special case that $L = 0$, equations 18 and 18' are equivalent and

$$\mu_{\text{eff}} = 2[S(S+1)]^{1/2}\mu_B = [8C_{\text{mol}}]^{1/2}\mu_B \tag{20'}$$

II. Molecules and Solids

A. LOCALIZED VERSUS COLLECTIVE ELECTRONS

If atoms are condensed into a molecule or a crystalline array, the outer electrons in partially filled shells are strongly perturbed by the neighboring atoms. In fact, these electrons determine the strength and direction of the binding forces between the atoms of a crystalline array, and the character of a bonding electron may be quite different in a crystal from what it is in the free atom. At the heart of any understanding of the magnetic properties of matter is an adequate description of the bonding and nonbonding electrons outside of atomic closed shells. Although quantum mechanics provides the necessary physical concepts for such a description, the mathematical difficulties associated with the many-body problem have forced the introduction of serious simplifications into the theory.   Therefore studies of the magnetic properties of matter should provide important clues to and checks for our descriptions of the chemical bond.   It is this aspect of magnetism that is probably of greatest interest to the chemist, and it is from this perspective that magnetism in solids will be discussed.

The chemist is accustomed to think of the chemical bond from the valence-bond approach of Pauling (505), for this approach enables construction of simple models with which to develop a "chemical intuition" for a variety of complex materials.   However, this approach is necessarily qualitative in character so that at best it can serve only as a useful device for the correlation and classification of materials.   Therefore the theoretical context for the present discussion is the Hund (290)–Mulliken (457) molecular-orbital approach. Nevertheless an important restriction to the application of this approach must be emphasized at the start; viz. an apparently sharp breakdown of the collective-electron assumption for interatomic separations greater than some critical distance, R_c.   In order to illustrate the theoretical basis for this breakdown, several calculations will be considered, the first being those for the hydrogen molecule.

1. *The Hydrogen Molecule*

The Schroedinger equation for the hydrogen molecule that corresponds to equation 1 for the atom is

$$(H_0 + H')\Psi = E\Psi \tag{21}$$

$$H_0 = -\frac{\hbar^2}{2m}(\nabla_1^2 + \nabla_2^2) - \frac{e^2}{r_1} - \frac{e^2}{r_2}$$

$$H' = \frac{e^2}{R} + \frac{e^2}{r_{12}} - \frac{e^2}{r_{1B}} - \frac{e^2}{r_{2A}}$$

where R is the intermolecular distance between atoms A and B, which is assumed fixed relative to the electronic motions (84), and r_{12} is the interelectronic distance.   In this nonrelativistic approximation, the electrical interactions between particles do not depend upon their spins, so that the solution to equation 21 may be written in the form of a product

$$\Psi = \psi(\mathbf{r}_1, \mathbf{r}_2)\chi(\sigma_1, \sigma_2)$$

where ψ is a function of the coordinates only and χ of the spins only. Despite the fact that the electrical interaction of the particles is independent of their spin, the energy of the system depends upon its total spin. This arises from the principle of indistinguishability of similar particles, which forces the wave function to be symmetrical or antisymmetrical. (If there is no overlap of the wave functions of two particles, they can be distinguished.) Therefore solution of Schroedinger's equation gives two energy levels, corresponding to a symmetrical and an antisymmetrical wave function $\psi(\mathbf{r}_1,\mathbf{r}_2)$. The total wave function for a system of electrons, particles with half-integral spin, must be antisymmetric (Pauli principle). Therefore if the space part of the function is symmetric, the spin part must be antisymmetric, i.e. the spins of the two electrons are antiparallel. Conversely, if the space part is antisymmetric, the spin part must be symmetric, i.e. the spins of the two electrons are parallel. Therefore the possible energy value for the system depends upon its total spin. The peculiar, purely quantum mechanical interaction that gives rise to this dependence is called *exchange interaction*.

A general formulation for the symmetric and antisymmetric co-ordinate wave function is

$$\psi(\mathbf{r}_1,\mathbf{r}_2) = [u_1(1)u_2(2) \pm u_2(1)u_1(2)] \qquad (22)$$

$$u_1 = c_{11}\phi_a + c_{12}\phi_b \qquad u_2 = c_{21}\phi_a + c_{22}\phi_b$$

where ϕ_a and ϕ_b are hydrogen wave functions for nucleus a and b, respectively. In the molecular-orbital (MO) approach, each of the two electrons of the hydrogen molecule is assumed to belong equally to the two hydrogen nuclei. In this approach the ground state has $c_{11} = c_{21} = c_{12} = c_{22}$ and the plus sign in equation 22. At large nuclear separations, this assumption is obviously poor: it is more accurate to describe the system as two separate hydrogen atoms, but with some stabilization as a molecule as a result of a finite probability of *exchanging* the electrons on the two atoms (i.e. electrons are considered indistinguishable). In this latter description, called the Heitler-London (266) approach (HL), $c_{12} = c_{21}$ and $c_{11} = c_{22}$. (The simple HL formulation neglects polar terms, i.e. terms in $\phi_a(1)\phi_a(2)$ and $\phi_b(1)\phi_b(2)$, so that $c_{12} = c_{21} = 0$. If orthogonalized HL wave functions are the basis set, $c_{12} = c_{21} \neq 0$ and stabilization of the molecule can only be achieved by further addition of polar terms.) In general, the c_{ij} are subject to the normalization conditions

$$c_{11}^2 + c_{12}^2 + 2\alpha'c_{11}c_{12} = 1$$
$$c_{21}^2 + c_{22}^2 + 2\alpha'c_{21}c_{22} = 1 \qquad (23)$$

where $\alpha' \equiv \int \phi_a \phi_b \, d\tau$ is the overlap integral. [$\int d\tau$ is an integral over coordinate space.] If the two possible spin states for an electron are designated α and β, the ground-state, two-electron wave function for the molecule is

$$\Psi = [u_1(1)u_2(2) + u_2(1)u_1(2)][\alpha(1)\beta(2) - \alpha(2)\beta(1)]/\sqrt{2} \quad (24)$$

where the symmetric space part allows for an accumulation of electronic charge between the positive nuclei to bind them together. Pratt (529) set himself the problem of determining, for a given interatomic separation R, the values of the c_{ij} that minimize the energy of the molecule. These c_{ij} then give the best description of the electrons. With the use of a variational procedure subject to the normalization conditions of equation 23, he obtained six possible solutions for the c_{ij} as a function of R, two of which are shown in Figure 4. The striking feature of these curves is the rapid breakdown of the MO description for $R > 1.6R_0$, where R_0 is the equilibrium separation. Similarly, detailed calculations for the N_2 molecule by Nesbet (479) indicate a breakdown of the MO description for interatomic separations greater than $\sim 2R_0$.

Mattheiss (415) and Slater (585) have carried out a complete calculation, given fixed nuclear positions, for a six-membered ring of hydrogen atoms. They find that the transition from MO electrons to HL electrons is not as sharp as is suggested from calculations for the H_2 molecule. However, these calculations indicate that a simple MO description is adequate only to $\sim 0.75R_0$, that with second-order perturbation theory (configuration interactions neglected) it is possible to modify a simple MO theory for $R = R_0$, but that for $R > 2R_0$ it is necessary to use a HL description for the electrons. [The orthogonal HL description used by Mattheiss consists of a calculation, which incorporates polar terms via a second-order perturbation method proposed by Kramers (373), of the "effective" Heisenberg exchange integral appropriate at large internuclear separations. (The Heisenberg exchange integral is discussed in Chapter II.)]. Therefore although these calculations do not support the concept of a critical R_c at which there is a sudden transition from MO to HL bonding electrons, they demonstrate a transition from one description to the other within the interval $R_0 < R < 2R_0$. Although a HL description for the electrons does not require localized electrons, the breakdown of a MO description will be assumed to permit this, especially in

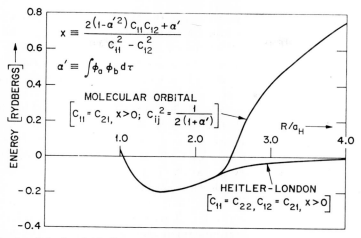

Fig. 4. Calculated binding energies for H_2 molecule (after Pratt (529)) as a function of interatomic distance R for two different relationships of the coefficients c_{ij} defined by Equation 22. (1 Rydberg = 13.6 eV.)

crystals where other mechanisms such as lattice polarization may be simultaneously present to stabilize electron localization.

Although Herring (271a) has raised a fundamental theoretical difficulty by showing that the HL description is incorrect at very large distances (> 50 atomic spacings), the HL approach is here assumed valid for the values of $R > R_c$ of physical interest.

2. *Problem of Ionic Terms*

Another criticism of the usual MO wave functions is that even at R_0 they overemphasize ionic terms since electron-electron interactions (electron "correlations") are not adequately introduced. According to the simple MO theory, the chance of a given electron being on a given atom is independent of whether another electron of opposite spin is already there. This cannot be true, and the problem of introducing into the formalism adequate electron correlations to account for this fact has proven a formidable obstacle for the theory of molecules and solids (400). If $\lambda = c_{12}/c_{11} = c_{21}/c_{22}$, the space part of equation 24, with normalization factor neglected, can be written in the form

$$\psi' = \{\phi_a(1)\phi_b(2) + \phi_b(1)\phi_a(2)\} + \mu\{\phi_a(1)\phi_a(2) + \phi_b(1)\phi_b(2)\} \quad (25)$$

$$\mu = 2\lambda/(1 + \lambda^2)$$

The expressions in the brackets are the HL covalent wave functions and the pure ionic wave functions, and μ shows the degree of mixing between them. In the MO theory $\lambda = \mu = 1$. In the simple HL theory, $\lambda = \mu = 0$. The ψ' of equation 25 are sometimes referred to as *semilocalized orbitals* (456). Values of μ which minimize the energy for the wave function of equation 25 have been calculated as a function of R by Coulson and Fischer (134) and are plotted in Figure 5(a). It is to be noted that the ionic contribution ("polar states") to the ionic-covalent hybrid decreases with increasing R. It is also to be noted how great an overemphasis there is on the ionic terms in the simple MO theory (i.e. at all distances $\mu < 1$). Therefore it is apparent that neglect of electron correlations cannot be considered insignificant, and any insights that empirical observations can give to this problem are important. (This is especially true for d electrons in solids where the interatomic separation is greater than the equilibrium separation for d-electron bonding.)

O'ohata (494) has recently used semilocalized orbitals to calculate the bonding energy of the C—C bond in the diamond crystals. The total electronic wave function Ψ for the crystal is expressed as an assembly of pairs of orbitals. These pairs include not only valence-orbital (hybrid s–p) pairs, but also core-electron pairs. The calculated binding energy of a C—C bond is plotted in Figure 5(b) as a function of λ. It is to be noted that the optimum value for λ is $\lambda = 0.16$. According to this calculation, the overemphasis of the polar terms in the MO approach fails to consider correlation effects that are responsible for binding energies of 0.4 eV per bond. For various diatomic molecules, the difference between the exact and the Hartree-Fock (parallel-spin correlations only are included) ground-state energies are $1 - 2$ eV. Since 1 eV = 23.07 kcal/mole, these errors are significant.

3. *Solids*

In the case of solids, Mott (454) has argued for a sharp breakdown of the MO approach at some critical separation R_c. Consider an array of noncovalent (alkali) atoms with interatomic separation R. If R is large, so that the overlap of the atomic wave functions on neighboring atoms is small, the HL approach should be used. Then each electron is described by an atomic wave function

$$\psi(\mathbf{r}) = \psi(\mathbf{r} - \mathbf{R}_n)$$

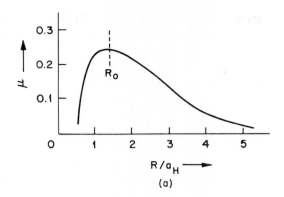

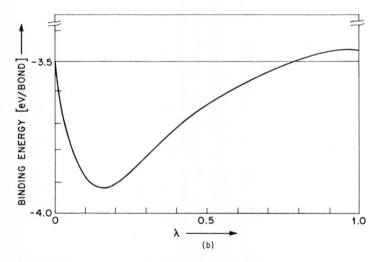

Fig. 5.   Contribution of ionic terms to the binding energy as a function of internuclear distance.   (a) Contribution μ of ionic terms for H_2 molecule (see equation 25) calculated with best screening constant of a Heitler-London wave function (after Coulson and Fischer (134)).   (b) Variation of the binding energy of diamond per C—C bond with $\lambda = c_{12}/c_{11} = c_{21}/c_{22}$ (after O'ohata (494)). The effect of nonorthogonality between a valence orbital of one atom and a core orbital of another reduces the calculated binding energy by 0.28 eV per bond, so that the complete theoretical binding energy is 3.64 eV per bond.

where $\mathbf{R}_n$ is the coordinate of the nth atom. The antisymmetrized wave function corresponding to these atomic wave functions is designated

$$\Psi_{nc}(q_1, q_2, \ldots)$$

where q_n are the electronic coordinates including spin and the subscript nc stands for nonconducting. That such a state is nonconducting is obvious since there are no "polar states." Although electrons can change places (electron exchange), there is always one electron per atom, so that *no net current can occur so long as the number of electrons per atom is unity* (or an integer if the ground state has orbital degeneracy: $l \neq 0$). [If an electron is removed, the "hole" left behind can move about and carry a current so long as electron-lattice interactions are small. Similarly an extra electron can move from atom to atom.]

At small R on the other hand, the antisymmetrized, many-electron wave function

$$\Psi_c(q_1, q_2, \ldots)$$

is composed of one-electron wave functions $\psi_{\mathbf{k}m}$ characteristic of running waves (MO electrons) in a periodic potential (see eq. 30). Such wave functions do not prevent two electrons from being located simultaneously at the same atom (although introduction of a "correlation hole" associated with each electron inhibits it), so that "polar states" and conductivity are possible. From the theory of the hydrogen molecule, such polar terms play an increasing role as the atoms are brought together (see Fig. 5). The same must be true for a crystalline array. However, there is an additional feature in the theory of the infinite lattice: *It is necessary to distinguish between free charge carriers and positive and negative carriers bound together as they are in an exciton.* This distinction does not occur for the molecule. Mott (453,454) has argued that a pair of carriers attract each other with a Coulomb force derived from the potential $-e^2/\kappa r$, where κ is the dielectric constant of the solid. They can therefore combine together to form a bound state at $T = 0°K$ similar to an exciton. For the example of a monovalent metal, the bound state would consist of an "extra" electron confined to move within the field of the "hole" from which it was excited. Such a bound pair is neutral and therefore cannot carry a current. The significance of this argument is simply that even at interatomic distances for which polar states exist ($\mu > 0$), the best wave function may be Ψ_{nc} rather than Ψ_c. However, if the number N_p of polar states is large, i.e. of the order of 0.1 to 1 state per atom, the attractive potential between two charge carriers is screened, or $V(r) = (-e^2/\kappa r) \exp[-\sigma r]$, where the screening parameter σ increases with N_p. At some critical number N_{pc}, the potential becomes too small to allow a bound state to form, and the carriers do not combine. Since N_p increases with decreasing R (see Fig. 5), it follows that there should be a critical distance R_c such that for $R < R_c$ the outer electrons are best described by running waves and Ψ_c, but for $R > R_c$ by atomic wave functions and Ψ_{nc}. Mott makes a rough estimate for a hydrogen array of $R_c \sim 2.1R_0$, which is comparable to the R_c determined for the hydrogen molecule.

The Mott argument is for the case where there are an integral number of outer electrons per interacting atom with a given pair of quantum numbers n, l. If there are overlapping d and s bands in a transition metal, such as nickel, there will be a fractional number of d and s electrons per atom so that the screening parameter σ is large, and from the Mott argument, collective-electron behavior is anticipated. However, even if there are nonintegral numbers of electrons per interacting atom as, for example, in the system $Li_x Ni_{1-x} O$, the electrical conductivity is not metallic (increasing resistivity with T) if the separation between transition-element atoms is $R_{tt} > R_c$, but has the characteristics of a semiconductor [$\rho = \rho_0 \exp(E_a/kT)$ or $\rho = T\rho_0 \exp(E_a/kT)$]. Therefore although the resistivity may be low (~ 1 ohm-cm), the conduction process cannot be described by the simple motion of a "bare" electron that is scattered by phonons, the quantized vibrational motions of the nuclei. If electron-phonon interactions are large, there are three possible assumptions:

(a) The energy gained by lattice polarizations about neighboring atoms of differing localized-electron occupations is greater than the energy gained from band formation, and conduction is due to a hopping of localized electrons over a potential barrier from a center of low valence to a center of higher valence. Such conductivity can be described by diffusion theory, and experimental support for this description for compounds with $R_{tt} > R_c$ is cited in Chapter III, Section I-A. This type of charge carrier has low mobility (~ 0.1 to 1 cm²/V-sec, or $\sim 10^{-3}$ to 10^{-5} cm²/V-sec if carrier hop is indirect).

(b) If electron motion is too fast for electron trapping by nearest-neighbor sites, strong electron-phonon interactions could nevertheless be reflected in a lattice distortion and polarization that moves with the travelling electron. Such collective, electron-lattice entities are called *polarons*. Polaron states lie in a narrow temperature-dependent range of energies, which means that polarons have a large, temperature-dependent effective mass (196,197,246,279,558,702).

(*c*) Localized electrons, which are trapped by lattice polarization and local distortion, can escape as a result of thermal activation (or phonon interaction). Such an electron travels many lattice spacings as a "bare," collective electron before it becomes trapped again. This mechanism implies a filled band or a set of traps (homopolar bonds, for example) that lie energetically $\sim kT$ below a conduction band. The mobility would depend upon the mean free path between hole-electron (or electron-electron) collisions.

4. Conclusions

Whether the number of electrons per atom is integral or nonintegral, the concept of a critical interatomic separation for collective-electron versus localized-electron theories seems to have physical significance. Further, two tentative conclusions are suggested:

(*a*) *For outer electrons characterized by the quantum numbers n and l, there is a critical internuclear separation* $R_c(n,l)$, *such that these electrons are best described as high-mobility collective (MO) electrons if the interatomic separation is* $R < R_c(n,l)$; *as low-mobility, localized (HL) electrons if* $R > R_c(n,l)$. (If $R \approx R_0^{nl}$, where R_0^{nl} is the equilibrium atomic separation for bonding via n, l electrons, the electron mobility is $\mu \sim 10^2 - 10^3$ cm²/V-sec. If $R \approx R_c$, $\mu \sim 1 - 10$ cm²/V-sec. If $R > R_c$ and electrons hop through an intermediary anion, $\mu \sim 10^{-3} - 10^{-5}$ cm²/V-sec.)

(*b*) *For bonding outer s and p electrons there is always* (the case of impurity doping in semiconductors that is discussed by Mott is an obvious exception and special case) *the relation* $R < R_c(n,l) \approx 2R_0^{nl}$, *but for outer d and f electrons the relation may be reversed since the interatomic distance R is determined by bonding s and p electrons of higher principal quantum number n, i.e. of larger mean radial extension (see eq. 5).*

To pursue this second conclusion, it follows from equations 5″ and 6 that the interatomic spacing, which is determined by outer s and p electrons of principal quantum number n', is

$$R \approx R_0^{nl} \left(\frac{Z_{\text{eff}}^{nl}}{Z_{\text{eff}}^{n'0}} \right) \frac{3n'(3n' + 1)}{(3n - l)(3n - l + 1)}$$

$$= R_0^{nl} \left(\frac{E_{nl}}{E_{n'0}} \right)^{1/2} \left(\frac{n}{n'} \right) \frac{3n'(3n' + 1)}{(3n - l)(3n - l + 1)} \quad (26)$$

where R_0^{nl} is the equilibrium separation for bonding via electrons with quantum numbers n, $l = 2$ or 3 and it is assumed that R/R_0^{nl} is in the ratio of the mean radii of the electrons. Although the assumption is arbitrary, it should be reasonable for qualitative arguments. Since partially filled d or f shells only occur where $E_{nd} \approx E_{(n+1)s}$ or $E_{nf} \approx E_{(n+2)s}$, it follows that $(E_{nl}/E_{n'0})^{1/2} \approx 1$. (It is only if the outer d or f shells are filled that $(Z_{\text{eff}}^{nl}/Z_{\text{eff}}^{n'0}) > 1$.) This gives

$$R \approx R_0^{nl}(n/n')3n'(3n' + 1)/[(3n - l)(3n - l + 1)] \quad (26')$$

In the case of the rare earth metals, it is observed that the 4f electrons are always best described as localized, HL electrons, which means that the near-neighbor separation $R_{nn} = 2.53R_0^{4f} > R_c(4f)$. On the other hand, *there are no localized electrons in face-centered cubic palladium* (although introduction of iron atoms into the structure induces localized moments on the neighboring palladium atoms), which means that $R_{nnn} = 2.47R_0^{4d} < R_c(4d)$. This implies that

$$R_c(nl) \approx 2.5R_0^{nl} \quad (27)$$

which is reasonably consistent with the various estimates of R_c discussed in the preceding paragraphs.

In the case of $3d$ electrons, equations 26′ and 27 give

$$R_{nn} \approx 2.09R_0^{3d} < R_c(3d)$$

so that the near-neighbor-directed $3d$ electrons in transition metals are collective, MO electrons. In the body-centered-cubic structure, $R_{nnn} = 2R_{nn}/\sqrt{3} = 2.41R_0^{3d} < R_c(3d)$, and all the $3d$ electrons are collective. However, for a face-centered-cubic structure, $R_{nnn} = \sqrt{2}R_{nn} = 2.96R_0^{3d} > R_c(3d)$, so that the next-near-neighbor-directed $3d$ electrons may be localized, HL electrons. The possibility that collective and localized $3d$ electrons may be simultaneously present at a given atom resides in the highly anisotropic character of the d orbitals (see Fig. 2). Further, in ionic compounds containing transition element cations it is anticipated that the intercation distance is $R_{tt} > R_c$ if the anions are significantly larger than a transition metal atom.

In metals of the second and third long periods, the significant interatomic distances for the face-centered-cubic structure are $R_{nnn} = 2.47R_0^{4d} \lesssim R_c(4d)$ and $R_{nnn} = 2.22R_0^{5d} < R_c(5d)$, since equation 27 was chosen to be compatible with collective states for all outer $4d$, and therefore also all outer $5d$, electrons. This choice was made because of the contrast in magnetic properties that are observed for close-packed elements of the first versus the second and third long periods, and it was found to be compatible with semiquantitative estimates of $R_c \sim 2R_0$ for outer s electrons. With this reasoning, it is to be anticipated that in ionic compounds containing $4d$ and $5d$ cations, an intercation separation $R_{ll} \lesssim R_c$ would be encountered more frequently than in those containing $3d$ cations. Indeed in primarily ionic rare earth or actinide compounds collective $5d$- or $6d$-electron levels may even form bands of sufficient breadth to overlap the localized f levels and introduce metallic properties. This appears to be illustrated by $Ce_{2+\delta}S_3$ (22,218,379), which is a material of interest for thermoelectric devices.

Since the magnitude of the atomic moment will be shown to depend sharply upon the collective versus localized character of the electrons, magnetic as well as electric data will be found (see Chapter III) to support these tentative conclusions. Therefore, a brief summary is given of the formal results and of the assumptions made for the collective (MO) versus localized (HL) descriptions of electrons in crystals.

B. BAND MODEL FOR COLLECTIVE ELECTRONS

1. *Major Assumptions*

The band model results from application of the MO approach to the giant molecule of the crystal. Just as in the case of atoms, the many-electron problem for the solid is treated as a single electron moving in a screened potential arising from the averaged behavior of the nuclei and all the other electrons. This potential is derived by the self-consistent techniques originally developed by Hartree (254) for the atom. Further, the atomic cores, nuclei plus closed-shell electrons, are assumed fixed so as to give rise to a potential that has the periodicity of the crystalline lattice. Therefore this one-electron treatment contains three major assumptions:

(a) *A description of the outer (outside of closed shells) electrons may* be built up from solutions of a single electron moving in a periodic potential.

(b) There is a disregard of any multiplet structure on individual atoms. The electron is treated as a single electron outside closed shells.

(c) Electron-lattice interactions due to thermal vibrations of the atomic cores or to lattice defects are treated as a small perturbation.

2. Consequences of Lattice Periodicity

As in the case of atoms, the starting point is the Schroedinger wave equation corresponding to equation 1:

$$\nabla^2\psi + \frac{2m}{\hbar^2}(E + eU(\mathbf{r}))\psi = 0 \tag{28}$$

where the periodic-potential function is

$$U(\mathbf{r}) = U(\mathbf{r} + \mathbf{R}) \qquad \mathbf{R} = n_1\mathbf{a}_1 + n_2\mathbf{a}_2 + n_3\mathbf{a}_3 \tag{29}$$

and the $\mathbf{a}_i$ are primitive translation vectors of the crystal lattice. The most important qualitative properties of the eigenfunctions and energy spectrum follow simply from the periodicity of $U(\mathbf{r})$. They are independent of how tightly bound the electrons are to the nuclei, i.e. to the degree of overlap of the atomic wave functions (provided $R_0 < R_c$). It is these features that are of principal interest.

(a) To obtain the "bulk" properties of the crystal, the crystal is assumed infinite and the boundary condition for ψ is periodicity within one arbitrary domain containing a large number of unit cells. This boundary condition gives rise to solutions (79) that are running waves modulated by a function $u_{\mathbf{k}m}(\mathbf{r})$ that has the periodicity of $U(\mathbf{r})$,

$$\psi_{\mathbf{k}m} = \exp[i\mathbf{k}\cdot\mathbf{r}]u_{\mathbf{k}m}(\mathbf{r}) \tag{30}$$

where the quantum number m indicates that for each value of the wave vector $\mathbf{k}$, there is a series of different solutions for u, each corresponding to a different energy.

(b) Substitution of equation 30 into equation 28 gives

$$[\nabla^2 + 2i\mathbf{k}\cdot\nabla]u_{\mathbf{k}}(\mathbf{r}) + \frac{2m}{\hbar^2}\left[\left(E_{\mathbf{k}} - \frac{\hbar^2\mathbf{k}^2}{2m}\right) + eU(\mathbf{r})\right]u_{\mathbf{k}}(\mathbf{r}) = 0 \tag{31}$$

The term $2i\mathbf{k}\cdot\nabla$ is often treated as a perturbation, and then to second order in $\mathbf{k}$

$$E_{\mathbf{k}} - \frac{\hbar^2\mathbf{k}^2}{2m} = E_0 + \mathbf{k}^2Q$$

where the quantity Q is independent of $\mathbf{k}$, so that

$$E_{\mathbf{k}} = E_0 + \frac{\hbar^2 \mathbf{k}^2}{2m^*} \qquad (32)$$

has the form of a free electron with momentum $\hbar \mathbf{k}$ and an effective mass m^*. Thus $\mathbf{k}$ attains the meaning of a wave number ($|\mathbf{k}| = 2\pi/\lambda$). For an anisotropic energy surface, the effective mass is a tensor with components

$$\left(\frac{m}{m^*}\right)_{ij} = \frac{m}{\hbar^2} \frac{d^2 E_{\mathbf{k}}}{d\mathbf{k}_i \, d\mathbf{k}_j} \qquad (33)$$

which is immediately seen to be consistent with equation 32. The significance of the effective-mass concept lies in the fact that, *if correlation and exchange effects are included in the theory, the basic formalism is not altered* since, as was pointed out by Kohn (356), these effects are confined to such phenomenological, measurable parameters as m^* and the dielectric constant κ.

(c) From equation 30 it follows that

$$\psi_{\mathbf{k}m}(\mathbf{r} + \mathbf{R}) = \exp\left[i\mathbf{k} \cdot \mathbf{R}\right]\psi_{\mathbf{k}m}(\mathbf{r}) \qquad (34)$$

If a set of vectors $\mathbf{K}$ is so defined that

$$\exp\left[i\mathbf{K} \cdot \mathbf{R}\right] = 1 \qquad (35)$$

then it may be immediately verified that

$$\mathbf{K} = 2\pi(h_1\mathbf{b}_1 + h_2\mathbf{b}_2 + h_3\mathbf{b}_3) \qquad \mathbf{a}_i \cdot \mathbf{b}_j = \delta_{ij} \qquad (36)$$

where h_1, h_2, h_3 are integers. The totality of points defined by all the vectors $\mathbf{K}$ drawn from a common origin constitutes a lattice. This lattice is the reciprocal lattice, and the vectors $\mathbf{K}$ are called reciprocal-lattice vectors. If the real-lattice vectors are chosen so as to generate a Bravais lattice, the reciprocal lattice is unique. If $\mathbf{k}' = \mathbf{k} + \mathbf{K}$, then it follows from equations 34 and 35 that the wave functions corresponding to $\mathbf{k}$ and $\mathbf{k}'$ have indistinguishable translational symmetry and

$$\psi_{\mathbf{k}'m}(\mathbf{r}) = \psi_{\mathbf{k}m}(\mathbf{r}) \qquad E_m(\mathbf{k}') = E_m(\mathbf{k}) \qquad (37)$$

Therefore $\mathbf{k}$ is generally restricted (hence referred to as the reduced wave vector) to a region of $\mathbf{k}$ space such that no two points in this region are separated by any vector $\mathbf{K}$. This is a unit cell in reciprocal space, and is referred to as the *first Brillouin zone*.

The boundaries of the Brillouin zone can be constructed with the aid of the Bragg reflection conditions

$$(\mathbf{k} + \mathbf{K})^2 = |\mathbf{k}|^2 \tag{38}$$

or

$$2\mathbf{k}\cdot\mathbf{K} + |\mathbf{K}|^2 = 0$$

Zones bounded by planes defined by equation 38 are consistent with the reduced-vector zones. These reciprocal-lattice planes are simply the planes bisecting the vectors $\mathbf{K}$ and normal to them. It is noteworthy that lattices with the same type of translational symmetry have equivalent zone patterns since zone structure is determined by the $\mathbf{K}$ vectors, and these are determined by the primitive translation vectors.

(d) Bragg reflection is characteristic of wave propagation in periodic structures, and therefore it must be a feature of electron waves in crystals. The most important consequence of this Bragg reflection is that it leads to gaps in the distribution of energy states. If the Bragg condition is satisfied, the solution is a standing wave, rather than a travelling wave, since the waves are Bragg reflected equally in opposite senses. There are two independent standing-wave solutions: one concentrates electronic charge at the region of large potential, the other in the region of small potential, depending upon whether there is a node or antinode at the reflecting plane. The former solution is more stable, the latter less stable than a free-electron solution, which distributes electron charge uniformly. With equation 32 and its modification by these concepts, the $E_\mathbf{k}$ vs. $\mathbf{k}$ plot of Figure 6 is drawn. Thus the energy scale is broken up into a number of allowed bands, which are separated by forbidden bands. Within a Brillouin zone the energy is quasi-continuous, not continuous, because of the imposition of boundary conditions. Across a zone boundary the energy may be discontinuous. Two problems of importance are: the magnitude of the energy gaps and the number of electronic states in a Brillouin zone.

1. The magnitude of the energy gap depends upon the periodic potential. The potential at any point $\mathbf{r}$ in the space lattice may be expanded as a Fourier series

$$U(\mathbf{r}) = \sum_{\text{all } K} U_\mathbf{K} \exp\left[i\mathbf{K}\cdot\mathbf{r}\right] \tag{39}$$

For the case of weak binding, i.e. periodic potential small relative to

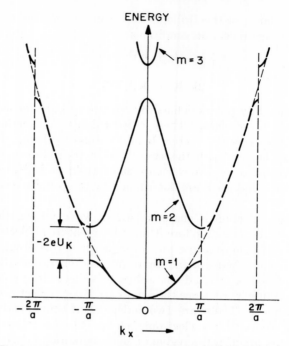

Fig. 6.   Energy of an electron in a crystal plotted against wave number k_x for a simple-cubic lattice with Brillouin-zone boundaries at $k_x = \pm(\pi/a), \pm(2\pi/a)$. Solid line is for reduced wave number $-(\pi/a) \leq k_x \leq (\pi/a)$.   Heavy dashed line is for k_x defined in range $-\infty < k_x < \infty$.   Light dashed line is solution for a constant potential.   Quantum number m defines the band.   Effective mass of interest is

$$\frac{1}{m^*} = \frac{1}{\hbar^2}\frac{d^2E}{dk_x{}^2}\bigg|_{E=E_F}$$

the mean energy $\langle E_\mathbf{k} \rangle$, Brillouin (103) has used a degenerate-perturbation calculation to show that the energy gap is

$$E_g = -2eU_\mathbf{K} \tag{40}$$

Therefore if $U_\mathbf{K} = 0$ at a zone boundary, there can be no energy discontinuity across this boundary.   For a structure with s atoms per unit cell, the Fourier coefficients of the potential may be written

$$U_\mathbf{K} = \sum_{t=1}^{s} A_{\mathbf{K}t} \exp\left[i\mathbf{K}\cdot\mathbf{n}_t\right] \tag{41}$$

where $\mathbf{n}_t$ gives the positions in real space of the atoms of the unit cell. If all the atoms in the unit cell are identical, then all $A_{\mathbf{K}t}$ with the same value of $\mathbf{K}$ are equal so that

$$U_{\mathbf{K}} = A_{\mathbf{K}}S_{\mathbf{K}} \qquad S_{\mathbf{K}} = \sum_{t=1}^{s} \exp\left[i\mathbf{K}\cdot\mathbf{n}_t\right] \tag{42}$$

$S_{\mathbf{K}}$ is simply the structure factor that enters determinations of x-ray intensities for scattering from crystal planes with Miller indices (h_1,h_2,h_3). Therefore, if the structure factor vanishes, there is no energy discontinuity across the corresponding plane in $\mathbf{k}$ space. However, it should be noted that an energy E, which is forbidden for a particular direction of propagation $\mathbf{k}$, may be allowed for another direction of propagation $\mathbf{k}'$. Therefore the experimental energy gap E_g^{eff}, which measures the overlap of forbidden energy for all directions of propagation, is considerably reduced from equation 40 and may even disappear. In this latter case the bands are said to overlap. Another type of band overlap may occur if the atomic energy levels are so broadened into bands of allowed energy states that the breadth of the allowed bands is greater than the energy separation of the atomic levels, as shown in Figure 7, which shows calculations for copper by Krutter (375).

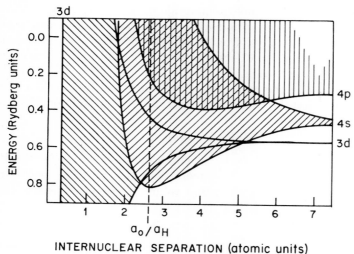

Fig. 7.   Energy bands in copper as a function of internuclear separation (after Krutter (375)).

Greater binding of the electrons to the atomic cores means larger A_K and therefore larger energy gaps, narrower bands of allowed energy. Electrons for which $R > R_c$ occupy atomic levels, but those for which $R < R_c$ occupy bands whose width is proportional to $\gamma = \int \phi^*(\mathbf{r} - \boldsymbol{\rho})[U(\mathbf{r}) - Z_{\text{eff}}e/r]\phi(\mathbf{r}) \, d\tau$, where $\phi(\mathbf{r})$ is the free-atom wave function, $\boldsymbol{\rho}$ is a vector joining near neighbors, and the deviation of $U(\mathbf{r})$ from a periodic array of free-atom potentials is treated as a small perturbation (79). Therefore the width of a band increases as $\boldsymbol{\rho}$ decreases due to increased overlap of the wave functions on neighboring atoms. For transition metals, the overlap of the outer s and p electrons is significantly greater than that of the d electrons, and the d bands are correspondingly narrower (see Fig. 7).

From the definition in equation 33 of the effective mass as the curvature of the $E_\mathbf{k}$ vs. $\mathbf{k}$ curve, it is apparent that near the top of the band $m^* < 0$. Therefore equation 32 may be written

$$E_k = E_0 \pm \frac{\hbar^2 \mathbf{k}^2}{2|m^*|} \tag{43}$$

where the positive sign is used near the bottom of a band, the negative sign near the top of a band. In the case of overlapping bands, there are strong interactions between states of comparable symmetry and energy so that the simple assumption $m^* = $ constant in equation 43 holds only near the top and bottom of the band and then only in the energy regions removed from those where overlap occurs. Nevertheless it will be used in Chapter III to give a semiempirical estimate of the various d subbands.

2. To obtain the number of electronic states in a Brillouin zone, it is noted that the Heisenberg uncertainty principle prohibits resolution of a state to

$$dx \, dy \, dz \, dp_x \, dp_y \, dp_z = h^3 \tag{44}$$

Since dp_x, dp_y, dp_z may be taken as quantum numbers, the Pauli exclusion principle prohibits more than two electrons, one of each spin, from occupying the same volume h^3 of phase space. Since $\mathbf{p} = \hbar \mathbf{k}$, it follows that the density of states in $\mathbf{k}$ space is

$$\rho_k = 2V/(2\pi)^3 \tag{45}$$

where V is the volume of the crystal. The volume of the first Brillouin zone is $(2\pi)^3/\Omega$, where Ω is the volume of the primitive cell of the crystal lattice.   This means that with one atom per unit cell of the Bravais lattice, a Brillouin zone contains $2N$ states, where N is the number of atoms in a crystal.   Since the volume of the first zone depends upon Ω, with ν atoms per unit cell the number of states it contains is $2N/\nu$.   If the atomic states contain an orbital degeneracy $(2l + 1)$ that is preserved by the crystal symmetry, this degeneracy is reflected in the quantum numbers $dp_x\, dp_y\, dp_z$.   Therefore the number of states in the first Brillouin zone is

$$n(BZ) = 2(2l + 1)N/\nu \tag{46}$$

(e) Thus far the discussion has been concerned with a single electron moving in the average potential of all the other electrons. Electrons corresponding to the same atomic states all move in the same average potential: therefore the occupation at $T = 0°\mathrm{K}$ of the one-electron states of a band is simply determined by putting in one electron per state in accordance with the Pauli principle.   Thus for metallic sodium, with one outer s electron ($l = 0$) per atom and one atom per primitive unit cell ($\nu = 1$), the Brillouin zone is half filled.

Wilson (685) has pointed out that if a Brillouin zone is full, the electrons occupying the states of this zone can make no contribution to the electric current. This fact follows from the definition of the zone as a region enclosing all reduced wave vectors.   Imagine all electrons of Figure 6 shifted Δk_x by an external field.   The electrons in states within Δk_x of the zone boundary are reflected to the opposite zone boundary, so that the zone remains filled and there is no transfer of charge.   This observation permits a sharp distinction between metallic conductors, semiconductors, and insulators.   Because of the high density of states in a band, a crystal with partially filled bands is a metallic conductor.   If all occupied zones (or bands) are filled, the crystal is a semiconductor if $E_g^{\text{eff}} \sim kT$, is an insulator if $E_g^{\text{eff}} \gg kT$. Although this distinction appears to explain the conductivities of most materials, the fact that ionic compounds containing transition elements are generally insulators or semiconductors, even though treatment of the d electrons by the band approach would call for partially filled d bands, supports the assertion that there is an R_c such that if $R > R_c$, the band approach is not applicable.

(f) A quantity that is important because it is related to m^* is the density of electron states $N(E)$, which is defined as

$N(E)\ dE$

$$= \frac{\text{Number of electronic states with energy between } E \text{ and } E + dE}{\text{Volume of the crystal}}$$

$$\tag{47}$$

It follows from equations 44 and 32 that

$$N(E)\ dE = \frac{1}{h^3}\ 4\pi p^2\ dp = \frac{1}{2\pi^2}\ k^2\ dk = \frac{1}{4\pi^2} \left(\frac{2m^*}{\hbar^2}\right)^{3/2} E^{1/2}\ dE \quad (48)$$

where $E = E_{\mathbf{k}} - E_0$. Precisely the same expression holds for the top of the band provided $E = E_{\text{top}} - E_{\mathbf{k}}$. For asymmetric bands defined by

$$E = \frac{\hbar^2}{2m}\ (\alpha_1 k_x^2 + \alpha_2 k_y^2 + \alpha_3 k_z^2) \tag{49}$$

instead of by equation 32, the density of states is given by

$$N(E)\ dE = \frac{1}{4\pi^2}\ \frac{2m}{\hbar^2}\ \frac{E^{1/2}\ dE}{(\alpha_1 \alpha_2 \alpha_3)^{1/2}} \tag{48'}$$

For a general $E_{\mathbf{k}}$ vs. $\mathbf{k}$ relation, equation 48 may be written

$$N(E) = \frac{1}{8\pi^3} \iint_{E sfc} \frac{dS}{|\nabla_{\mathbf{k}} E_{\mathbf{k}}|}$$

To obtain the variation of $N(E = E_F(0))$ with the number of electrons $N z_e$, where z_e is the number of electrons per atom in the band, use is made of the relation (for $T = 0°\text{K}$)

$$N z_e = 2 \int_0^{E_F(0)} N(E)\ dE = \frac{1}{3\pi^2} \left(\frac{2m^*}{\hbar^2}\right)^{3/2} [E_F(0)]^{3/2} \tag{50}$$

where the factor 2 enters because of the spin degeneracy and the Fermi energy $E_F(0)$ is the maximum energy of the occupied states at $T = 0°\text{K}$. Therefore

$$N(E_F(0)) = \frac{m^*}{2\pi\hbar^2} \left(\frac{3N z_e}{\pi}\right)^{1/3} = \frac{3N z_e}{4 E_F(0)} \tag{51}$$

provided equation 32 or 43 gives a reasonable description of $E(\mathbf{k})$.

3. *The Fermi Surface*

From the above discussion of the simple band model (no electron interactions are included), it follows that there is a surface in phase space at $T = 0°\text{K}$ across which there is a discontinuity in the occupation of electronic states, all states of lower energy having a unit probability of being occupied and all those of higher energy having a zero probability. This surface is called the Fermi surface. If electron interactions are introduced, it is apparent that no electron can continue permanently in a state of a particular momentum. The electrons must suffer accelerations, some of which put the electrons in states of higher energy than the Fermi surface E_F. Therefore the occupation probability is no longer one below E_F or zero above E_F. Nevertheless recent many-body theories (200) indicate that even if electron interactions are included, there exists a surface in momentum or k space for the electrons across which the occupation probabilities of the possible one-electron states are discontinuous and in the neighborhood of which there can exist quasi particles capable of carrying a current, contributing to the electronic specific heat, Hall coefficient, diamagnetic susceptibility, etc. Further, Luttinger (406) has shown that as for the simple band model, so for any model of interacting electrons for which perturbation series converge, the volume of k space enclosed by the Fermi surface is exactly proportional to the number of electrons per unit volume. Therefore *the Fermi surface is believed to have physical significance for the case of collective electrons in partially filled bands. There is no Fermi surface for localized electrons. For filled bands of collective electrons, the Fermi energy is in the gap of forbidden electron energies, and physical phenomena characteristic of a high density of states at the Fermi surface do not occur.* Experimental evidence for the physical reality of a Fermi surface has been obtained in several types of experiments that employ high magnetic fields at low temperatures: cyclotron resonance (721), anomalous skin effect (525), Hall effect (85,607), magnetoresistance (85), magnetic susceptibility (422). This type of experiment promises to provide important information in the next few years.

In conclusion, the principal features of collective electrons that appear to have physical significance are the Brillouin zone and bandstructure concepts that follow from the lattice periodicity and the concept of a Fermi surface.

C. MAGNETIC PROPERTIES OF COLLECTIVE ELECTRONS

According to the collective-electron model developed in the last paragraph, each state is filled with two electrons, one of each spin, up to the Fermi surface.   This means that in the absence of a magnetic field, an atom carries no net spin, and therefore no atomic moment.   It follows that any atomic moments due to collective electrons are induced either by internally or externally generated magnetic fields.   Whereas field-induced moments might be expected to contribute only negative terms to the magnetic susceptibility in accordance with Lenz's law, it is found that collective electrons also contribute a positive term arising from alterations by **H** of the spin

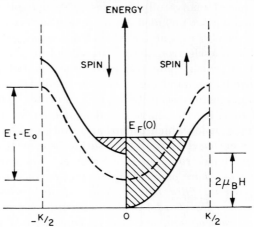

Fig. 8.   Induced, spin-originated atomic moment in the presence of a magnetic field H at $T = 0°K$.   At higher temperatures electrons near Fermi level spread out.   Internal magnetic fields induce spontaneous magnetization.   External fields induce weak (Pauli) paramagnetism.   If $E_F(0) < E_0 + \mu_B H$ or $E_F(0) > E_t - \mu_B H$, atomic moments are saturated.

populations of electron states.   (The negative term is due to alterations in the spatial orbits of the electrons.)   In order that the collective electrons be magnetized to saturation, it is necessary for these fields to split the spin degeneracy of each state by an energy that is greater than the width of the occupied (or unoccupied) portion of the band, as is illustrated in Figure 8.   From this it follows that for a given splitting of the levels, the induced spin-originated moment is larger the greater $N(E_F)$, and saturation requires a relatively narrow band.

In the case of free atoms, it was shown possible to understand intuitively how the exchange correlations give rise to internal magnetic fields responsible for Hund's maximum-$(2S + 1)$ rule.   In the case of collective electrons, in the absence of any simultaneously present, localized $(R > R_c)$ electrons outside of closed shells (i.e. contributing a net atomic spin), there is no comparable mechanism for generating large, internal magnetic fields at the atoms.   In fact the electron–atomic core electrostatic interactions may induce anti-parallel-spin correlations that are stronger than the parallel-spin cor-relations due to electron-electron interactions.   The homopolar bond of the hydrogen molecule, which forms the basis of covalent-bond concepts, illustrates forcefully how much stronger the antiparallel-spin correlations may be in the case of molecules and solids.   (For further discussion of electron correlations, see Section II-D).   It is assumed, therefore, that *in a solid, if all electrons outside of closed shells are collective $(R < R_c)$ electrons, as is the more general situation, any magnetic moment is induced by external fields.*   (Intersublattice exchange may induce localization of $R \approx R_c$ intrasublattice electrons, which in turn provides strong internal magnetic fields, as is pointed out in Chapter III in the discussion of b.c.c. transition metals.)

1. Molecules

If the collective electrons of a molecular system have no mag-netic moment in the ground state ψ_0, then the expectation value $\langle \mu_{||} \rangle \equiv (0|\mu_{||}|0) \equiv \int \psi_0^* \mu_{||} \psi_0 \, d\tau \, d\xi$ of the magnetic moment operator $\mu_{||}$ is zero.   However, the presence of an external field may induce an electron to change its spin, thus raising the system into an excited state ψ_n of energy $\Delta = E_n - E_0$ above the ground state.   If this is possible, it follows from standard perturbation methods that the ground and excited states are altered by the presence of even a small field $(H_{||} \ll \Delta)$ to become

$$\psi_0' = \psi_0 + \frac{H(n|\mu_{||}|0)}{\Delta} \psi_n \qquad \psi_n' = \psi_n - \frac{H(0|\mu_{||}|n)}{\Delta} \psi_0 \qquad (52)$$

where the matrix element $(n|\mu_{||}|0) = (0|\mu_{||}|n) \neq 0$, so that the new ground and excited states have induced moments

$$(0'|\mu_{||}|0') = 2H|(n|\mu_{||}|0)|^2/\Delta = 2H|(n|\mu|0)|^2/3\Delta = -(n'|\mu_{||}|n') \qquad (53)$$

Boltzmann statistics for the population of the two states gives

$$\langle \mu_{||} \rangle = \frac{2H|(n|\mu|0)|^2}{3\Delta} \cdot \frac{e^x - e^{-x}}{e^x + e^{-x}} \qquad x = \Delta/2kT \qquad (54)$$

Substitution into equation 9 and summation over all excited states and over N molecules gives

$$\chi_{mp}^{(1)}\binom{\text{collective}}{\text{molecular}} = \frac{N \sum_n |(n|\boldsymbol{\mu}|0)|^2}{3kT} \qquad (x \ll 1) \qquad (55)$$

$$\chi_{mp}^{(2)}\binom{\text{collective}}{\text{molecular}} = \frac{2}{3} N \sum_n \frac{|(n|\boldsymbol{\mu}|0)|^2}{E_n - E_0} \qquad (x \gg 1) \qquad (55')$$

The diamagnetic term for molecules is given by equation 12, just as in the case of atoms, except that the r_i for the electrons may be considerably greater in molecules than in atoms. Van Vleck (628) has emphasized that temperature-independent susceptibilities cannot be accounted for by equation 12 alone since contributions of the type expressed by equation 55' are always present and may even be of sufficient magnitude to give a net *positive*, temperature-independent susceptibility from field-induced atomic moments.

In a series of comprehensive magnetochemical investigations, Pascal (501,602) found that the molecular susceptibility of diamagnetic, organic compounds can be closely represented by

$$\chi_m/N = \sum n_A \chi_A + \eta$$

where n_A is the number of atoms of susceptibility χ_A in the molecule and η is a corrective constant that depends on the nature of the linkages between the atoms. In this expression, χ_A is not the free-atom (or ion) value, but that characteristic of the atom in single-bond ($\eta = 0$) coordination. The presence of double or triple bonds concentrates electronic charge in the bond and decreases the magnitude of the diamagnetic contribution. This decrease is accounted for in the corrective constant η. As would be expected from this relation, the susceptibilities of organic isomers are approximately the same. Nevertheless definite, though usually small, differences do exist (68).

2. Solids

In the case of solids, it is necessary to use Fermi-Dirac statistics rather than Boltzmann statistics. For a finite temperature T, these statistics give, for the number of occupied states of a given spin, not equation 50 but

$$N_s = \frac{1}{2} N z_e = \int_0^\infty N(E) f(E)\, dE$$

$$f(E) = 1/\{\exp\left[(E - E_F)/kT\right] + 1\} \qquad (56)$$

From Figure 8, the net magnetization is

$$M = [N_s(\uparrow) - N_s(\downarrow)]\mu_B$$

$$= \mu_B \int_0^\infty [N(E + \mu_B H) - N(E - \mu_B H)]f(E)\,dE$$

which for small H and series expansion of $N(\epsilon) \sim \epsilon^{1/2}$ (equation 48 which is based on 32), is

$$M \approx 2\mu_B^2 HI \qquad I = \int_0^\infty \frac{dN(E)}{dE} f(E)\,dE \qquad (57)$$

The integral I is a standard integral of the Fermi-Dirac statistics with the solution (419):

$$I = N(E_F) + \frac{\pi^2}{6}(kT)^2 \frac{d^2N(E)}{dE^2}\bigg|_{E_F} + \dots$$

At low temperatures the higher terms are negligible, and equation 57 reduces, with the aid of Equation 51 and

$$E_F = E_F(0)\left[1 - \frac{\pi^2}{12}\left(\frac{kT}{E_F(0)}\right)^2 + \dots\right],$$

to

$$\chi_{mp} = 2\mu_B^2 N(E_F) \approx 2\mu_B^2 N(E_F(0)) = 3Nz_e\mu_B^2/2E_F(0) \qquad (58)$$

This weak paramagnetism is known as *Pauli paramagnetism* (504). In the case of broad bands, the approximation $kT \ll E_F(0)$ is good even above room temperature. In the case of narrow bands and high temperatures, it may be necessary to include temperature-dependent terms.

Although classical mechanics does not provide a diamagnetic contribution to the susceptibility from collective electrons (induced internal currents and surface currents cancel one another out), Landau (383) discovered that the running waves of quantum mechanics are modified by $\mathbf{H}$ to give a diamagnetic susceptibility $-1/3$ that of the paramagnetic susceptibility. Thus

$$\chi_m \text{ (collective, solids)} = Nz_e\mu_B^2/E_F(0) \qquad (59)$$

provided equation 32 is a reasonable approximation for the $E_\mathbf{k}$ vs. $\mathbf{k}$ curve. (An expression for the diamagnetic term given a general $E_\mathbf{k}$ vs. $\mathbf{k}$ curve has been worked out recently by Hebborn and Sondheimer (261).) A diamagnetic correction for the positive atomic cores (eq. 12) must also be added. The various susceptibility possibilities are summarized in Table I.

TABLE I.   Magnetic Susceptibilities for Various Situations

[Paramagnetic electrons refer only to those outside of close shells; diamagnetic electrons include all electrons (r_{ci} refers to an ith core electron).][a]

Electrons	Paramagnetic			Diamagnetic
	$\Delta \ll kT$[b]	$\Delta \gg kT$[b]	Spin only	
	Free Atoms			
Collective	$\dfrac{N\mu_B^2}{3kT}[4S(S+1)+L(L+1)]$	$N\left(\dfrac{\mu_J^2}{3kT}+\alpha_p\right)$	$N\dfrac{4S(S+1)\mu_B^2}{3kT}$	$-\dfrac{Ne^2}{6mc^2}\sum_i \overline{r_i^2}$
		Molecules		
Collective	$\dfrac{N}{3kT}\sum_n |(n|\mu|0)|^2$	$\dfrac{2N}{3}\sum_n \dfrac{|(n|\mu|0)|^2}{E_n-E_0}$	As given for $\Delta \ll kT$, $\Delta \gg kT$	$-\dfrac{Ne^2}{6mc^2}\sum_i \overline{r_i^2}$
Localized	$\dfrac{N\mu_B^2}{3kT}[4S(S+1)+L(L+1)]$	$N\left(\dfrac{\mu_J^2}{3kT}+\alpha_p\right)$	$N\dfrac{4S(S+1)\mu_B^2}{3kT}$	$-\dfrac{Ne^2}{6mc^2}\sum_i \overline{r_i^2}$
Loc. + coll.	Strong internal, molecular field H_{ex} induces a contribution to the localized moment from the collective electrons equal to χ_{mp}(coll.) H_{ex}			
		Solids		
Collective	$\dfrac{3Nz_i\mu_B^2}{2kT_F}$		$\dfrac{3Nz_i\mu_B^2}{2kT_F}$	$-\dfrac{Nz_i\mu_B^2}{2kT_F}-\dfrac{Ne^2}{6mc^2}\sum_i \overline{r_{ci}^2}$
Localized	$\dfrac{N\mu_B^2}{3kT}[4S(S+1)+L(L+1)]$	$N\left(\dfrac{\mu_J^2}{3kT}+\alpha_p\right)$	$N\dfrac{4S(S+1)\mu_B^2}{3kT}$	$-\dfrac{Ne^2}{6mc^2}\sum_i \overline{r_i^2}$
Loc. + coll.	Strong internal, molecular field H_{ex} induces a contribution to the localized atomic moment from the collective electrons of			

$$\mu_c = \sum_i z_i q_i \mu_B \quad \text{with} \quad q_i \equiv 3\mu_B H_{ex}/2kT_{Fi}$$

[a] $\mu_J = g[J(J+1)]^{1/2}$, $g \equiv 1 + [J(J+1) + S(S+1) - L(L+1)]/2J(J+1)$, $\alpha_p = [\mu_B^2/6(2J+1)][E(J+1)/(E_{J+1}-E_J) - F(J)/(E_J - E_{J-1})]$, $F(J) = J^{-1}[(S+L+1)^2 - J^2][J^2 - (S-L)^2]$, $kT_F \equiv E_F(0)$.

[b] Δ refers to multiplet splitting in case of localized electrons, to $E_n - E_0$ in case of collective electrons.

3. *Localized Electrons Simultaneously Present*

Localized electrons in a partially filled shell carry a net spin (provided Hund's rule is obeyed), and interactions between these localized electrons and the collective electrons gives rise to a large effective field $\mathbf{H}_{ex}$ acting on the collective electrons. Since the intraatomic exchange correlations minimize the electrostatic interactions between electrons of parallel spin, $\mathbf{H}_{ex}$ is directed parallel to the atomic moment due to localized electrons. Below a magnetic-ordering temperature, this internal field induces a contribution to the atomic moment from the collective electrons whether the localized electrons are ordered parallel or antiparallel. From equation 58, this contribution is

$$\mu_c = \sum_i z_i q_i \mu_B \qquad q_i \equiv 3\mu_B H_{ex}/2[E_F(0)]_i \leq 1 \qquad (60)$$

where z_i is the number of electrons per atom in the ith band if it is less than half filled, and $[E_F(0)]_i$ is the Fermi surface relative to the bottom of this band; but z_i is the number of holes per atom in the ith band if it is more than half filled, and $[E_F(0)]_i$ is the Fermi surface relative to the top of this band. For a broad s band, this contribution may be (527) 0.1 to $0.2z_i\mu_B$ and for a narrow d band it may therefore be as high as 0.5 to $0.7z_i\mu_B$. In the case of ferromagnetic order, this contribution may attain its maximum value of $z_i\mu_B$ (see Section II-D and Chapter III, Section III).

D. ELECTRON CORRELATION CONSIDERATIONS

There are two points to be emphasized:

1. It is observed empirically that atoms with two or more p electrons (four or more s–p electrons) in outer, unfilled shells tend to form homopolar bonds with one another, thus giving the $(8 - N)$ rule, and to form covalent or ionic bonds with other atoms, the degree of covalence depending upon the electronegativity difference.

2. In the MO approach appropriate to outer s and p electrons, the simple formalism does not distinguish between a covalent-ionic band and a metallic band. The use of determinantal (antisymmetrized) wave functions automatically introduces correlations between electrons of parallel spin. Traditionally the many-electron wave function has, at best, been represented by a single Slater determinant of one-electron wave functions (Hartree-Fock approximation), whereas the true wave function would be given by a series of such determi-

nants, the additional determinants representing *configuration inter-actions*. Overhauser (497) has shown that within the Hartree-Fock approximation, relaxation of the usual spin restriction, viz. that the spin part of the one-electron wave functions can always be factored out, gives a free-electron ground state in which there is also consid-erable antiparallel-spin correlation. These correlations have the form of spirals and are called *spin-density waves*. Since this type of correlation involves a rearrangement of states at the Fermi surface, it is only applicable to partially filled bands. Except for one or two cases, which are mentioned in the text, these correlations are prob-ably not important for the materials under discussion, and so this concept is not developed here. Löwdin (400) has also pointed out that part of the antiparallel-spin correlation can be obtained by *letting electrons with different spins occupy different orbitals in space*, so that they can get a chance to avoid each other. This is partic-ularly appropriate for a two-sublattice structure with filled bonding states, empty antibonding states, and he calls his method of treating the relaxed Hartree-Fock equations the *alternant molecular-orbital method*. Other attempts to consider the correlations between elec-trons of antiparallel spin usually are concerned with the ground-state energy for a system of interacting, free electrons in *a uniform* back-ground of positive charge (see for example the work of Bohm and Pines (524)).

The fact that Pauling's valence-bond approach, which assumes stability for the covalent-bond configuration, is so useful a guide for chemical intuition strongly suggests that in covalent-ionic crystals electron pairs are a more fundamental unit than single electrons moving in an average potential. In the case of diatomic H_2 the stability of the singlet relative to the triplet states falls out of the formalism discussed earlier. This conclusion is also reached from consideration of the fact that electrons of like spin exclude one another from the same region of space (720), so that there is less electronic charge for binding in the region of orbital overlap if the spins are parallel (triplet) than if they are antiparallel (singlet). The problem for solids, therefore, is to explicitly introduce into the formalism a mechanism whereby those crystalline symmetries that avoid the necessity of electron exclusion in the region of orbital overlap are stabilized relative to those that do not. This is done in a qualitative way by Pauling (505). Like Löwdin (400), Slater (582) has pointed out that with a two-sublattice structure, it is possible to relax the requirement that orbitals of different spin are identical, and Slater and Koster (586) have used this MO formalism to obtain a qualitative description of the antiferromagnetism of metallic Cr. O'ohata (494), in discussing diamond, considers an assembly of orbital pairs.

It therefore appears that the following three concepts must be explicitly introduced into any formal description of the chemical bond if chemical intuition is to be maintained:

1. A distinction must be made between those structures that are composed of two sublattices such that an atom of one has only nearest neighbors belonging to the other (hereafter referred to as a *two-sublattice structure*) and those that are not.

2. In a two-sublattice structure with half-filled, overlapping atomic orbitals, the spins associated with the two sublattices must be spin paired within any near-neighbor bond. This was done by O'ohata for diamond by the construction of a total wave function that is the product of pairs of semilocalized wave functions, the valence-electron pairs always consisting of an electron orbital from each sublattice. If an atomic wave function overlaps equally atomic orbitals of more than one near neighbor, construction of suitable orbital pairs is complicated by the fact that a single pair is shared over more than one bond. This situation corresponds to Pauling's synchronous and pivotal resonances. However, Van Vleck (634) has pointed out that if an s band is half full (one conduction s electron per atom), it is possible to construct linear combinations of $4s$ wave functions such that the spin of the $4s$ band alternately points north and south as one passes from one sublattice to another and such that the translational kinetic energy is equivalent to that for the conventional set of wave functions. Analogy between a pair of electrons, one from each sublattice, with the electron pair of the H_2 molecule, one from each atom, is obvious; and it appears that, *if the near-neighbor-overlapping atomic orbitals of a two-sublattice structure are half filled, optimum binding occurs when the electron pairs are singlets.* (See the discussions of Heisenberg exchange integrals, Chapter III, Section I-B, for further justification.) The general conclusions of the simple band theory, which depend only upon the periodicity of the lattice and the concept of a Fermi surface, are simultaneously maintained.

3. If the two-sublattice condition were not fulfilled or if the overlapping atomic orbitals were more than half filled, it would be im-

possible to avoid electron exclusions in all near-neighbor bonds simultaneously, and parallel-spin correlations become important. Therefore three types of collective-electron bands can be distinguished (217): bonding, antibonding, and metallic.

Bonding and antibonding bands are associated with two-sublattice structures, metallic bands with other structures. Given a two-sublattice structure with near-neighbor-overlapping atomic orbitals half or less filled, the band of allowed energy states separates into a bonding portion (no electron exclusion from region of overlap of near-neighbor atomic functions) and a portion containing less stable, antibonding states (electrons in these states are forced to exclude electrons from the region of overlap of near-neighbor atomic orbitals). If the atoms of the two sublattices differ in kind (as in NaCl) or in the orientation of their near-neighbor configurations (as in Ge), the bonding and antibonding portions of the band may be split by a discrete energy gap since there are two atoms per unit cell.* The lower band is called a bonding band, the upper an antibonding band. If the orbitals are half filled, the bonding band is full, the antibonding band empty; and the material may be a semiconductor or an insulator, depending upon the size of E_g^{eff} between the two subbands. If there is a large electronegativity difference and a large anion/cation size ratio between the two sublattices, the bonding electrons belong to the electronegative sublattice, and the antibonding states are associated with the electropositive sublattice. The larger the electronegativity difference and/or anion/cation size ratio the larger the potential difference at the two sublattices and therefore the greater E_g^{eff}. Thus ionic materials tend to be insulators, covalent crystals to be semiconductors. However, it must be borne in mind that if the electropositive sublattice contains transition element cations with partially filled d shells, then metallic conductivity can occur on the transition element sublattice should the transition element separation be $R_{tt} < R_c(nd)$, where n is the principal quantum number of the outer d electrons. The importance of this fact is discussed in Chapter III, Section II.

Given a two-sublattice structure with near-neighbor-overlapping atomic orbitals that are more than half filled, it is no longer possible

---

* The b.c.c. metals do not have two atoms per unit cell (unless antiferromagnetic and below the spin-ordering temperature), so that there is no splitting of the bonding and antibonding portions of the band.

to avoid exclusion of electronic charge from the region of strong atomic-orbital overlap. The situation is analogous to the three-electron bond of H_2^- which is stabilized by a sharing of the antiparallel electron between two hydrogen atoms whose electron spins are parallel. Such a bond is about half as strong as the electron-pair bond of H_2 (see Pauling (505)). Intuitively it follows that in a solid the collective electrons may give rise to a net moment equivalent to a magnetization of the electrons in excess of half filled, overlapping atomic orbitals, the maximum moment occurring with atomic orbitals $3/4$ filled. Conceptually this is equivalent to a spin-paired bonding band and a magnetized antibonding band. Illustration of these concepts comes from the magnetic susceptibilities of N_2, NO, and O_2. In these diatomic molecules the σ bond is split into stable, occupied bonding states and unstable, empty antibonding states. In N_2 the π bonds are similarly split, so that N_2 is exceptionally stable (bonding energy = 225.2 Kcal/mole), whereas NO and O_2 have one and two extra π electrons, respectively. Thus the π orbitals of O_2 are $3/4$ filled, and the binding energy of O_2 is 117.3 Kcal/mole. Significantly, N_2 is diamagnetic and has a singlet ground state whereas paramagnetic NO and O_2 have doublet and triplet ground states, respectively.

If the two-sublattice condition does not exist, there can be no electron correlations that avoid exclusion of electron charge from the region between positive atomic cores. Therefore the bottom of the valence-electron band should be less stable than that of a corresponding bonding band, the top more stable than that of a corresponding antibonding band. Such a band is called metallic as it is characteristic of the close-packed metals.

It should be noted that the greater stability of a bonding vs. a metallic band favors a two-sublattice structure that permits a filled bonding band, an empty antibonding band. Although the core-core repulsive forces favor close-packed structures, this effect is rarely decisive if there are several electrons outside of closed shells. Thus if the collective electrons are all outer s and p electrons, bonding-band formation gives rise to the electron ordering responsible for the $(8 - N)$ rule. In the case of d electrons, similar electron ordering may occur below the melting point (entropy favors disorder and crystallization is due largely to outer s and p electrons). Such ordering gives rise to a martensitic phase change, the low-temperature phase being a two-sublattice structure.

Further, it is observed experimentally that electron-pair bonds are frequently associated with anisotropic, i.e. directed, atomic orbitals. This gives rise to "open" structures. However, the electrostatic (Madelung) energy associated with ionic crystals favors close packing: Therefore largely ionic crystals favor more close-packed, two-sublattice structures such as rock salt versus zinc blende. In the case of two-sublattice structures induced by d electrons, electron-pair bonds are generally prohibited by the metallic or ionic outer s and p electrons that favor close packing. Nevertheless, it will be found in Chapter III, Section II that, if transition element cations are small relative to the anion interstice and simultaneously have $R_{tt} \approx R_c$, electron-pair bonds may be formed below a critical temperature.

The significance of these considerations for magnetism lies in the fact that *the predominant coupling between atomic moments due to localized electrons is usually indirect, the collective electrons playing the role of intermediary. Conversely, a knowledge of the type of magnetic coupling provides information about the correlations among the collective electrons.*

E. LOCALIZED ELECTRONS IN A CRYSTALLINE FIELD

Localized electrons are atomic-like, so that the considerations for the free atom are pertinent provided three additional effects are taken into account: the strong crystalline (ligand) fields, which reflect the symmetry of the lattice, and the elastic and magnetic coupling between neighboring atoms. In this section the results of ligand-field theory are briefly reviewed. (An excellent presentation of the subject is given in reference 233a.) In a crystal, only d and f outer electrons can be localized $(R > R_c)$. (Localized s–p electrons at an impurity center in a semiconductor represent a special case that is not pertinent to the present discussion.)

1. *The Hamiltonian*

In a solid, if the electrons outside of closed shells are not s electrons, the Hamiltonian for localized outer electrons with the same quantum numbers n, l is

$$H = \sum_k \left(\frac{p_k^2}{2m} - \frac{Z_{\text{eff}}e^2}{r_k} \right) + \sum_{j<k} \frac{e^2}{r_{jk}}$$
$$+ V_{LS} + V_{cf} + V_\lambda + \sum_{ij} J_{ij}\mathbf{S}_i \cdot \mathbf{S}_j \quad (61)$$

where the interaction between the magnetic moment of the nucleus and the magnetic field set up by the orbital and spin moments of the electrons (energy $\sim 10^{-2}$ cm^{-1}) (175) is omitted, V_{cf} represents the ligand-field potential, V_{LS} represents the magnetic interactions between the electron spins and the orbits, and the subscripts j, k refer to the outer electrons.   For Russell Saunders coupling, that is if the states have definite L and S, the spin-orbit interaction is given by equation 8.   These first four terms describe the free-ion problem, and the last two terms introduce coupling between the ions, V_λ giving any elastic coupling due to distortions of the cation interstices and the last term the magnetic-exchange coupling.

Solution of the Schroedinger equation, $H\psi = E\psi$, appropriate to this problem has only been accomplished by means of successive perturbation calculations.   The zero-order approximation is a "spherical" approximation in which a given outer electron is assumed to move in the *average* potential of the other outer electrons as well as of the core electrons.   Then the free-ion Hamiltonian becomes

$$H = \sum_k \left(\frac{p_k^2}{2m} - \frac{Z'_{\text{eff}} e^2}{r_k} \right) + V_{\text{el}} + V_{LS} + V_{cf} \qquad (61')$$

where V_{el} is the correction to the spherical approximation for the true electrostatic interaction between outer electrons.   The portion of the Hamiltonian that is in parentheses has the form of equation 1, so that the angular dependence of the wave equation in zero-order approximation is immediately known from equation 2.   This starting point contains the assumption that the term splittings are much greater than any splittings due to V_{el}, V_{LS}, or V_{cf}.

From symmetry considerations alone, it is possible to determine qualitatively how the term degeneracies of the zero-order problem are split by the perturbations.   Since several complicated effects contribute simultaneously to the strength of the ligand fields (see footnote, page 52), the magnitude of the potential V_{cf} cannot, at present, be calculated from first principles, and it is best to obtain the magnitude of the splittings it induces from the experimental Stark splittings observed in the optical spectra of these crystals.

Investigation of the experimental data indicates that the strengths of the ligand fields fall into three groups:

1. *Strong fields* with $\Delta_{LS} \ll \Delta_{\text{el}} \lesssim \Delta_{cf}$, where the electrostatic splitting is $\Delta_{\text{el}} \sim 10^4$ cm^{-1}: This situation occurs only with d electrons,

and then only if there is considerable covalent bonding between the paramagnetic ion and the ligands. This occurs principally in the $4d$ and $5d$ series, but it is also found in the $3d$ series, especially if the cation is in an abnormally high valence state, i.e. Fe^{4+}, Ni^{3+}, Co^{3+}. Strong fields may be manifest by a breakdown of Hund's rule: the cations are then said to be in a *low-spin state*.

2. *Medium fields* with $\Delta_{LS} \lesssim \Delta_{cf} \ll \Delta_{el}$: It is the relative energies that are important; the multiplet splitting may vary from 10^{-1} to 10^4 cm^{-1} (see Sommerfeld's (594) fine structure formula). In this case V_{el} is the first perturbation effect, and the cubic part of V_{cf} is treated as a perturbation before spin-orbit effects are calculated. For distortions from cubic symmetry, it is necessary to consider carefully the relative magnitudes of V_t (that part of V_{cf} due to departures from cubic symmetry) and V_{LS}.

3. *Weak fields* with $\Delta_{cf} \ll \Delta_{LS}$: In this case the ligand fields merely perturb the multiplet structure of the free atom.

In the $3d$ iron transition group, the ligand fields are usually of moderate strength whereas in the $4d$ and $5d$ palladium and platinum groups the ligand fields are strong. In the $4f$ and $5f$ rare earth and actinide groups, the ligand fields acting on the f electrons are considerably weaker than the spin-orbit coupling. Materials of principal interest in magnetism are those containing iron group atoms or ions, and in this brief review attention is almost entirely confined to the iron group elements, compounds, and alloys, which usually represent the medium field case.

The standard perturbation procedure is to consider only those matrix elements that connect the various $3d$ orbitals. With $\Delta_{el} > \Delta_{cf}$, free-atom considerations provide the number of possible terms resulting from V_{el}, and Hund's rule gives their order. The lowest term may be n-fold degenerate. Then matrix elements with the cubic-field potential between these n-fold degenerate states give the splittings and ordering of the terms resulting from the cubic part of the ligand fields. The various terms can be obtained from relatively simple group-theoretical arguments, but the magnitude of the splittings and their order can only be obtained by actual calculations of the matrix elements. The eigenfunctions are, as usual, obtained by finding that linear combination of the degenerate orbitals that diagonalizes the various $\nu_i \times \nu_i$ submatrices, where $\sum_i \nu_i = n$ and i designates the various terms due to ligand-field splitting. If the orbital angular momentum is quenched by the cubic ligand fields, then Δ_{LS} is very small. In this case splittings due to distortions from cubic symmetry Δ_t are $\Delta_t > \Delta_{LS}$, so that if noncubic fields are present or if the ground state is still degenerate, matrix elements with V_t are considered next for the small $\nu_i \times \nu_i$ submatrices. Again simple group-theoretical arguments give the number of terms into which the degenerate states are split, but an actual calculation of the eigenfunctions and matrix elements is required for a proper ordering of the terms and for the magnitude of the splittings. If the orbital angular momentum is not quenched, then Δ_{LS} may be larger than any Δ_t that might be spontaneously generated to remove a ground state degeneracy (see discussion of Jahn-Teller effect). In all of the above cases, it is possible to ignore the spin part of the wave functions. For the spin-orbit perturbations V_{LS}, however, the complete wave function must be considered, and the complete degeneracies, including spin, are important for possible term splittings. Again group-theoretical arguments provide the various possible terms into which the degenerate levels may be split, but actual calculation of the matrix elements is required in this case to determine whether all of the possible splittings occur. Only the original degenerate submatrix is diagonalized in the determination of the eigenfunctions: the introduction of off-diagonal matrix elements outside of this submatrix introduces only higher order effects.

2. Symmetry of the Zero-Order Functions

From equation 2, the angular dependencies for the zero-order d wave functions are:

$$\left.\begin{aligned} \psi_{\pm 2} &\sim \sin^2 \theta \exp (\pm i2\phi) \\ \psi_{\pm 1} &\sim \sin \theta \cos \theta \exp (\pm i\phi) \\ \psi_0 &\sim (3 \cos^2 \theta - 1) \end{aligned}\right\} \tag{62}$$

where the subscripts refer to the magnetic quantum number m_l. In order to obtain the real functions that are plotted in Figure 2, the following linear combinations of degenerate wave functions are used:

$$\begin{aligned} A &\equiv \psi_0 \sim [2z^2 - x^2 - y^2]/r^2 = [(z^2 - x^2) + (z^2 - y^2)]/r^2 \\ B &\equiv [\psi_2 + \psi_{-2}]/\sqrt{2} \sim [x^2 - y^2]/r^2 \\ C &\equiv [\psi_2 - \psi_{-2}]/\sqrt{2} \sim xy/r^2 \\ D &\equiv [\psi_1 + \psi_{-1}]/\sqrt{2} \sim zx/r^2 \\ E &\equiv [\psi_1 - \psi_{-1}]/\sqrt{2} \sim yz/r^2 \end{aligned} \tag{63}$$

3. Ligand-Field Splittings

To find the splittings that are caused by the ligand fields, it is assumed that $V_{cf} = V_c^t + V_t$ consists of a large term V_c^t of cubic symmetry with a smaller term V_t to describe departures from cubic symmetry. (Consideration of hexagonal symmetry is omitted from the present discussion.) Therefore the first task is to determine the cubic-field splittings of the localized-$3d$-electron levels; the relative magnitudes of V_t and V_{LS} must be considered subsequently. Various authors (1,46,66) have treated this problem with the aid of group theory. The mathematical problem requires a representation of the ligand-field potential and calculation of the matrix elements between the fivefold degenerate orbital states. The surrounding ligands are regarded as point charges that do not overlap the paramagnetic ion,*

* Although this assumption provides an acceptable formalism for the theory, there is as yet no conclusive theory of the origins of the ligand fields, so that the magnitudes of the splittings are best obtained experimentally. The point-charge model neglects the overlap of the electron clouds of neighboring atoms, and these overlap effects have several important consequences. In the first place, the potential satisfies Poisson's, not Laplace's equation; and attempts (351,452) to calculate this "classical" effect of the overlap show that in the case of cubic symmetry, it reduces, or even reverses (contrary to experiment), the level splittings obtained from the point-charge model. Tanabe and Sugano (611) have pointed out that the nonorthogonality of the overlapping orbitals corrects for the "classical" effect. Cation electrons are excluded from the overlapping, nonorthogonal orbitals because the anion orbitals are full. Another mechanism that will cause splitting of the orbital levels is possible coordinate covalence between an anion and an empty overlapped, nonorthogonal cation orbital. Owen (498) has pointed out how this effect can explain the discrepancy between optical and magnetic determinations of level splittings of some hydrated salts. Related to this is the partial covalency of the superexchange mechanism responsible for indirect coupling of the atomic moments. Since coordinate-covalent stabilization is greatest if the anion orbitals overlap empty cation orbitals and is greater if the cation orbitals are half filled (corresponding to three-electron bond) than if full, this effect also acts as a repulsive potential for the cation electrons. Kanamori (318) has shown that for FeO and CoO this effect amounts to an energy of several thousand inverse centimeters. Thus the magnitude of the splittings must be considered the combined result of these various complicated effects. Phillips (514) has recently presented a method for calculating crystal-field splittings that also provides a qualitative justification for the empirical success of the Van Vleck point-ion approximation in deriving the ligand-field potential. However, there is considerable experimental evidence that covalent bonding effects play an appreciable role, and that the surrounding ions cannot be treated as simple point charges. Therefore the point-charge model is not a fundamental theory even though it has provided a semi-empirical basis for the interpretation of a wide range of phenomena.

so that the electrostatic potential is assumed to obey Laplace's equation $\nabla^2 V_c^l = 0$. Since the solutions of this equation are Legendre polynomials, the potential is expanded in terms of spherical harmonics. The first term in the expansion is a constant and $V_c^l = V_0 + V_c$. The constant term V_0 shifts all of the levels of a given configuration by the same amount. Therefore it has no significance for the magnetic symmetry and optical properties of crystals containing transition elements. However, it strongly influences the lattice energy and the heat of solution of the paramagnetic ion. Symmetry considerations are used to drastically reduce the number of terms in the expansion of V_c.

In order to determine into how many Stark terms a given energy level splits when put into a ligand field without making a detailed calculation of the values, the group-theoretical methods of Bethe (66) are convenient. In this method it is noted that the spherical harmonics $Y_l^{m_l}(\theta,\phi)$ transform according to the lth irreducible representation of the continuous rotation group. (The ligand fields perturb the spatial part of the electron orbitals directly; they may influence the spin only indirectly via the spatial part of the orbitals and the Pauli exclusion principle.) That is, for a given angular momentum l, the spherical harmonics give the basis of a $(2l + 1)$-dimensional representation D^l of the continuous rotation group. The character of these representations for the class of rotations through an angle ψ is given by

$$\chi^l(\theta) = \sin (l + \tfrac{1}{2})\psi / \sin \tfrac{1}{2}\psi \qquad (64)$$

The symmetry group of the electron of a free ion is the full rotation group since the electron wave functions are invariant under rotation about, and inversion in, the origin of the central force field, the nucleus. It is for this reason that each level l for the free atom belongs to the l representation group D^l. All the ligand-field groups are subgroups of the continuous rotation group and possess lower symmetry. Because of this lower symmetry, the originally irreducible representations for the free ion will, in general, become reducible if the ion is placed in a crystal. Now a theorem of group theory states: *The character of a reducible representation can be expressed as a linear combination of the characters of the irreducible representations contained within it.* Therefore to find the Stark splitting caused by a ligand field of a given symmetry, it is only necessary to find the number of times each irreducible representation of the crystal point group is contained in the l representation. This is done by means of the group-theoretical relation

$$\sum_\kappa g(\kappa)\chi^\alpha(\kappa)\chi(\kappa) = ha_\alpha \qquad (65)$$

where $g(\kappa)$ is the number of elements in the class κ, h is the number of elements in the group, a_α is the number of times the α irreducible representation with character χ^α is repeated in the reducible representation with character χ. The character table for the irreducible representations of the cubic group is given in Table II. Decom-

TABLE II

Character Table for the Cubic Group with Its Five Classes

[κ_1 contains the identity operation; κ_2 contains three 180° rotations about x, y, z axes, respectively; κ_3 contains six 90° rotations ($+$ and $-$) about the x, y, z axes; κ_4 contains six 180° rotations about the six $\langle 110 \rangle$ axes; κ_5 contains eight 120° rotations ($+$ and $-$) about the four $\langle 111 \rangle$ axes. The d wave functions are even and therefore operations involving inversion provide a redundant set. The degeneracy within a representation is given by κ_1. The Bethe (66) and Mulliken (457a) notations are compared.]

Representation		$\kappa_1 = E$ (1 el.)	$\kappa_2 = C_2$ (3 el.)	$\kappa_3 = C_4$ (6 el.)	$\kappa_4 = C_2$ (6 el.)	$\kappa_5 = C_3$ (8 el.)
Bethe	Mulliken					
Γ_1	A_{1g}	1	1	1	1	1
Γ_2	A_{2g}	1	1	-1	-1	1
Γ_3	E_g	2	2	0	0	-1
Γ_4	T_{1g}	3	-1	1	-1	0
Γ_5	T_{2g}	3	-1	-1	1	0

position of the $(2l + 1)$-fold degenerate levels by cubic-field symmetry is given in Table III for various values of l. Distortions from cubic to a lower symmetry may further remove the degeneracies. Similar considerations for tetragonal and trigonal symmetry give the decompositions of the cubic-field representations shown in Table IV. These latter splittings are small compared to the cubic-field splittings since $V_t \ll V_c$.

A number of interesting facts emerge from this treatment. It is seen that P states remain threefold degenerate in cubic fields, but are split by a tetragonal distortion into a twofold and singlefold degenerate state. For a D state, or one d electron outside of closed

TABLE III

Character of Classes of Cubic Symmetry in the $(2L+1)$-Dimensional Representation D^L of the Continuous Rotation Group and Their Resolution into Irreducible Representations of Cubic Symmetry

		Character table				Decomposition, or a_α					No. of terms
	E	C_z	C_4	C_2	C_3						
L	$\psi = 0$	$\psi = \pi$	$\psi = \pi/2$	$\psi = \pi$	$\psi = 2\pi/3$	Γ_1	Γ_2	Γ_3	Γ_4	Γ_5	
S 0	1	1	1	1	1	1	0	0	0	0	1
P 1	3	−1	1	−1	0	0	0	0	1	0	1
D 2	5	1	−1	1	−1	0	0	1	0	1	2
F 3	7	−1	−1	−1	1	0	1	0	1	1	3
G 4	9	1	1	1	0	1	0	1	1	1	4
H 5	11	−1	1	−1	−1	0	0	1	2	1	4
I 6	13	1	−1	1	1	1	1	1	1	2	6

shells, the fivefold-degenerate state of the free ion splits into a threefold and a twofold degenerate level. (The twofold spin degeneracies associated with each orbital are to be considered separately. For a single outer electron $V_{el} = 0$.) The reason for this splitting is intuitively obvious from a consideration of the symmetry of the d wave functions of equation 63 shown in Figure 2 and the four-, six-, eight-, and twelve-coordinated cubic interstices shown in Figure 9. In the six-coordinated structure (octahedral interstice), the two functions A, B are directed towards the ligands whereas C, D, E are directed away from them. The equivalence of the functions C, D, E is

TABLE IV

Relationship of Irreducible Representations
for Tetragonal and Trigonal Symmetry
to Those for Cubic Symmetry

Cubic	Tetragonal	Cubic	Trigonal
Γ_1	$\rightarrow$ Γ_{t1}	Γ_1	$\rightarrow$ Γ_{T1}
Γ_2	$\rightarrow$ Γ_{t2}	Γ_2	$\rightarrow$ Γ_{T2}
Γ_3	$\rightarrow$ $\Gamma_{t1} + \Gamma_{t2}$	Γ_3	$\rightarrow$ Γ_{T3}
Γ_4	$\rightarrow$ $\Gamma_{t3} + \Gamma_{t5}$	Γ_4	$\rightarrow$ $\Gamma_{T2} + \Gamma_{T3}$
Γ_5	$\rightarrow$ $\Gamma_{t4} + \Gamma_{t5}$	Γ_5	$\rightarrow$ $\Gamma_{T1} + \Gamma_{T3}$

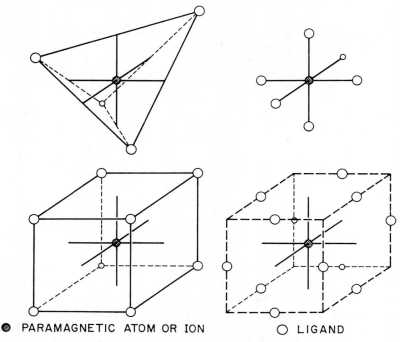

● PARAMAGNETIC ATOM OR ION   ○ LIGAND

Fig. 9. Symmetries of four-, six-, eight-, and twelve-coordinated ligands relative to Cartesian reference frame for d wave functions of Figure 2.

immediately obvious. The electrons of the corresponding threefold degenerate state Γ_5 are designated γ_5 or d_ϵ (Bethe) or t_{2g} (Mulliken). The equivalence of A, B can be seen from equation 63 where A is written as a linear combination of functions similar to B. The electrons of the corresponding twofold degenerate state Γ_3 are designated γ_3 or d_γ (Bethe) or e_g (Mulliken). Further, the six-coordinated structure generally occurs in ionic compounds in which the ligands are anions, the paramagnetic ion is a cation. In this case the γ_3 (d_γ or e_g) electrons in the Γ_3 orbitals suffer a greater electrostatic repulsion from the negatively charged anion than do the γ_5 (d_ϵ or t_{2g}) electrons, so that the Γ_3 level is at a higher energy than the Γ_5 level. This splitting is generally designated in the literature as $\Delta = 10Dq$, where Dq is defined by

$$-4Dq \equiv (C|V_c|C) \tag{66}$$

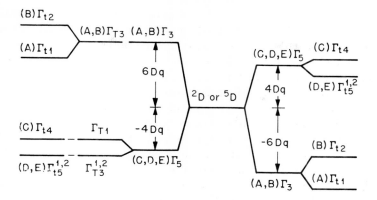

Fig. 10.   One-electron ligand-field splittings.   Trigonal-field and tetragonal-field splittings of $\gamma_3(e_g)$ and $\gamma_5(t_{2g})$ levels are each inverted for distortions of opposite sign.   Letters refer to wave functions of equations 63 and 68.   For cases d^4 and d^6, assume moderate field splitting with Hund's rule satisfied.   (a) Six-coordinated cation with outer-electron configuration d^1 ^2D or d^6 ^5D and four-, eight-, or twelve-coordinated d^4 ^5D or d^9 ^2D cations.   (b) Four-, eight-, or twelve-coordinated d^1 ^2D or d^6 ^5D cation and six-coordinated d^4 ^5D or d^9 ^2D cation.

Since perturbation theory requires conservation of energy relative to the degenerate level, the Γ_3 level is raised $6Dq$ and the Γ_5 level is lowered $4Dq$ relative to the fivefold degenerate D level, as is indicated in Figure 10(a).*   In the four-, eight-, and twelve-coordinated structures, on the other hand, the Γ_5 orbitals are directed toward the

* It should be appreciated that this statement is only correct for a point-charge model.   Actually coordinate covalence between cation and anion, which is responsible for anion polarization, introduces mixing of s and p states into the d-state manifold, and this mixing destroys the conservation of energy of the original degenerate level.   This fact is of major importance in any quantitative estimate of site-preference energies.   Unfortunately quantitative estimates of the ligand-field contribution to site-preference energies (156,431) have not taken this fact into account.   Since the point-charge model is known to be inaccurate (polarization energies are usually a large fraction of the energy of ionization), these estimates of site-preference energy cannot be taken quantitatively.

anions and are the more strongly perturbed.　Therefore if the ligands are anions, the cubic-field splitting is inverted as shown in Figure 10(b).　If the D level corresponds to nine outer d electrons, i.e. to one d hole in the fivefold degenerate level, it is the hole which must be considered so that the conclusions for the electron are just inverted. Further, so long as Hund's rule is valid, the two half shells may be considered separately and four outer d electrons correspond to one d hole, six outer d electrons to one d electron.

For an F state, or for a single f electron outside of closed shells, the levels split into a singlefold and two threefold degenerate levels.　For two outer d electrons, the maximum L is $L = 4$, so that there are S, P, D, F, and G states.　By the first half of Hund's rule, the triplet $(2S + 1 = 3)$ states ^3P and ^3F are more stable than the singlet states ^1S, ^1D, ^1G for the free ion.　Of these, the ^3F state possesses the greater angular momentum, so that by the second half of Hund's rule the ^3F state is the ground state.　Therefore the perturbation V_{el} splits the twenty-fivefold degenerate (orbital part only) state into the five terms shown in Figure 11.　If $V_{el} \gg V_c$, it follows from Table III that the free-atom terms are split by V_c into the various levels indicated in Figure 11.　(It is to be noted that if $V_c \gg V_{LS}$, J is no longer a good quantum number and the irreducible representations Γ_n are used as quantum numbers.)　To obtain the order of the splittings and their separations, it is necessary to solve the matrices and to find the eigenfunctions and eigenvalues for a given symmetry.　For calculation of the matrix elements, reference is made to the operator equivalent

TABLE V

Eigenfunctions (Not Normalized) for Two d Electrons outside of Closed Shells in ^3F Ground State

Representation	Eigenfunction	One-electron notation	
Γ_2	$[B(1)A(2)]^-$	e_g^2	
Γ_4^1	$[(B(1) + A(1))D(2) + 8C(1)E(2)]^-$		
Γ_4^2	$[(B(1) - A(1))E(2) + 8D(1)C(2)]^-$	$(t_{2g}^2)_{1-\delta} + (e_g t_{2g})_\delta$	$\delta \ll 1$
Γ_4^3	$[2C(1)B(2) + 8E(1)D(2)]^-$		
Γ_5^1	$[(3B(1) - A(1))D(2)]^-$		
Γ_5^2	$[(3B(1) + A(1))E(2)]^-$	$e_g t_{2g}$	
Γ_5^3	$[C(1)A(2)]^-$		

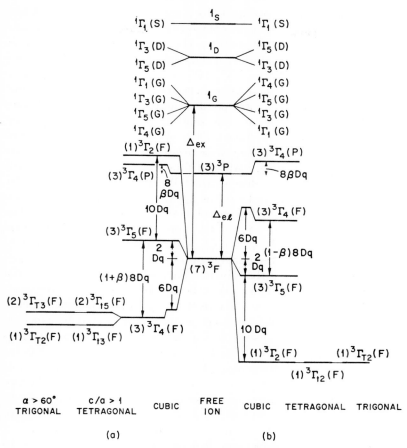

Fig. 11. Ligand-field splittings for a d^2 ^3F cation. Trigonal- and tetragonal-field splittings of $^3\Gamma_4(F)$ level are inverted for distortions of opposite sign. However, it should be noted that sign of distortion is related to relative magnitudes of Δ_c, Δ_{el} and Δ_t, $\Delta_{t'}$ or Δ_T, $\Delta_{T'}$ where Δ refers to splittings of A and B levels to one-electron problem, Δ' to C, D, E, levels. Thus for example, $^3\Gamma_{t3}(F)$ may be lowest for $c/a < 1$ if $\Delta_{el} \gg \Delta_c$ and $\Delta_t > 6\Delta_{t'}$. Numbers in parentheses refer to orbital degeneracy. The splitting Δ_{ex} indicates the stabilization of the high-spin state. (a) Cation in a six-coordinated interstice. (b) Cation in a four-, eight-, or twelve-coordinated anion interstice.

method developed by Stevens, Elliott, and Judd (167,313,314,600) for calculations of the splittings for the rare earth ions. Tabulated summaries are given by Low (404). The eigenfunctions are given in Table V, where the notation Γ_n^i means the ith row of the nth representation and $[B(1)A(2)]^- = [B(1)A(2) - B(2)A(1)]$ corresponding to a triplet state. That these are eigenfunctions can be seen in the fact that the seven functions correspond either to different representations or to different rows of the same representation since an important theorem of group theory states: *There can be no matrix elements connecting functions unless they arise from the same row of the same irreducible representation.* All the functions corresponding to the same representation are degenerate. With Table V and Figure 10, it is easy to deduce the order of the levels. The $^3\Gamma_2(F)$ level contains only the AB product and therefore corresponds to γ_3^2 (or e_g^2). The $^3\Gamma_5$ level contains only $\gamma_3\gamma_5$ (or $e_g t_{2g}$) products, and the $^3\Gamma_4(F)$ level contains predominantly γ_5^2 (or t_{2g}^2) with a small portion of $\gamma_3\gamma_5$ (or $e_g t_{2g}$). Thus for a paramagnetic cation in an octahedral interstice, the order of the levels is that given in Figure 11(a). For a tetrahedral interstice, or for two d holes, the order of the ^3F splittings is reversed, as shown in Figure 11(b). The reader may wonder why the ground state for an octahedral field is not simply γ_5^2, as would be expected were $V_c \gg V_{el}$. The answer lies in the fact that the $\gamma_3\gamma_5$ states as well as the γ_5^2 states for $V_c \gg V_{el}$ contain $^3\Gamma_4$ states, and that for $V_{el} > V_c$ ^3P and ^3F both contain $^3\Gamma_4$ states. The orthogonality theorem quoted above does not rule out matrix elements between the two $^3\Gamma_4$ levels. Since the operators V_c and L^2 do not commute, the levels perturb one another. The amount of admixing of $\gamma_3\gamma_5$ into γ_5^2 in $^3\Gamma_4(F)$ depends upon the ratio V_c/V_{el}. Kanamori (318) has shown that the true energy separation between the Γ_4 and Γ_5 levels is, in first approximation, given by

$$\Delta E = (1 + \beta)\Delta_c \qquad (67)$$

where

$$\beta = \Delta_c/(4\Delta_{el} + 3\Delta_c)$$

and Δ_c is the separation between the Γ_4 and Γ_5 levels on the basis of no mixing of $\gamma_3\gamma_5$ with γ_5^2, and Δ_{el} is the splitting by V_{el} between the F and P terms. For Co^{2+}, with two electrons outside of a closed half-shell in CoO, the splitting between ^4P and ^4F is about 14,800 cm^{-1}, according to spectroscopic data (31), and Kanamori was able

TABLE VI

States and Energies in Moderate Fields

(In Dq units)

Ground state of free ion	Octahedral states and energies	Tetrahedral states and energies
d: ^2D	t_{2g} $^2\Gamma_5(-4)$; $^2\Gamma_3(+6)$	e_g $^2\Gamma_3(-6)$; $^2\Gamma_5(+4)$
d^2: ^3F	$(t_{2g}^2)_{1-\delta}(e_g t_{2g})_\delta$ $^3\Gamma_4(-6-8\beta)$; $^3\Gamma_5(+2)$; $^3\Gamma_2(+12)$	e_g^2 $^3\Gamma_2(-12)$; $^3\Gamma_5(-2)$; $^3\Gamma_4(+6-8\beta)$
d^3: ^4F	t_{2g}^3 $^4\Gamma_2(-12)$; $^4\Gamma_5(-2)$; $^4\Gamma_4(+6-8\beta)$	$(e_g^2 t_{2g})_{1-\delta}(e_g t_{2g}^2)_\delta$ $^4\Gamma_4(-6-8\beta)$; $^4\Gamma_5(+2)$; $^4\Gamma_2(+12)$
d^4: ^5D	$t_{2g}^3 e_g$ $^5\Gamma_3(-6)$; $^5\Gamma_5(+4)$	$e_g^2 t_{2g}$ $^5\Gamma_5(-4)$; $^5\Gamma_3(+6)$
d^5: ^6S	$t_{2g}^3 e_g^2$ $^6\Gamma_1$	$t_{2g}^3 e_g^2$ $^6\Gamma_1$
d^6: ^5D	$t_{2g}^4 e_g^2$ $^5\Gamma_5(-4)$; $^5\Gamma_3(+6)$	$e_g^3 t_{2g}^3$ $^5\Gamma_3(-6)$; $^5\Gamma_5(+4)$
d^7: ^4F	$(t_{2g}^5 e_g^2)_{1-\delta}(t_{2g}^4 e_g^3)_\delta$ $^4\Gamma_4(-6-8\beta)$; $^4\Gamma_5(+2)$; $^4\Gamma_2(+12)$	$e_g^4 t_{2g}^3$ $^4\Gamma_2(-12)$; $^4\Gamma_5(-2)$; $^4\Gamma_4(+6-8\beta)$
d^8: ^3F	$t_{2g}^6 e_g^2$ $^3\Gamma_2(-12)$; $^3\Gamma_5(-2)$; $^3\Gamma_4(+6-8\beta)$	$(e_g^4 t_{2g}^4)_{1-\delta}(e_g^{3,5} t_{2g})_\delta$ $^3\Gamma_4(-6-8\beta)$; $^3\Gamma_5(+2)$; $^3\Gamma_2(+12)$
d^9: ^2D	$t_{2g}^6 e_g^3$ $^2\Gamma_3(-6)$; $^2\Gamma_5(+4)$	$e_g^4 t_{2g}^5$ $^2\Gamma_5(-4)$; $^2\Gamma_3(+6)$

to estimate from available paramagnetic data a $\beta = 0.185$. Typically β is small for the moderate field case ($3d$ elements) but is particularly important for the strong field case ($4d$ and $5d$ elements). In Table · VI are listed the states and energies for various d-shell configurations for the moderate field case, i.e. β small and Hund's rule fulfilled.

Splittings due to deviations from cubic symmetry, i.e. to V_t, are generally small compared to those due to V_c. The procedure for calculating these splittings is completely analogous to the cubic-field case, and the results are shown in Figures 10, 11. For the one-electron case (Fig. 10), the eigenfunctions of the singlefold Γ_{T1} and twofold Γ_{T3} levels into which the threefold Γ_5 level is split by the trigonal field are given by

$$
\left.
\begin{aligned}
\Gamma_{T1} &= \psi_0' \sim (2z'^2 - x'^2 - y'^2)/r^2 \\
\Gamma_{T3}^1 &= \sqrt{(2/3)}\psi_{-2}' + \sqrt{(1/3)}\psi_1' \\
\Gamma_{T3}^2 &= \sqrt{(2/3)}\psi_2' - \sqrt{(1/3)}\psi_{-1}'
\end{aligned}
\right\}
\tag{68}
$$

where the prime indicates that the trigonal axis has been taken as the z axis.

4. Spin-Orbit Splittings

For the $3d$ elements, the cubic ligand-field splittings are generally greater than the spin-orbit splittings, so that J is no longer a good quantum number. Therefore to calculate the effects of spin-orbit interactions in solids, the procedure is to first find the number of levels into which L is split by V_c and then to find the additional splittings through the action of the spin-orbit coupling. Frequently it is necessary to consider whether $\Delta_{LS} > \Delta_t$, where Δ_t is a splitting due to distortions from cubic symmetry. For this purpose it is necessary to have an estimate of the degree of "quenching" of the orbital momentum as a result of the cubic ligand fields V_c. This estimate comes from a consideration of equations 62 and 63. Cubic-field splitting defines two real functions B and C in place of two complex functions $B \pm iC$. Since the $\mathbf{L}$ operator is imaginary, the angular momentum of B and C is no longer observable. Therefore in a cubic field, the magnetic quantum numbers associated with the wave functions of equation 63 are $m_l = 0$, for A, B, C; $m_l = \pm 1$ for D, E. This means that the angular momentum is small for octahedral-site, high-spin-state (Hund's rule valid) cations with outer-electron configuration d^3, d^4, d^5, d^8, d^9; and for tetrahedral-site cations with outer-electron configuration d^1, d^2, d^5, d^6, d^7. For these ions it is reasonable to assume $V_t > V_{LS}$ so that any splittings Δ_t due to distortions from cubic symmetry must be considered before V_{LS}. However, for octahedral-site, high-spin-state d^1, d^2, d^6, d^7 cations or tetrahedral-site d^3, d^4, d^8, d^9 cations, the relationship $V_{LS} > V_t$ may occur.

Since V_{LS} has the form of equation 8, it is necessary to consider the spin as well as the orbital part of the wave function. For the free atom, the spin is represented by the continuous rotation group D^S appropriate to a given spin angular momentum S. In a crystal this is reduced to the irreducible representation appropriate for the

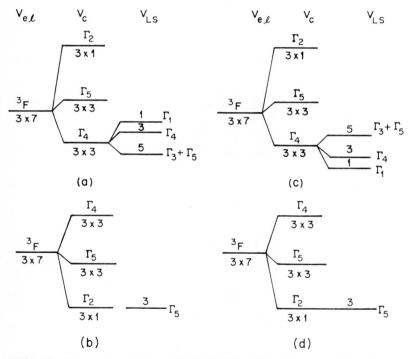

Fig. 12. First-order splittings for $V_{el} \gg V_c > V_{LS}$. The spin-orbit splittings are drawn to an arbitrary scale. The numbers indicate the total degeneracy. (a) d^2 in octahedral interstice. (b) d^8 in octahedral interstice. (c) d^8 in tetrahedral interstice. (d) d^2 in tetrahedral interstice

cation symmetry. Thus for two outer electrons with $S = 1$, the irreducible representation is Γ_4 corresponding to $L = 1$. With spin included, the $^3\Gamma_4(F)$ ground state for two outer electrons is no longer threefold degenerate, but ninefold degenerate corresponding to $\Gamma_4(L = 3) \times \Gamma_4(S = 1)$. Multiplication of corresponding elements of the character tables and reduction to irreducible representations by equation 65 gives

$$\Gamma_4(L = 3) \times \Gamma_4(S = 1) \rightarrow \Gamma_1 + \Gamma_3 + \Gamma_4 + \Gamma_5 \qquad (69)$$

To obtain the order and magnitude of the possible splittings, it is necessary to find the eigenfunctions of the 9×9 matrix and to evaluate the matrix elements

$$(\Gamma_4(L) \times \Gamma_4(S)|\mathbf{L}\cdot\mathbf{S}|\Gamma_4(L) \times \Gamma_4(S))$$
$$= \sum_{j=x,y,z} (\Gamma_4(L)|L_j|\Gamma_4(L))(\Gamma_4(S)|S_j|\Gamma_4(S)) \quad (70)$$

The qualitative results of these calculations are summarized in Figure 12.

In the case of one outer electron, $S = 1/2$ is nonintegral, and the spin part requires the twofold degenerate double group Γ_6. The relevant spin-orbit splittings for one d electron, or one d hole, are summarized in Figure 13(a), (b). Whereas the ligand-field splittings for d^1 and d^6, or for d^2 and d^7, are similar, this is not at all the case for spin-orbit splittings because of the different multiplicities $(2S + 1)$. This is demonstrated by a comparison of Figures 13(c), (d), which show the spin-orbit splittings for d^6 and d^7 in octahedral interstices, with Figures 12(a) and 13(a).

5. *The Jahn-Teller Effect*

From Figures 10 and 11, it is apparent that in cubic ligand fields (V_{LS} neglected) the cation ground state may be degenerate. Jahn and Teller (301,302) have pointed out that: *A cation with a ground state that is degenerate, but not a Kramers' doublet, may be stabilized by a distortion of the interstice to some lower symmetry that removes the ground-state degeneracy.* The physical reason for this is that in first-order perturbation theory, the center of gravity of the levels remains the same after a perturbation that splits the levels, so that removal of the degeneracy, or splitting of the levels, results in a ground state that decreases linearly with the distortion. Since the elastic energies vary quadratically, a minimal total energy can be achieved by a finite distortion. This is illustrated in Figures 10 and 11. [That there is no Jahn-Teller distortion if the ground state is a Kramers' doublet follows from the fact that in any external electric field (there being no magnetic field) there is a symmetry with respect to a change in the sign of the time. Kramers (372) has shown that an electric

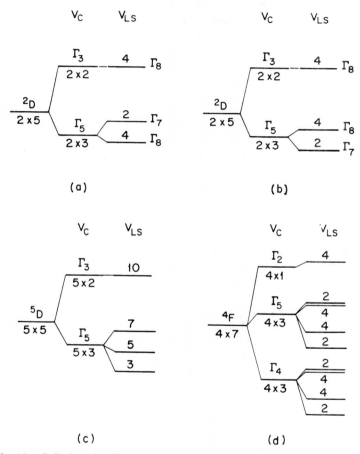

Fig. 13. Splittings for $V_c > V_{LS}$. The spin-orbit splittings are drawn to an arbitrary scale and represent first-order theory only. The numbers indicate total degeneracy. (a) d^1 in an octahedral interstice. (b) d^9 in a tetrahedral interstice. (c) d^6 in an octahedral interstice. (d) d^7 in an octahedral interstice.

field can completely remove the degeneracy only for a system with an integral value of the sum of the spins of the particles. For a system with half-integral value of this sum, in an arbitrary electric field, all the levels must be doubly degenerate.]

There are five points that should be made in connection with this theorem:

(*i*) If $\Delta_{LS} > \Delta_t$, the spin-orbit effects will quench out the Jahn-Teller mechanism. Therefore a Jahn-Teller distortion is to be unambiguously anticipated only if the orbital angular momentum is quenched by the ligand fields, i.e., for d^4 and d^9 cations in octahedral interstices, d^1 and d^6 cations in tetrahedral interstices.

(*ii*) If the spins are ordered collinearly below a spin-ordering temperature, spin-orbit interactions will also cause a cooperative crystal distortion from cubic to lower symmetry, but the sign of this distortion is opposite to that predicted for the Jahn-Teller mechanism since here the ground state must be degenerate lest L be quenched. Such distortions should be distinguished from cooperative Jahn-Teller distortions.

(*iii*) A d^4 or d^9 cation in an octahedral interstice, or a d^1 or d^6 cation in a tetrahedral interstice, may obtain equal stabilization by a distortion to tetragonal symmetry with $c/a > 1$ as with $c/a < 1$. This follows from the fact that the Γ_3 level is only twofold degenerate and the center of gravity of the level is preserved by the distortion. In such a case, the system may resonate between the two stable configurations unless some other effect that favors one is simultaneously present. Therefore in a crystal the composite electronic and vibrational problems must be considered, and the presence of Jahn-Teller cations may not lead to configurations of lower symmetry, but rather to a special coupling between vibrational modes and low-frequency electronic motion. This is known as the *dynamic Jahn-Teller effect*. This is particularly true for higher temperatures, where entropy favors resonance between several unique axes, or for relatively dilute concentrations of Jahn-Teller ions. Moffitt *et al.* (395,444,445) find that if the forces tending to remove the degeneracies are not strong, the degenerate vibrational levels may be split without removal of the electronic degeneracy.

(*iv*) Since distortions to lower crystalline symmetry require cooperative distortions (via V_λ of equation 61) about the Jahn-Teller ions, spontaneous electron ordering to render a low-temperature structure of lower symmetry can only occur if the concentration of Jahn-Teller cations is greater than some critical fraction. Such electron-ordering transformations are martensitic. Since they are cooperative phenomena, they may exhibit thermal hysteresis.

(v) Since the Jahn-Teller effect is due only to lattice-orbital interactions, it is independent of spin and therefore of spin ordering at a Curie or Néel temperature. This also can provide an experimental distinction between the cooperative Jahn-Teller distortions and the cooperative spin-orbit distortions that occur at a temperature below which the spins are ordered collinearly.

6. *Spin Quenching by Large Ligand Fields*

In strong ligand fields with $\Delta_c > \Delta_{ex} \sim \Delta_{el}$, where Δ_{ex} is the splitting of the free-atom ground state and a state of lower $(2S + 1)$, the spin angular momentum may be partially, or completely, quenched. This is manifest by a breakdown of Hund's highest $(2S + 1)$ rule, and the cations are said to be in a *low-spin state*. In the strong-field case, it is possible to use the one-electron model of Figure 10. From this model follow the electron configurations and net atomic spins for cations in large cubic and tetragonal fields that are summarized in Table VII.

TABLE VII

Electron Configurations and Net Spins for Transition Element Cations
in Strong Cubic and Tetragonal Octahedral Fields

(Comparison of net spins of cations in strong ligand fields with those for the free
cation illustrates spin quenching.)

Free cation		Cubic field		Tet. $(c/a > 1)$ field		Tet. $(c/a < 1)$ field	
Config.	Spin	Config.	Spin	Config.	Spin	Config.	Spin
d^1	$1/2$	t_{2g}^1	$1/2$	$(D,E)^1$	$1/2$	C^1	$1/2$
d^2	1	t_{2g}^2	1	$(D,E)^2$	1	C^2	0
d^3	$3/2$	t_{2g}^3	$3/2$	$(D,E)^3$	$1/2$	$C^2(D,E)^1$	$1/2$
d^4	2	t_{2g}^4	1	$(D,E)^4$	0	$C^2(D,E)^2$	1
d^5	$5/2$	t_{2g}^5	$1/2$	$(D,E)^4C^1$	$1/2$	$C^2(D,E)^3$	$1/2$
d^6	2	t_{2g}^6	0	t_{2g}^6	0	t_{2g}^6	0
d^7	$3/2$	$t_{2g}^6 e_g^1$	$1/2$	$t_{2g}^6 A^1$	$1/2$	$t_{2g}^6 B^1$	$1/2$
d^8	1	$t_{2g}^6 e_g^2$	1	$t_{2g}^6 A^2$	0	$t_{2g}^6 B^2$	0
d^9	$1/2$	$t_{2g}^6 e_g^3$	$1/2$	$t_{2g}^6 A^2 B^1$	$1/2$	$t_{2g}^6 B^2 A^1$	$1/2$

7. *The g Factor*

From Figure 3 it was shown that if a free ion with a resultant angular momentum J (large L-S coupling) is placed in a magnetic field **H**, the degenerate energy level is split and the magnitude of the splittings relative to the field-free level are given by

$$\Delta_H = g\mu_B H M_J \qquad (71)$$

where g is given by equation 13. To obtain an experimental value for g, paramagnetic-resonance techniques are frequently employed. In this method, a paramagnetic material is placed in a large d.c. field **H**, and a small a.c. field is applied at right angles. The a.c. field induces magnetic-dipole transitions according to the selection rule $\Delta M_J = \pm 1$. Therefore a resonance absorption of energy is observed if the a.c. frequency ν corresponds to

$$h\nu = g\mu_B H$$

and

$$g = 21.4178/\lambda H \qquad (72)$$

where H is measured in kilogauss and $\lambda = c/\nu$ is measured in centimeters.

If a cation is placed in a ligand field, J is generally no longer a good quantum number, and the experimental g factor is no longer a measure of the Landé g factor of equation 13. Rather it is a measure of the complicated term splittings that result not from interactions of **J** with **H**, but of Γ_n's with **H**. It depends upon the orientation of **H** with respect to the symmetry axis of the ligand field. Therefore the experimental g factor is a tensor and reflects the anisotropy of the ligand fields. This experimental g is called the *spectroscopic splitting factor*.

From equations 10 and 13, it follows that for a free ion

$$\mathbf{M}_J = \gamma\mathbf{J} \qquad \gamma = ge/2mc \qquad (73)$$

Since the classical equation of motion equates the rate of change of angular momentum **J** to the applied torque $\mathbf{M}_J \times \mathbf{H}$, the equation of motion for the magnetization of a solid is (damping terms neglected)

$$\dot{\mathbf{M}}_J = \gamma\mathbf{M}_J \times \mathbf{H} \qquad (74)$$

where g is no longer equal to equation 13, but reflects the ligand-field splittings. Ferromagnetic-resonance experiments similar to the paramagnetic experiments provide a measure of γ, and therefore of g. The exact relationship between the a.c. frequency and γ depends, for ferromagnetic resonance, upon the geometry and magnetization of the sample (346).

The spectroscopic splitting factor g that is determined from resonance experiments must be distinguished from the g factor determined by gyromagnetic experiments (347,526,632). In a gyromagnetic experiment (Einstein-DeHaas (164) or Barnett (40) methods), what is measured is the magnetomechanical ratio (see eq. 73)

$$\frac{g'e}{2mc} \equiv \frac{\Delta M_{\text{obs}}}{\Delta J_{\text{obs}}} = \frac{\Delta(M_S + M_L + M_{\text{lattice}})}{-\Delta J_{\text{lattice}}} = \frac{\Delta(M_S + M_L)}{\Delta(J_S + J_L)} \quad (75)$$

where the lattice contribution to the magnetic moment M_{lattice} is negligible and $-\Delta J_{\text{lattice}} = \Delta(J_S + J_L)$ follows from the conservation of the total angular momentum, $\Delta(J_{\text{lattice}} + J_S + J_L) = 0$. From equation 7, the spin-only ratio $M_S/J_S = e/mc$. If the ratio of orbital to spin angular momentum is

$$J_L/J_S = 2\epsilon \quad (76)$$

then

$$M_L/M_S = \epsilon$$

so that for $\epsilon \ll 1$,

$$g' \approx 2(1 - \epsilon) \quad (77)$$

If the orbital angular momentum is quenched by the crystalline fields, so that ϵ is small, then it is possible to show (347) that for a resonance experiment the spectroscopic splitting factor g is given by

$$g \approx 2(1 + \epsilon) \quad (78)$$

where the definition of ϵ corresponding to equation 76 is

$$2\epsilon = (\psi|L_z|\psi)/(\psi|S_z|\psi) \qquad \psi = \psi_0 - i\lambda_1\psi_1/2\Delta_1 - \ldots \quad (79)$$

and Δ_1 is the splitting between the states ψ_0 and ψ_1, λ_1 is the spin-orbit coupling parameter defined by equation 8. This gives the following theoretical relationship between the two experimentally determined g factors:

$$g - 2 \approx 2 - g' \quad (80)$$

In practice it is found that the values of ϵ determined from resonance experiments are appreciably ($\sim$ factor of two) higher than those found from gyromagnetic measurements, and this discrepancy is attributed by Kittel and Mitchell (350) to an apparent tendency of the g values to decrease as the resonant frequency is increased.

Smit and Wijn (590) have pointed out that if the atomic moments are oriented purely parallel or antiparallel to the magnetic field, i.e., the orbital angular momentum is quenched, in first approximation, by the crystalline fields ($\epsilon \ll 1$), then

$$\gamma = \frac{\Delta M_S + \Delta M_L}{\Delta J_S} \quad \text{and} \quad g = 2\frac{\Delta(M_S + M_L)}{\Delta M_S} \tag{81}$$

whereas from equation 75

$$g' = 2\frac{\Delta(M_S + M_L)}{\Delta(M_S + 2M_L)} \tag{82}$$

From equations 81 and 82 there follows the relation

$$\frac{1}{g} + \frac{1}{g'} = 1 \tag{83}$$

which is only equivalent to equation 80 if $M_L \ll M_S$, i.e. if $(g - 2) \ll 1$. This distinction between equations 80 and 83 is important for the case of compensated ferrimagnetics (ferrimagnetism is defined in Chapter II) in which M_S may be extremely small.

In the case of the transition element atoms or ions, the orbital angular momentum is usually quenched, and it has become customary to define the spectroscopic splitting factor g by equation 81 rather than by equation 13. Then equation 20 becomes

$$\mu_{\text{eff}} = g[S(S + 1)]^{1/2}\mu_B = [(3k/N)C]^{1/2} = [8C_{\text{mol}}]^{1/2}\mu_B \tag{84}$$

and the spontaneous magnetization at $T = 0°K$ is

$$\mathbf{M}_0 = -Ng\mathbf{S}\mu_B \tag{85}$$

III. Magnetism and the Chemical Bond

To this point there has been a review of the description of the electrons on free atoms and their interaction with an external magnetic field. There has also been a discussion of the two principal approaches to a quantitative description of the outer electrons of atoms that have condensed into molecules or solids: the MO or collective-electron approach and the HL localized-electron approach. It was pointed out that there probably is a critical distance $R_c(n,l)$ such that for interatomic distances $R < R_c(n,l)$, outer electrons with quantum numbers n, l are best described by the MO approach, whereas if $R > R_c(n,l)$, these electrons are best described by a HL approach. The localized orbitals to be used in the HL description are atomic orbitals that have been perturbed by the crystalline (or ligand) fields. The simple HL theory (or valence-bond approach of Pauling) uses nonorthogonal orbitals and therefore is applicable quantitatively only to diatomic molecules. If orthogonalized atomic orbitals are used as the initial HL wave functions, then binding can only be obtained if polar terms are included; and failure to include polar terms leads to serious errors. This is especially true if a HL approach is used for collective electrons, in which case the polar terms must include more than just the nearest neighbors. The calculational difficulties associated with the inclusion of polar terms for more than nearest neighbors makes the HL approach practicable only for the case of localized $(R > R_c)$ electrons.

The essential features of the MO, collective-electron theory follow from the crystal structure and the Pauli exclusion principle (Fermi-Dirac statistics). The principal assumptions of the MO approach were emphasized. Its weaknesses are an overemphasis of polar states because of inadequate treatment of electron correlations and treatment of electron-phonon interactions as small perturbations even for relatively large interatomic separations. Qualitative arguments have been proposed for the principal correlations to be anticipated among the collective electrons. The valence-bond approach of Pauling was seen to provide an important intuition for the electron correlations that is suggestive for improvements to the MO approach. In the case of localized HL electrons, a multi-electron problem is solved for the outer atomic orbitals, so that crystal structure and the Pauli exclusion principle determine not only the interatomic electron correlations via couplings between neighboring atomic moments (these couplings are discussed in Chapters II and III), but also the intra-atomic exchange correlations and multiplet structure. The weakness of the present ligand-field theory is the assumption of point charges for the construction of the ligand-field potential.

Spontaneous atomic moments were claimed to occur only if localized electrons are present, and expressions were developed for the magnitudes of spontaneous atomic moments, including contributions from the collective electrons as a result of internal exchange fields. Various contributions to the magnetic susceptibility were also examined.

Thus far there has been no discussion of the mechanisms of coupling between neighboring atomic moments. For the most part these mechanisms are indirect, the localized electrons coupling to the collective electrons, the role of the collective-electron intermediaries being determined in metals by the collective-electron correlations and in ionic compounds by covalent terms induced by the interactions of those overlapping orbitals from neighboring atoms that are ultimately responsible for the magnitude and sign of the ligand fields. It is just for this reason that magnetic studies can provide direct information about the electron correlations or about the origins of the ligand-field potentials.   Therefore magnetic studies have more profound implications than just an adequate description of the magnetic properties of matter.

In Chapter II those magnetic properties of solids that are due to the presence of localized electrons are developed in a purely phenomenological manner.   The approach is that of the Weiss molecular field in which the magnitude of the atomic moments and the sign of the couplings between them are assumed given.   From this starting place, it is possible to obtain the temperature dependence of the magnetic susceptibility and of the magnetization.   It is also possible to obtain the type of magnetic order.   Since neutron diffraction provides an experimental technique whereby the magnitude of the atomic moments and the magnetic order can be directly determined, it is possible to work backwards from this information, together with temperature-dependent measurements of susceptibility and magnetization, to obtain a measure of the magnitude of the individual atomic moments and of the sign and strength of the couplings (called exchange integrals) between them.   The first piece of information provides a direct check of the theory for localized, HL electrons as well as an empirical estimate of R_c for the $3d$ electrons, and the second permits the observation of certain regularities for the sign of the exchange integrals that give rise to the formulation of empirical rules. These empirical rules can be rationalized by qualitative physical arguments that provide a basis for understanding the origins of the molecular fields, or exchange integrals, and their relation to bond stabilization.   Some of these rules have been relatively firmly established by more quantitative calculations, while others will be seen to be still speculative and the subject of considerable controversy in the literature.   In Chapter III, atomic moments and their cooperative interactions for three different classes of materials are considered: insulators and semiconductors, metals and alloys, and ionic compounds with metallic-type conductivity. After a brief description of the outer electrons, qualitative arguments are used to develop a set of rules for the sign and relative magnitudes of the couplings between atomic moments. This theoretical model is used to interpret magnetic, crystallographic, and electrical data for all typical compounds of each class.

It should be noted that two phenomena that are important for the theory of magnetism and that are relevant to the present discussions are not treated at all. These phenomena are magnetic anisotropy and magnetostriction. Also there is no discussion of the rare earth and actinide metals or compounds, for which much of the present discussion serves as a necessary introduction.

CHAPTER II

Types of Magnetic Order

I. Ferromagnetism

A. WEISS MOLECULAR FIELD AND HEISENBERG EXCHANGE HAMILTONIAN

Introduction of interatomic coupling permits the possibility of a spontaneous ordering of the atomic moments below some critical temperature. A substance is generally called ferromagnetic if it possesses a spontaneous magnetic moment at low temperatures.* The saturation magnetization $\mathbf{M}_s$ is defined as the spontaneous magnetic moment per unit volume (in technical literature the saturation flux density $\mathbf{B}_s = \mathbf{H} + 4\pi\mathbf{M}_s$, where $\mathbf{H} \ll 4\pi\mathbf{M}_s$ is the external magnetic field used to align the moments of the various domains, is often used), and the critical temperature below which the spontaneous long-range ordering occurs is called the Curie temperature T_c. However, it should be noted that weak ferromagnetism may occur in substances where the magnetic ordering is antiferromagnetic and that moderate ferromagnetism may occur in chemically ordered substances with predominantly antiferromagnetic (antiparallel moments) interactions. These latter situations are distinguished from substances with ferromagnetic (parallel moments) coupling by the designations *parasitic ferromagnetism* and *ferrimagnetism*, respectively.

For the case of *ferromagnetism*, i.e. all interactions favoring a parallel alignment of the atomic moments, introduction of a simple phenomenological coupling term has proven extremely successful for describing several important attributes. This term is called the Weiss molecular field $\mathbf{H}_w$, after its inventor Pierre Weiss (655). It is assumed that the interatomic coupling can be represented by an

---

* Because of domain formation, which permits minimization of internal demagnetizing fields at the expense of a fraction of the coupling energy, it is usually necessary to align the moments of the various domains by an external field in order to determine the magnitude of the spontaneous moment.

effective magnetic field that acts on each atomic moment and is proportional to the magnetization $\mathbf{M}$:

$$\mathbf{H}_w = W\mathbf{M} \qquad (86)$$

where the proportionality constant W is called the *Weiss field constant* or the *molecular field constant*.

This is the form of the Lorentz correction for magnetic coupling of a paramagnetic solid. Consider a small sphere of radius R cut out of the paramagnetic medium. This induces a magnetic pole density at the surface of the sphere of $\omega^* = \mathbf{M} \cdot \mathbf{n}$, where $\mathbf{n}$ is the unit vector normal to the surface. These poles, after integration over the entire surface, produce a field at the center of the sphere $\mathbf{H}'$ that, by spherical symmetry, has only a component along the direction of $\mathbf{M}$ of magnitude

$$H' = \int_0^\pi \left(\frac{\cos\theta}{R^2}\right) \omega^* 2\pi R \sin\theta \cdot R \, d\theta$$

$$= 2\pi M \int_{-1}^1 \cos^2\theta \, d(\cos\theta) = \frac{4\pi}{3} M$$

However, if $W = 4\pi/3$, ferromagnetism would occur only below 1°K.

To obtain an estimate of the magnitude of $\mathbf{H}_w$, it is noted that the orienting effect of the interatomic coupling is opposed by the thermal energy associated with random motions of the moments. At the Curie point, the ordering and disordering energy must be equal, so that for a single atomic moment μ,

$$\mu H_w \approx kT_c \qquad (87)$$

For iron, $T_c \approx 1000°\text{K}$ and $\mu \approx 2\mu_B$ so that $H_w \approx 5 \times 10^6$ oe. This field is much stronger than that produced by the magnetic moments of all the other ions (the dipole-dipole interactions), which are only $\sim (4\pi/3)M \sim 10^3$ oe. Internal fields due to crystalline anisotropy are generally several orders of magnitude smaller than H_w also, so that anisotropy effects, which are neglected in this book, may be treated as a perturbation.

Heisenberg (265) showed that the physical origin of the Weiss field is in the quantum mechanical exchange integral. The form of the "exchange Hamiltonian" that is generally used in the literature was derived by Heisenberg from a Heitler-London description of the outer electrons. Slater (584) has strongly criticized calculations that are based on the Heisenberg exchange Hamiltonian because the non-orthogonality of the atomic wave functions used in the Heitler-London approximation vitiates their use in a many-electron problem. Van Vleck (631) was able to justify use of this expression given certain limiting conditions, and more recently Nesbet (477) and Slater (585) have argued that the form of the expression, which is given in equation 90, is more generally valid. It is the starting point of the present discussion. However, the magnetic interaction is not *exactly* described by equation 90, and for certain problems it may prove necessary to use a more fundamental approach (415).

In the discussion of the hydrogen molecule, it was pointed out that there are two energy levels, E_I corresponding to a symmetrical co-ordinate wave function (singlet spin function) and E_{II} corresponding to an antisymmetrical coordinate wave function (triplet spin functions). If the part of the Hamiltonian labeled H' in equation 21 is treated as a perturbation, the energies of the singlet and triplet states are

$$E_{I,II} = 2E_0 + (1 \pm \alpha'^2)^{-1}(J_c \pm J_e) \qquad (88)$$

where the plus sign is associated with the singlet state E_I and the minus sign with the triplet state E_{II} (266). E_0 is the energy of an unperturbed, free atom, α' is the overlap integral of equation 23,

$$J_c = \int |u_1(1)|^2 H' |u_2(2)|^2 \, d\tau_1 \, d\tau_2$$

is the Coulomb energy, and

$$J_e = \int u_1^*(1)u_2^*(2)H'u_2(1)u_1(2) \, d\tau_1 \, d\tau_2$$

is the exchange integral. It follows that the effective spin coupling between orbits ϕ_a and ϕ_b with spin angular momenta $\mathbf{S}_a$ and $\mathbf{S}_b$ is equivalent to a potential energy of the form

$$V_{ab} = -2J_{ab}\mathbf{S}_a \cdot \mathbf{S}_b \qquad (89)$$

where

$$J_{ab} = \tfrac{1}{2}(E_I - E_{II}) = (J_e - \alpha'^2 J_c)/(1 - \alpha'^4)$$

Thus the stability of the singlet versus the triplet state depends upon the sign of J_{ab}. If $J_{ab} > 0$, then the triplet state is more stable, so that a positive exchange integral is associated with ferromagnetic coupling. Similarly a negative exchange integral is associated with antiferromagnetic coupling since the singlet state is stabilized by

$J_{ab} < 0$.   In Chapter II the exchange integrals are treated as phenomenological constants.   In Chapter III the sign of the exchange
integrals is argued for several bonding situations and classes of
materials: The rules thus developed are compared with experiment.
However, some comment on the historical speculations about the sign
of J_{ab} should be made at this point.

Early workers assumed $J_{ab} = J_e$, neglecting terms to order α^2 and
higher.   Heisenberg suggested that although $J_e < 0$ in the hydrogen

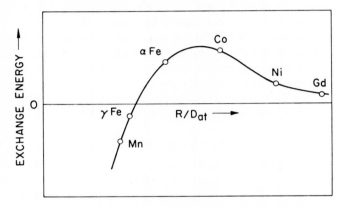

Fig. 14.   Bethe's (595) curve relating the exchange energy of magnetization
to the distance R between atomic centers having a fixed diameter D_{at} of active
shell.   This curve is now considered incorrect.

molecule, beyond some critical ratio of internuclear distance to mean
radial extension of atomic orbitals the exchange integral must change
sign.   This ratio was chosen empirically so as to account for the
ferromagnetism of Fe, Co, Ni.   That this possibility exists is immediately seen from the expression for H' in equation 21: the first two
terms are positive, the last two are negative, and all four are of the
same order of magnitude.   It was Bethe (595) who provided plausible
arguments why J_e might be positive in the ferromagnetic elements.
He pointed out that for a simple HL model ($u_1 = \phi_a$ and $u_2 = \phi_b$)
the term e^2/r_{12} would dominate the others if all the overlap between
ϕ_a and ϕ_b were concentrated in a small region away from the nuclei.
He suggested that this would be the case if ϕ_a and ϕ_b had (1) small
amplitude at their parent nuclei, (2) angular lobes pointing towards
and overlapping one another, and (3) small radial extent compared

to the internuclear spacing R.   All three of these conditions are satisfied by the $3d$ electrons of the ferromagnetic metals.   From general arguments Bethe (595) suggested that J_e varied as shown in Figure 14, the negative value at small R resulting because condition (3) is not satisfied.   Subsequently the validity of Bethe's argument was severely questioned, and it has been suggested by Van Vleck (634), Slater (580,584), and Zener (716) that J_e could never be positive, but simply varied monotonically from a large negative value at small R to an exponentially small negative value at large R.   Four explicit calculations of J_{ab} have been attempted: The first, by Wohlfarth (687), replaced the $3d$ wave functions by spherically averaged functions, violating condition (2), and indicated that J_e is always negative. Kaplan (324) took proper account of the angular variation of the wave functions, but made only one accurate estimate of J_e, which turned out to be positive for a small internuclear separation.   Both Wohlfarth and Kaplan took $\alpha' = 0$.   Subsequently Stuart and Marshall (605) evaluated J_{ab} and found it to be positive for all internuclear separations, but of the order 70 times too small to account for the experimentally determined exchange constants in iron, cobalt, and nickel.   Freeman and Watson (193) showed that the Stuart-Marshall calculation, which assumed hydrogenic orbitals or a point-charge model with $Z = 1$ in equation 1, is not applicable for atoms like iron, cobalt, and nickel.   If realistic effective Z_A and Z_B are taken, then it is necessary to add to the numerator of J_{ab} the term

$$J' = \alpha'\left\{ \int \phi_b^* H_{0b}\phi_a \, d\tau + \int \phi_a^* H_{0a}\phi_b \, d\tau \right.$$
$$\left. - \int \phi_b^* H_{0b}\phi_b \, d\tau - \int \phi_a^* H_{0a}\phi_a \, d\tau \right\}$$

Calculations of J_{ab} for σ, π, and δ bonding orbitals (one electron per orbital) for a fictitious Co_2 molecule were made for the unrealistic, but previously assumed, case $J' = 0$ (or $Z = 1$) and for the case $J' \neq 0$.   For the first case it was found that $J_{\sigma\sigma}$ is everywhere positive, but too small to account for ferromagnetism, and that $J_{\pi\pi}$ and $J_{\delta\delta}$ were even smaller and negative at the appropriate internuclear distance.   These results do not support either of the earlier speculations about the behavior of J_{ab} as a function of internuclear separation R.   In the second case ($J' \neq 0$) the various exchange integrals were found to be *large* and *negative*.   Although Freeman and Watson were disturbed by this result because it did not predict ferromagnetism (i.e. J_{ab} was not positive), it is to be noted that they chose the optimum case for bonding, that is one electron per atom in the overlapping orbitals. The qualitative arguments of Chapter III for the sign of J_{ab} anticipate a large, negative J_{ab} for this case. It is argued in Chapter III that a positive J_{ab} should be found if there is more than one electron per atom in the overlapping orbitals.

Nesbet (480) has pointed out that a Hamiltonian of the form of equation 90 is the simplest scalar quantity that can be constructed to describe two interacting spins of fixed magnitude. A satisfactory theory for this phenomenological equation must account for the following properties of the Heisenberg interaction: (1) linearity in $\mathbf{S}_a \cdot \mathbf{S}_b$, (2) additivity (the coupling between atoms A and B must not interfere with that between A and C), (3) dependence on total atomic spin, not the $\boldsymbol{\sigma}_i \cdot \boldsymbol{\sigma}_j$ for the individual electrons, (4) distinction between spin coupling and covalent bonding, (5) sign and magnitude of J_{ab}, and (6) some indications of the limits of applicability of equation 90. The only theoretical derivation of even equation 89 that is intended to satisfy these criteria has been developed by Nesbet (477,479) and his conclusions are compatible with the semiempirical postulates (214,216,217) that are presented in Chapter III.

Generalization of equation 89 to the many-electron system of a crystal is given by the Heisenberg exchange Hamiltonian

$$H_{\mathrm{ex}} = -\sum_{ij} J_{ij} \mathbf{S}_i \cdot \mathbf{S}_j \tag{90}$$

where J_{ij} is the effective exchange integral between atoms i and j having total spins $\mathbf{S}_i$ and $\mathbf{S}_j$ and the factor 2 is omitted because the summation includes each pair twice. Since the exchange integral is sensitive to orbital overlap, interactions on the same atom (intra-atomic) or between neighboring atoms (interatomic) alone are important, except for the special case of indirect coupling via metallic s–p electrons, which is apparently encountered in rare earth metals and dilute transition metal alloys. This case is outside the scope of this summary. Within an atom the orbitals are orthogonal, and *for orthogonal orbitals* $(\alpha' = 0)$, $J_{ab} = J_e > 0$.* (In an atom the only term in J_e comes from the positive term e^2/r_{12} of q. 21.) Therefore

---

* $J_e = \int \rho_{\mathrm{ex}}(r)\phi(r)\,d\tau$, where $\phi(r) = \int \rho_{\mathrm{ex}}(r')|r - r'|^{-1}\,d\tau$, $\rho_{\mathrm{ex}}(r) = eu^*(r)u_2(r)$, and $\nabla^2\phi(r) = \int \rho_{\mathrm{ex}}(r')\nabla^2|r - r'|^{-1}\,d\tau' = -4\pi\rho_{\mathrm{ex}}(r)$. Now $\nabla \cdot \phi\nabla\phi = |\nabla\phi|^2 + \phi\nabla^2\phi$, so that $4\pi J_e = -\int \phi\nabla^2\phi\,d\tau = \{\int |\nabla\phi|^2\,d\tau - \int_{sfc} \phi\nabla\phi \cdot dS\} > 0$ since the surface integral vanishes for large r.

intraatomic exchange interactions favor a maximum $(2S + 1)$, which is the physical origin of Hund's rule.

B. TEMPERATURE DEPENDENCE OF THE MAGNETIZATION AND THE SUSCEPTIBILITY

To introduce the effect of interatomic coupling, it is only necessary to replace H in equation 14 by the effective internal field $H_i = H + H_w$. This gives

$$M(H) = N\mu = NJg\mu_B B_J[Jg\mu_B(H + WM)/kT] \qquad (91)$$

Since $B_J(T = 0)$ and $B_J(\infty) = 1$, equation 91 is written in the following parametric form and solved graphically:

$$M/M_0 = B_J(y') \qquad (92)$$

$$y' = \frac{M_0 H}{NkT} + \left(\frac{WM_0^2}{NkT}\right)\frac{M}{M_0}$$

where

$$M_0 \equiv M(T = 0°K) = NJg\mu_B$$

Comparison with equation 85 shows that J of this expression is generally replaced by S because of the quenching of the orbital angular momentum. This involves g as defined by equation 81.

The graphical solutions (with $H = 0$ and therefore $M = M_s$) are the intersections of the two curves shown in Figure 15. From equation 15 it was shown that

$$B_J(y')|_{y'\to 0} = (J + 1)y'/3J$$

Therefore the decrease in M_s/M_0 follows a continuous curve until it vanishes at that value of temperature T_c for which the straight line becomes tangent to $B_J(y')|_{y'\to 0}$, so that the Curie point is given by:

$$\frac{(J + 1)}{3J} = \frac{NkT_c}{WM_0^2}$$

$$T_c = Wg\mu_B M_0(J + 1)/3k = NWg^2\mu_B^2 J(J + 1)/3k \qquad (93)$$

For iron, $M_0 \approx 10^3$ emu and $10^{3°}K \approx T_c \approx 0.05W°K$, so that $W \approx 2000$, in agreement with the estimate from equation 87. Further, from Figure 15 it is seen that the curve for $J = 1/2$ gives the best fit with experimental data. This is compatible with quenching of the orbital angular momentum, and therefore with the replacement of J by S (subject to the proper definition of g). In the case of iron,

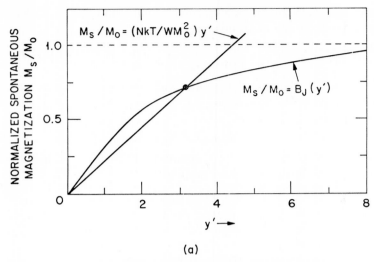

(a)

Fig. 15. Spontaneous magnetization vs. temperature, according to Weiss (655) theory. (a) Graphical solution. The value of M_s/M_0 is given by the intersection of the two curves. (b; see facing page) Reduced-scale plot. The solid lines represent the Weiss field theory for $J = 1/2$, 1. The experimental (dashed) curves for iron and nickel fit more closely the theoretical curve for $J = 1/2$. (After Bozorth (92)).

there is a fairly marked departure from the shape of the Brillouin curve. This suggests that either the atomic moment or the Weiss-field constant is not temperature-independent, as assumed by equation 91. A small increase with temperature in the atomic moment, i.e. in the product gJ, would account for the discrepancy. Comparison of μ_{eff} and μ_0 for α-iron suggests such an increase.

From the Weiss field model, the relation between J_{ex}, the effective exchange integral of equation 90, and T_c for the case $L = 0$ can be derived from the fact that the energy of interaction with the Weiss field, $-\boldsymbol{\mu}\cdot\mathbf{H}_w = -gS\mu_B H_w$, is equal to the exchange energy, $-J_{\text{ex}} \sum_{ij} \mathbf{S}_i\cdot\mathbf{S}_j = -2zJ_{\text{ex}}S^2$, where z is the number of nearest neighbors. This, together with equation 93, gives

$$H_w = WM_0 = 2zSJ_{\text{ex}}/g\mu_B = 3kT_c/g\mu_B(S + 1)$$

$$J_{\text{ex}}/kT_c = 3/[2zS(S + 1)] \tag{94}$$

It should be realized, however, that the Weiss field model first con-

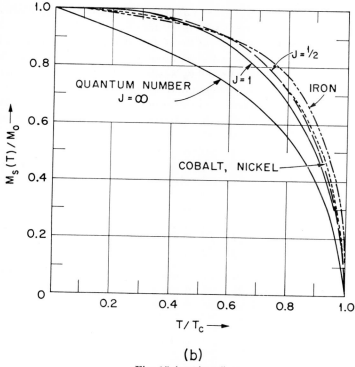

(b)

Fig. 15 (*continued*)

siders the effect on a given spin of the average spin of the neighboring atoms and then averages, whereas in the Heisenberg formulation $\langle \mathbf{S}_i \cdot \mathbf{S}_j \rangle$ must be considered. Therefore any relationships between J_{ex} and W can only be valid at $T = 0°K$. In addition, the effects of short-range order just above T_c are neglected. More exact quantum statistics (107,496,658,715), which include short-range order above T_c, give results for J_{ex}/kT_c that are about a factor 3/2 larger.

Above the Curie temperature, the magnetic field entering the Curie law of equation 19 is H_i, not H, so that to account for interatomic coupling this law must be rewritten as

$$M/(H + WM) = C/T \tag{95}$$

Since the measured susceptibility is $\chi_m = M/H$, it follows that

$$\chi_m = M/H = C/(T - \theta_p) \qquad \theta_p \equiv CW \tag{96}$$

where, as can be verified from equations 20 and 93, $\theta_p = T_c$ in the Weiss field theory.   Equation 96 is known as the *Curie-Weiss law*, and it is found to describe quite well the observed susceptibility variation of ferromagnets in the paramagnetic region above the Curie point.   That a separate symbol θ_p is used for the paramagnetic Curie temperature and for the ferromagnetic Curie point T_c used to indicate the actual order $\rightleftharpoons$ disorder transformation temperature is due to the fact that experimentally θ_p is frequently found to be somewhat greater than T_c.   (The effects of short-range order above T_c are neglected in the simple molecular-field treatment.)

Because of the decrease in M_s with increasing temperature, there is a change with temperature in the total exchange energy

$$W_m = -\int_0^{M_s} \mathbf{H}_w \cdot d\mathbf{M}_s = -\tfrac{1}{2}WM_s^2$$

which gives rise to an extra contribution to the specific heat

$$C_m = dW_m/dT = -\tfrac{1}{2}Wd(M_s^2)/dT \tag{97}$$

From the curves of Figure 15, it is apparent that C_m rises to a sharp maximum just below T_c and drops abruptly to zero for $T > T_c$. Such a variation in the specific heat is characteristic of a second-order transition.

C. COMMENTS ON THE WEISS FIELD THEORY

The Weiss field theory neglects two physical phenomena, one of which is important at very low temperatures and the other at and just above the Curie point.   First, it is assumed that a single spin interacts with a uniform field parallel to the net magnetization.   In reality it would be better to say that it interacts with a field that is parallel to the magnetization of its neighbors.   This permits a small deviation of an atomic moment from alignment with its neighbor which can continue progressively from atom to atom.   If $\mathbf{M}$ (atomic moments precess about $\mathbf{M}$) is perpendicular to the x-y plane, it is possible to have a small, periodic variation in the amplitude of the x-y components of successive atomic moments without much loss in coupling energy.   This is illustrated in Figure 16.   By this means it is possible for $\mathbf{M}$ to be decreased by $2\mu_B$ at the cost of considerably less energy than is required for a spin flip.   These sinusoidal variations in the basal-plane components of the atomic spins are called *spin waves*.   Since spin waves are readily excited at low temperatures,

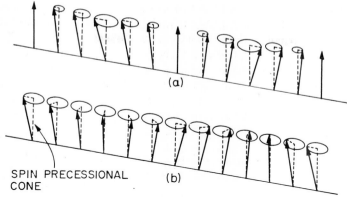

SPIN PRECESSIONAL CONE

Fig. 16. (a) Stationary and (b) travelling spin wave on a line of atoms.

the magnetization decreases much more rapidly than follows from the Weiss theory. Calculation of the temperature dependence of M_s at low temperatures as a result of spin wave excitation was first performed by Bloch (80, see also 160,495) who obtained, with the aid of the Heisenberg exchange Hamiltonian,

$$M_s(T) = M_0[1 - (T/T_B)^{3/2} - \ldots] \qquad (98)$$

where for a b.c.c. structure and spin S,

$$T_B = 21S^{5/3}J_{\mathrm{ex}}/k \qquad (99)$$

Equation 98 is known as the Bloch $T^{3/2}$ law. It is in good agreement with experiment at very low temperatures; other phenomena begin to appear at somewhat higher temperatures. An interesting phenomenon that demonstrates the existence of spin waves is the spin wave resonance spectrum recently observed in Permalloy films (554,612).

At the Curie point, the Weiss theory predicts that for $T > T_c$, in the absence of an external field, the spin order vanishes completely. Actually there is considerable short-range order just above T_c, as has been verified by neutron diffraction experiments (405,675). It is the problem of short-range order that is tackled by the more exact quantum statistics mentioned in connection with equation 94. At very high temperatures $(T \gg T_c)$, there is no short-range order, and the experimental curve approaches the Curie-Weiss curve asymptotically. Theory shows that the possibility of short-range ordering lowers the experimental T_c for long-range order below that calculated from the Weiss model. The discrepancy is rather small in most cases (20 to 30° for nickel), but it does introduce the distinction between θ_p and T_c noted earlier. Also because T_c may be quite high, it frequently happens that the experimental $1/\chi_m$ vs. T curve does not reach the true asymptote, so that too low a slope, and therefore too high a C_{mol}, is obtained. Care must be exercised in drawing conclusions from the $1/\chi_m$ vs. T curve.

II. Antiferromagnetism, Ferrimagnetism, and Parasitic Ferromagnetism

A. TWO-SUBLATTICE, COLLINEAR MODEL

If the exchange integral is $J_{ab} < 0$, antiferromagnetic coupling results. The simplest configuration, given $J_{ab} < 0$, consists of two sublattices such that an atom of one sublattice interacts most strongly only with atoms of the other sublattice. The ordered configuration then consists of ferromagnetic sublattices that are coupled antiparallel to one another. Two situations can arise: either the moments of the two sublattices are equal so that the net moment of the substance is zero, or the moments of the two sublattices are unequal so that there is a net spontaneous magnetization M_s. Substances belonging to the first class are called *antiferromagnets*, substances of the second are called *ferrimagnets*. As in the case of ferromagnets, there is a second-order transformation at the order $\rightleftharpoons$ disorder transition temperature that is marked by anomalies in the specific heat, thermal expansion coefficient, electrical resistivity, and magnetic susceptibility. These transitions sometimes display thermal hysteresis: the physical origins of this hysteresis, which suggests a first-order transition, are discussed in Chapter III.

Although a two-sublattice model and the concept of antiferromagnetic order is used for the case of an antiferromagnet consisting of identical sublattices, it should be realized that there is no long-range order in the classical sense of a net spin on each sublattice. The net spin of each sublattice is, on the average, zero. However, it can be shown (528) that there is a definite sublattice correlation of the electron spins that is detectable by neutron diffraction. It is this correlation that justifies arguments in terms of the classical concepts.

To calculate the temperature dependence of the magnetization or magnetic susceptibility of these substances, Néel (471) generalized the concept of the Weiss molecular field.   An ion of a given sublattice interacts with neighbors belonging to the two sublattices (or in general to the ν sublattices).   Interactions within and between sublattices are assumed to give rise to distinct internal fields, so that the total Weiss field acting at an atom of the ith sublattice is

$$H_{wi} = \sum_{j=1}^{\nu} W_{ij}M_j \qquad (100)$$

For $J_{ij} < 0$, the $W_{ij} < 0$; and since action is equal to reaction, $W_{ij} = W_{ji}$.   Since all interactions between sublattices are assumed to be contained within the Weiss field, it follows that the magnetization and the susceptibility of each sublattice are described by equations 91 and 95 provided the Weiss fields of equation 100 are used.

1. *Paramagnetism above the Curie Point*

Substitution of equation 100 for the Weiss field in equation 95 gives the set of equations

$$M_iT - C_i\left[H + \sum_{j=1}^{\nu} W_{ij}M_j\right] = 0 \qquad (101)$$

(To make contact with Néel's original notation, it should be noted that $C_1 = C\lambda$, $C_2 = C\mu$, where $\lambda + \mu = 1$.)   The total moment is

$$\mathbf{M} = \sum_{j=1}^{\nu} \mathbf{M}_j \qquad (102)$$

For the two-sublattice model, $\nu = 2$, and elimination of the M_i from equations 101 and 102 gives

$$\frac{1}{\chi_m} = \frac{1}{C}\left[T - \theta_a - \frac{\theta_b^2}{T - \theta}\right] \qquad (103)$$

where $C = C_1 + C_2$.   The Curie constants C_1 and C_2 for the respective sublattices depend upon the properties of the ions in these sublattices as given in equations 20 and 84.   If there is more than one kind of ion on a given sublattice, a suitable average is generally used. For antiferromagnetic coupling between sublattices, $W_{12} < 0$.   It is customary in the literature to use the following definitions:

$$n \equiv -W_{12} \qquad n\alpha \equiv W_{11} \qquad n\beta \equiv W_{22} \qquad (104)$$

and then the parametric temperatures entering equation 103 are given by

$$\theta_a = \frac{-n(2C_1C_2 - \alpha C_1^2 - \beta C_2^2)}{C_1 + C_2} \tag{105}$$

$$\theta = \frac{nC_1C_2(2 + \alpha + \beta)}{C_1 + C_2} \tag{106}$$

$$\theta_b = \frac{n\sqrt{(C_1C_2)}}{C_1 + C_2} \left[C_1(1 + \alpha) - C_2(1 + \beta) \right] \tag{107}$$

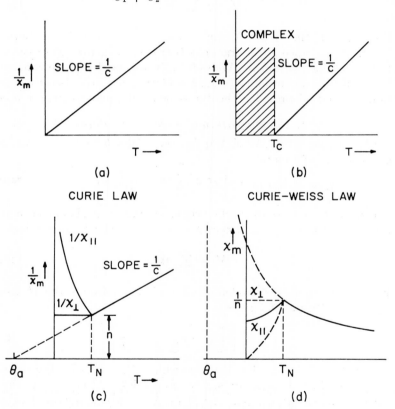

MOLECULAR-FIELD MODEL FOR ANTIFERROMAGNETISM

Fig. 17.   Molecular field $1/\chi_m$ vs. T curves for (a) free atoms (no interactions), (b) ferromagnetism, (c) and (d) antiferromagnetism. (See following page for Fig. 17(e).)

Schematic diagrams for typical paramagnetic behavior of ferromagnetic, antiferromagnetic, and ferrimagnetic compounds are shown in Figure 17. The curvature of the $1/\chi_m$ vs. T curve is due to θ_b. For an antiferromagnetic material composed of two identical sublattices, $C_1 = C_2$ and $\alpha = \beta$ so that $\theta_b = 0$. If $\theta_b = 0$, equation 103 reduces to the Curie-Weiss law of equation 96. For $T \gg \theta$, the paramagnetic susceptibility approaches a Curie-Weiss asymptote. In contrast to the ferromagnetic materials where $\theta_p > 0$, the asymptotic paramagnetic Curie point θ_a for antiferromagnetic and ferrimagnetic materials is $\theta_a < 0$, as can be seen from equation 105. This follows directly from the negative sign for the intersublattice interactions. Theoretically, the relative couplings n, α, β can be obtained by determining the parametric temperatures θ_a, θ, θ_b from a plot of $1/\chi_m$ vs. T (see Fig. 17e). Attempts (118,475) have been made to do this for several ferrimagnetic spinels, but the results are questionable as they are quite sensitive to the ionic distributions over the tetrahedral and octahedral sites. Further, how meaningful such parameters are in view of the known limitations of the Weiss field approximation is also debatable. Failure to account for short-range order leads to too high values, especially for α. The geometric relations between the parametric temperatures and the hyperbola of equation 103 are indicated in Figure 17e.

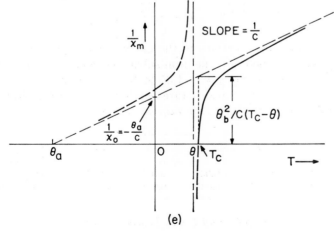

(e)

NÉEL LAW

Fig. 17 (continued). (e) Molecular field $1/\chi_m$ vs. T curves for ferrimagnetism.

Aléonard (5) has applied the method to the ferrimagnetic garnets, where the ionic distributions are known. He includes, to first order, the temperature dependence of the molecular field constants, $n = n_0(1 + \gamma T)$, that was first formulated by Néel (472). The coefficient $\gamma \approx 10^{-4}$ is proportional to the coefficient of thermal expansion. Then equation 103 becomes

$$\frac{1}{\chi_m} = \frac{1}{C'}\left[T - \theta_a' - \frac{\theta_b'^2}{T - \theta'}\right]$$

where

$$1/C' = (1 - \theta_a\gamma)/C \qquad \theta' = \theta/(1 + \theta\gamma)$$

$$\theta_a'/C' = (\theta_a + 2\gamma\theta_b^2)/C \qquad \theta_b'^2/C' = \theta_b^2(1 - 3\gamma\theta)/C$$

and C', θ_a', $\theta_b'^2$ are the experimental parameters. If the Curie constant C is known from independent paramagnetic measurements, the parameter γ can be obtained. In the case of the garnets, Aléonard obtained γ, n, α, β for the two iron sublattices by measuring $1/\chi_m$ for $Y_3Fe_5O_{12}$ and $Lu_3Fe_5O_{12}$. Since interactions between the rare earth ions can be shown to be $\sim 10^{-2}$ that between the two iron sublattices, they are neglected. Therefore the molecular field constants for the interactions of Y-substituted rare earths with the two iron sublattices can be obtained from the three-sublattice expression

$$\frac{1}{\chi_m} = \frac{1}{C'}\left[T - \theta_a' - \frac{\theta_b'T + \theta_m'^3}{T^2 - \theta'T + \theta_l'^2}\right]$$

where $\theta_m'^3$ and $\theta_l'^2$ are functions of the molecular field constants. In this way he obtained for the iron-sublattice constants $n = 48.4$, $\alpha = -0.51$, $\beta = -0.29$, $\gamma = -1.35 \times 10^{-4}$. The molecular field constants coupling the various rare earth ions to tetrahedral and octahedral iron, respectively, are $n\alpha_t$, $n\alpha_0$ where

	Gd	Tb	Dy	Ho	Er	Tm	Yb
$-\alpha_0$	0.035	0.047	0.037	0.025	0.010	0.000	0.091
$-\alpha_t$	0.012	0.045	0.035	0.041	0.006	0.000	0.010

2. Néel and Curie Temperatures

To determine the order $\rightleftharpoons$ disorder transition temperature, which is usually called the *Néel temperature* T_N in antiferromagnets, but the

Curie temperature T_c in ferromagnets and ferrimagnets, it is only necessary to set equal to zero the determinant for the coefficients of the M_i of equation 101 with $H = 0$ as this determines the temperature $T = T_c$ at which the magnetization has a nontrivial solution in zero external field. This gives an equation of the nth degree in T_c. Since all the sublattices are tied together, only one transition temperature is realized physically; this is the one corresponding to the largest real root. Other real solutions correspond to less stable phases. If there are no real roots, there is no two-sublattice, collinear atomic moment configuration. For $\nu = 2$, solution of the determinantal equation gives

$$T_c = (n/2)\{[(C_1\alpha - C_2\beta)^2 + 4C_1C_2]^{1/2} + C_1\alpha + C_2\beta\} \quad (108)$$

For an antiferromagnet with both sublattices identical, this reduces to

$$T_N = nC'(1 - \epsilon) \quad (109)$$

where $C_1 = C_2 = C'$ and $\alpha = \beta = -\epsilon$. A measure of the relative intrasublattice coupling ϵ for antiferromagnets is then given by a comparison of the ratio

$$|\theta_a|/T_N = (1 + \epsilon)/(1 - \epsilon) \quad (110)$$

From equation 110 it would appear that the ratio $|\theta_a|/T_N$ could be made arbitrarily large by having ϵ sufficiently close to one. Actually this is not the case, for the minimum-energy configuration need not be the two-sublattice configuration that leads to equation 110. In fact, for $\epsilon > \epsilon_c$, where the critical value $\epsilon_c < 1$, a different type of magnetic order becomes energetically more favorable. This point has been discussed by Anderson (17) and Van Vleck (633) for several types of chemical structures. In a body-centered-cubic (b.c.c.) array of magnetic atoms, the two-sublattice structure, called *ordering of the first kind*, is only realized if the nearest-neighbor (n.n.) interactions predominate. If the next-near-neighbor (n.n.n.) interactions predominate, there will be *ordering of the second kind*. (See Figure 18 for illustrations of the different types of magnetic order.) With this type of order, the Weiss constant W_{12} between the two simple-cubic (s.c.) sublattices is $W_{12} = 0$, so that equation 101 becomes

$$M_{ia} = \frac{nC}{4T}(H - 2\epsilon M_{ib}) \qquad M_{ib} = \frac{nC}{4T}(H - 2\epsilon M_{ia})$$

where $i = 1, 2$ and the subscripts a, b refer to the two magnetic

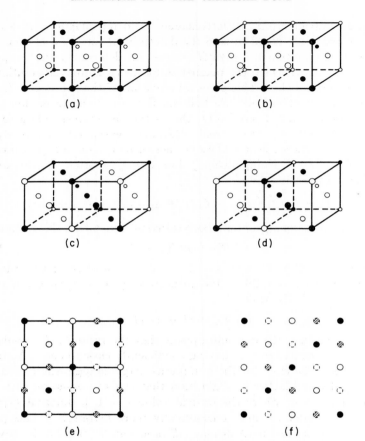

Fig. 18. Various types of collinear antiferromagnetic order found by neutron diffraction. • is plus spin and o is minus spin. (a) Face-centered first kind, (b) face-centered third kind, (c) face-centered second kind, type I, (d) face-centered second kind, type II, (e) face-centered fourth kind, type I, (f) face-centered fourth kind, type II. (See following pages for Figs. 18(g)–18(q).)

sublattices into which each s.c. sublattice is decomposed. Since there are four magnetic sublattices, each $C_{i\nu} = C/4$. With $H = 0$, solution of the secular equation gives

$$T_N = \tfrac{1}{2}n\epsilon C \qquad |\theta_a|/T_N = (1 + \epsilon)/\epsilon \qquad (110')$$

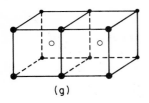

(g)

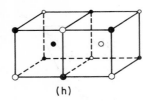

(h)

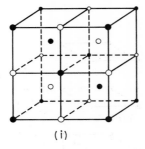

(i)

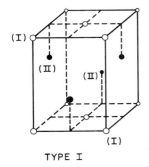

(I)

(II)

(II)

(I)

TYPE I

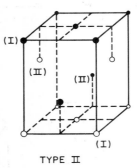

(I)

(II)

(II)

(I)

TYPE II

CATION (I) HAS TETRAHEDRAL, CATION (II) OCTAHEDRAL COORDINATION

(j)

Fig. 18 (*continued*). (g) Body-centered first kind, (h) body-centered second kind, (i) body-centered third kind, (j) Mn_2Sb-type. (Because the two sublattices of Mn_2Sb have manganese atoms of different moment, the structure is ferrimagnetic).

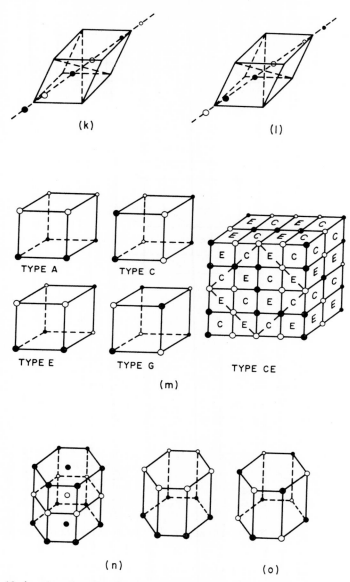

Fig. 18 (*continued*). (k) Corundum first kind, (l) corundum second kind, (m) simple cubic types *A*, *C*, *E*, *G*, and *CE*, (n) hexagonal type I, (o) hexagonal type II.

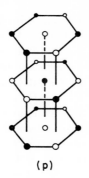

(p)

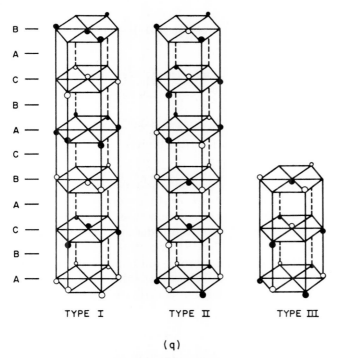

TYPE I   TYPE II   TYPE III

(q)

Fig. 18 (*continued*). (p) Hexagonal (close packed) third kind, (q) ilmenites.

The stable magnetic phase is that with the higher Curie temperature. Comparison of equations 110 and 110' show that $\epsilon_c = 1/2$, *where for* $\epsilon < \epsilon_c$ *there is ordering of the first kind, but for* $\epsilon > \epsilon_c$ *there is ordering of the second kind. The maximum value of* $|\theta_a|/T_N$ *is 3.* Body-centered ordering of the third kind would have no contribution from nearest neighbors and a $T_N = n\epsilon C/6$ were all interactions described by only two molecular field constants. Therefore *ordering of the third kind must be indicative of at least three constants, or more than one type of nearest-neighbor or next-nearest-neighbor interaction.*

In the case of rock salt, the cations form a face-centered-cubic (f.c.c.) array. Such an array is not compatible with a two-sublattice model, and there are four different types of magnetic order that can be considered (see Fig. 18). An f.c.c. structure is composed of four interpenetrating, simple-cubic (s.c.) sublattices. In *ordering of the first kind*, each s.c. sublattice is ferromagnetic and $\mathbf{M}_1 = -\mathbf{M}_2$, $\mathbf{M}_3 = -\mathbf{M}_4$ so that each cation has eight antiparallel and four parallel near neighbors. Then equation 101 becomes (all interactions assumed negative)

$$M_i = \frac{C}{4T}\left(H - nM_i - n\epsilon \sum_{j \neq i} M_j\right) \qquad i = 1, 2, 3, 4$$

$$\chi_m = \sum_i M_i/H = C/(T + \theta_a)$$

with

$$\theta_a = (1 + 3\epsilon)nC/4 \qquad (105')$$

and the secular equation for $H = 0$ gives

$$T_N = (\epsilon - 1)nC/4 \qquad |\theta_a|/T_N = (1 + 3\epsilon)/(\epsilon - 1)$$

Ordering of the first kind can only be stable if the next-near-neighbor interactions are zero or positive, or if there are more than two molecular field constants. With all interactions negative, *ordering of the third kind* (sometimes called improved ordering of the first kind) is obviously more stable (see Fig. 18) since this permits 1/3 of the next-nearest-neighbor interactions to be antiparallel without changing the ratio of antiparallel to parallel near neighbors. This is equivalent to reducing the next-near-neighbor contributions by 2/3, so that

$$T_N = (\epsilon - 1/3)nC/4$$

$$|\theta_a|/T_N = 3(3\epsilon + 1)/(3\epsilon - 1) \qquad (110'')$$

However, if the next-near-neighbor interaction predominates, then the stable configuration is *ordering of the second kind* (see Fig. 18).

With this configuration, there is no molecular field due to coupling between s.c. sublattices, and equation 101 reduces to

$$M_{ia} = \frac{C}{8T}(H - 2nM_{ib}) \qquad M_{ib} = \frac{C}{8T}(H - 2nM_{ia})$$

where the subscripts a, b refer to the two magnetic sublattices into which each of the four s.c. sublattices is decomposed. With $H = 0$, the secular equation gives

$$T_N = nC/4 \qquad |\theta_a|/T_N = (1 + 3\epsilon) \qquad (110''')$$

Comparison of equations 110'' and 110''' gives $\epsilon_c = 4/3$, *where with* $\epsilon < \epsilon_c$, *the stable configuration is ordering of the third kind. The maximum value of* $|\theta_a|/T_N$ *is 5.* (Where experimentally, see Table VIII, $|\theta_a|/T_N > 5$, there are two types of nearest-neighbor coupling: one is supplemented by 109° cation-anion-cation correlation superexchange, and the other is not.) *Ordering of the fourth kind* is similar to ordering of the second kind except that two of the next-near neighbors are parallel. This reduces the Néel temperature to $T_N = nC/12$, so that *this type of order is only found where there is a distortion of the structure from cubic symmetry, indicative of more than one type of near-neighbor interaction.*

The above arguments assume collinear spins. Loeb and Goodenough (398) have pointed out that if the next-nearest-neighbor interactions predominate in a rock salt structure, the four s.c. sublattices may have spin axes that make angles with one another without loss of exchange energy. In this case dipole-dipole interactions and/or crystalline anisotropy could determine the spin configuration. It was also shown (344,398) that multiaxis configurations can be present that satisfy the minimum dipole-dipole energy, but that these are degenerate with a collinear configuration. Removal of the degeneracy must be due to more subtle effects, such as magnetostrictive energy. Experimentally there is no conclusive evidence for a multiaxis spin configuration. However, careful measurements (544) of NiO indicate spontaneous formation of multidomain structures that are equivalent, on a macroscopic scale, to a multiaxis spin configuration. The ratios $|\theta_a|/T_N$ for several antiferromagnetic substances are given in Table VIII. Prediction of the type of order requires a knowledge of the coupling parameters W_{ij}, or of the exchange integrals J_{ij}. Conversely, knowledge of the magnetic order plus $|\theta_a|/T_N$ provides information about these parameters.

TABLE VIII
Illustrative Paramagnetic and Antiferromagnetic Data

Note the different types of magnetic order that occur for similar cation-sublattice structures and the variation in T_N for different cations in the same chemical structure. (Reported Néel points for a given compound often vary considerably as a result of different preparations.) For magnetic order, see Figure 18. Effective paramagnetic moment is $n_{eff} \equiv \mu_{eff}/\mu_B = \sqrt{(8C_M)}$, and the atomic moment in ordered state is $n_B^A = \mu_A/\mu_B$. Hydroxide impurities, which strongly influence magnetic data, tend to contaminate fluoride samples.

Row no.	Substance	Chem. structure	Crystal sym. $T > T_N$	Mag. cat. structure	n_{eff}	T_N, °K	$-\theta_a/T_N$
1	VO	Rock salt	Cubic	f.c.c.	( )[a]	117	
2	CrN	Rock salt	Cubic	f.c.c.	( )[a]	∼273	
3	MnO	Rock salt	Cubic	f.c.c.	5.95	122	5.0
4	α-MnS	Rock salt	Cubic	f.c.c.	5.6	130	3.1
5	β-MnS	Zinc blende	Cubic	f.c.c.	5.82	160	6.1
6	MnSe	Rock salt	Cubic	f.c.c.	5.7	∼173	2.1
7	Li$_{0.1}$Mn$_{0.9}$Se	Rock salt	Cubic	f.c.c.	4.76	71[b]	−0.8
8	FeO	Rock salt	Cubic	f.c.c.	4.6[d]	198	∼1.0[d]
9	CoO	Rock salt	Cubic	f.c.c.	5.1	291	1.1
10	NiO	Rock salt	Cubic	f.c.c.	4.6	520[c]	∼5
11	TbP	Rock salt	Cubic	f.c.c.		9	
12	ErP	Rock salt	Cubic	f.c.c.		3.1	
13	TbAs	Rock salt	Cubic	f.c.c.		12	
14	TbSb	Rock salt	Cubic	f.c.c.	9.9	14	
15	HoSb	Rock salt	Cubic	f.c.c.		9	
16	ErSb	Rock salt	Cubic	f.c.c	9.8	3.7	
17	γ-Mn	f.c.c.	Cubic	f c.c.		660	
18	MnS$_2$	Pyrite	Cubic	f.c.c.	6.30	<77	>8
19	MnSe$_2$	Pyrite	Cubic	f.c.c.	5.93	∼100	∼4.8
20	MnTe$_2$	Pyrite	Cubic	f.c.c	6.22	80	6.5
20a	FeS$_2$	Pyrite	Cubic	f.c.c.			
20b	CoS$_2$	Pyrite	Cubic	f.c.c.	1.85	$T_c = 110$	
20c	NiS$_2$	Pyrite	Cubic	f.c.c.	3.19		
21	CrF$_2$	Dist. rut.	Mono.	b.c. mono.	4.9	53	
22	CrCl$_2$	Dist. rut.	Ortho.	b.c. ortho.	5.1	40[h]	2.7
23	MnF$_2$	Rut.	Tet. $(c/a < 1)$	b.c. tet.	5.7	72	1.6
24	FeF$_2$	Rut.	Tet. $(c/a < 1)$	b.c. tet.	5.6	79	1.5
25	CoF$_2$	Rut.	Tet. $(c/a < 1)$	b.c. tet.	5.13	37	1.4
25a	CuF$_2$	Dist. rut.	Mono.	b.c. mono.		78	
26	NiF$_2$	Rut.	Tet. $(c/a < 1)$	b.c. tet.	3.5	78.5–83	∼2.0
27	VO$_2$	Rut.	Tet. $(c/a < 1)$	b c. tet.	1.73	343	2.1
28	CrO$_2$	Rut.	Tet. $(c/a < 1)$	b.c. tet.		$T_c = 394$	

TABLE VIII (continued)

Key: antiferro., antiferromagnetic; calc., calcite; cat., cation; chalcop., chalco-pyrite; chem., chemical; compl., complex; corund., corundum; diamag., diamag-netic; dist., distorted; el., electron; ferri., ferrimagnetic; ferro., ferromagnetic; hex., hexagonal; ilmen., ilmenite; mag., magnetic; met., metal; metal., metallic; metamag., metamagnetic; mono., monoclinic; ord., ordered; ortho., ortho-rhombic; paramag., paramagnetic; paras., parasitic; perov., perovskite; rut., rutile; s., simple; semicond., semiconductor; subl., sublattice; sym., symmetry; tet., tetragonal; trans., transition; trig., trigonal; vac., vacancy; wurz., wurtzite.

Mag. order	Spin axis	n_B^A	Remarks	Refs.	Row no.
			Semicond. $\rightleftharpoons$ met. at T_N	425, 442	1
f.c. fourth	$\parallel$ [010]	2.4	Metal. ortho. $\rightleftharpoons$ cubic at T_N	127	2
f.c. second (I)	$\parallel$ ferro. (111)	5.0	Trig. ($\alpha > 60°$) below T_N	72, 543, 570	3
f.c. second (I)	$\parallel$ ferro. (111)	5 0	Trig. ($\alpha > 60°$) below T_N	39, 126, 570	4
f.c. third	$\perp$ [001]	5.0	Tet. mag. cell	126	5
f.c. second (I)	$\parallel$ ferro. (111)	5.0	Different phases at low T	396, 557, 570	6
f.c. third	45° from [010][c]	4.2	Tet. (c[010]$/a \approx 1.02$) $\rightleftharpoons$ cubic at T_N	264, 523	7
f.c. second (I)	$\perp$ ferro. (111)	3.3	Trig. ($\alpha > 60°$) below T_N	72, 413, 543, 570	8
f.c. second (I)	$\sim \parallel$ [001]	3.8	Tet. ($c/a < 1$) below T_N	72, 570, 576	9
f.c. second (I)	$\parallel$ ferro. (111)	2.0	Trig. ($\alpha < 60°$) below T_N	72, 382, 512, 561, 570, 576	10
( )[f]	[111]	6.2	spin $\perp$ ferro. (111)	682	11
( )[f]	$\perp$ [111]	5.7	spins in ferro. (111)	682	12
( )[f]	[111]	7.7	spins $\perp$ ferro. (111)	682	13
( )[f]	[111]	8.2	spins $\perp$ ferro. (111)	682	14
( )[f]	[100]	9.3		682, 683	15
( )[f]	$\perp$ [111]	7.0	spins in ferro. (111)	682, 683	16
f.c. first	[001]	2.4	f.c. tet. ($c/a < 1$) below T_N	35, 432	17
f.c. third	$\parallel$ mag. [001]	5.0		260	18
( )[g]	$\parallel$ mag. [001]	5.0		260	19
f.c. first	$\parallel$ ferro. (001)	5.0		260	20
			Pauli paramag.	50	20a
ferro.(?)		0.84		251a	20b
			$\theta_a = -1500°$K	50	20c
b.c. first	32° from [001]	4.0	Any mono. $\rightleftharpoons$ tet. above 300°K	112	21
b.c. third	( )[i]	3.86	Any ortho. $\rightleftharpoons$ tet. above 300°K	112, 599, 604	22
b.c. first	[001]	5.0		72, 171	23
b.c. first	[001]	4.64		72, 171	24
b.c. first	[001]	3.0		71, 171	25
				70a, 550a	25a
b.c. first	( )[j]	2.0	Paras. ferro.	9, 71, 171	26
( )[k]			Semicond. $\rightleftharpoons$ met. at T_N)[l]	298, 333, 410, 442, 511, 547	27
Ferro.	40° to [100]	2.0	spins lie in (100)	121, 242, 121a	28

(continued)

TABLE VIII (*continued*)

Row no.	Substance	Chem. structure	Crystal sym. $T > T_N$	Mag. cat. structure	n_{eff}	T_N, °K	$-\theta_a/T_N$
29	MnO_2	Rut.	Tet. $(c/a < 1)$	b.c. tet.		84	
30	$MnAu_2$	CaC_2	Tet. $(c/a > 1)$	b.c. tet. $(c/a > 1)$		90	
30a	V	b.c.c.	Cubic	b.c.c.		250ma	
31	Cr	b.c.c.	Cubic	b.c.c.	$(\ )^a$	$\sim310, \sim475^n$	
32	MnCr	b.c.c.	Cubic	b.c.c.		$\gg300$	
33	$FeTe_2$	Marcasite	Cubic	s. tet. $(c/a < 1)$	0.2	85	3.8
34	MnAu	Dist. CsCl	Tet. $(c/a < 1)^q$	s. tet. $(c/a < 1)$		515	
35	FeSi	CsCl	Cubic	s.c.	2.55	443	0.24
36	FeRh	CsCl	Cubic	Two s.c.		$T_c = 675$	
37	VF_3	Dist. ReO_3	Trig.	$\sim$s.c.		<4	
37a	TaF_3	ReO_3	Cubic	s.c.	1.4		
38	CrF_3	Dist. ReO_3	Trig.	$\sim$s.c.	3.9	80	1.6
39	MoF_3	Dist. ReO_3	Trig.	$\sim$s.c.		185	
40	MnF_3	Dist. ReO_3	Mono.	$\sim$s. tet. $(c/a < 1)$	5.0	43–47	-0.2
41	FeF_3	Dist. ReO_3	Trig.	$\sim$s.c.	1.9	394	0.33
42	RuF_3	Dist. ReO_3	Trig.	$\sim$s.c.			
43	CoF_3	Dist. ReO_3	Trig.	$\sim$s.c.	2.5	460	
44	PdF_3	Dist. ReO_3	Trig.	$\sim$s.c.			
45	$KCrF_3$	Perov.	Ortho.	$\sim$s. tet. $(c/a < 1)$		<77	
46	$KMnF_3$	Perov.	Cubic	s.c.	5.94	88	1.8
47	$KFeF_3$	Perov.	Cubic	s.c.	5.38	113	
48	$KCoF_3$	Perov.	Cubic	s.c.	5.30	114	1.1
49	$KNiF_3$	Perov.	Cubic	s.c.	4.7	275	3.1
50	$KCuF_3$	Perov.	Tet. $(c/a < 1)$	s. tet. $(c/a < 1)$	2.0	243	1.5
51	$LaCrO_3$	Perov.	Ortho.	$\sim$s.c.	3.9	320	1.8
52	$LaMnO_3$	Perov.	Ortho.	$\sim$s. tet. $(c/a < 1)$	5.25	100	-0.5^u
53	$La_{0.65}Ca_{0.35}MnO_3$	Perov.	Trig.	$\sim$s.c.		$T_c = 250$	
54	$La_{0.4}Ca_{0.6}MnO_3$	Perov.	Mono.	$\sim$s. tet. $(c/a < 1)$		170	
55	$La_{0.2}Ca_{0.8}MnO_3$	Perov.	Tet. $(c/a > 1)$	s. tet. $(c/a > 1)$		165	
56	$CaMnO_.$	Perov.	Cubic	s.c.		110	

TABLE VIII (*continued*)

Mag. order	Spin axis	n_B^A	Remarks	Refs.	Row no.
Spiral[m]	⊥ [001]			72, 171, 706	29
Spiral[m]	⊥ [001]	3.0	Metamag.	269, 438	30
( )[k]		<0.1		108a	30a
b.c. first[o]	( )[p]	0.4		33, 111, 130, 255, 563, 567, 677	31
b.c. first		⟨0.85⟩		335	32
				178, 397	33
A	[010]	3.5		34, 208	34
				50	35
G ferro.[r]		( )[r]	Metamag.	65, 173, 368	36
( )[k]		~2.0[s]		696	37
				483	37a
G	‖ ferro. (111)	3.0	Paras. ferro.	96, 251, 696	38
G	⊥ [111]	3.0		696	39
A	⊥ [001]	4.0		96, 696	40
G	‖ ferro. (111)	5.0		73, 696	41
( )[k]			Low-spin Ru[III]	681	42
G	⊥ ferro. (111)	4.4		483, 696	43
( )[k]			Low-spin Pd[III]	681	44
A	⊥ [001]	4.3		553	45
G[t]	[100][t]	5.0	Tet. pseudocell $c/a > 1$ for $84°K < T < 184°K$, $c/a < 1$ for $T < 84°K$.	45, 261a, 275, 485, 553	46
G		4.4	Trig. ($\alpha < 60°$) below T_N	491, 492, 553	47
G		3.3	Tet. ($c/a < 1$) below T_N	491, 492, 553	48
G		2.2		491, 492, 553	49
( )[k]				491, 492, 553	50
G		2.8	Paras. ferro.	308, 354	51
A	[100]	3.9		308, 354, 694	52
Ferro.		⟨~3.7⟩		694	53
CE			71% Mn^{4+}	694	54
C	[001]	⟨3.0⟩		694	55
G		2.7	97% Mn^{4+}	694	56

(*continued*)

TABLE VIII (continued)

Row no.	Substance	Chem. structure	Crystal sym. $T > T_N$	Mag. cat. structure	n_{eff}	T_N, °K	$-\theta_a/T_N$
57	LaFeO₃	Perov.	Ortho.	∼s.c.	3–4.4	750	∼1.0
58	LaCoO₃	Perov.	Trig.	∼s.c.	4.5		
59	LaNiO₃	Perov.	Trig.	∼s.c.			
59a	K₂NiF₄	K₂NiF₄	Tet.	b.c. tet.		180	
60	TiS	NiAs	Hex.	s. hex.			
61	TiSe	NiAs	Hex.	s. hex.			
62	TiTe	NiAs	Hex.	s. hex.			
63	TiSb	NiAs	Hex.	s. hex.			
64	V$_x$S	NiAs	Hex.	s. hex.	3.76	1040	3.0
65	VSe	NiAs	Hex.	s. hex.	4.08	163	16
66	VTe	NiAs	Hex.	s. hex.	1.7		
67	CrS	Dist. NiAs	Mono.	Dist. hex.			
68	Cr₇S₈	Ord. NiAs	Hex.	Ord. hex.			
69	Cr₅S₆	Ord. NiAs	Hex.	Ord. hex.	4.8	$T_c = 305$	0.5
70	CrSe	NiAs	Hex.	s. hex.	4.9	320	0.63
71	Cr₃Se₄	Ord. NiAs	Mono.	Ord. hex.	2.4	80	0.04
72	CrTe	NiAs	Hex.	s. hex.	4.0	T_c: 350–360	−1.0
73	CrSb	NiAs	Hex.	s. hex.	4.3	723	1.4
74	CrTe₀.₂₅Sb₀.₇₅	NiAs	Hex.	s. hex.		520	−0.33
75	Cr₀.₈Mn₀.₂Sb	NiAs	Hex.	s. hex.	4.26	588	−0.14
76	MnAs	NiAs	Hex.	s. hex.	4.95	$T_c = 318^z$	−0.9
77	MnSb	NiAs	Hex.	s. hex.	4.1	$T_c = 587$	−1.0
78	MnBi	NiAs	Hex.	s. hex.		$T_c = 633^z$	
79	MnTe	NiAs	Hex.	s. hex.	6.1	323	2.2
80	FeS	NiAs	Hex.	s. hex.	5.25	600	1.9
81	Fe₁₋$_x$S	NiAs	Hex.	s. hex.		600	
82	Fe₀.₉S	NiAs	Hex.	s. hex.		( )ᵃᵇ	
83	Fe₇S₈	Ord. NiAs	Mono.	Ord. hex.	5.93	$T_c = 578$	3.4
84	Fe₇Se₈	Ord. NiAs	Ortho.	Ord. hex.		$T_c = 425$	6.1
85	Fe₃Se₄	Ord. NiAs	Mono.	Ord. hex.		$T_c = 320$	
86	FeTe	NiAs	Hex.	s. hex.	2.44	63	2.0
87	CoS	NiAs	Hex.	s. hex.	1.7	358	1.8
88	Co₀.₈Te	NiAs	Hex.	s. hex.	2.7		
89	CoSb	NiAs	Hex.	s. hex.	1.36	40	8.0
90	NiS	NiAs	Hex.	s. hex.	2.66	150	20
91	NiTe	NiAs	Hex.	s. hex.	0.99		
92	NiSb	NiAs	Hex.	s. hex.			
93	Fe₁.₂₂Sb	Ni₂In	Hex.	two hex.	2.7	$T_c = 4.2$	36

TABLE VIII (*continued*)

Mag. order	Spin axis	n_B^A	Remarks	Refs.	Row no.
G		4.6	Paras. ferro.	308, 354	57
( )^k			Neutron data for 10% Co^{IV}	311, 354	58
( )^k			Low-spin Ni^{III}	354	59
⇅ (in 001)	[001]	2.0	Ni^{2+}octahedron $c/a = 0.98$	38a, 392a	59a
			Pauli paramag.	3	60
			Pauli paramag.	3	61
			Pauli paramag.	3	62
			Pauli paramag.	3	63
			Probably $x \approx 0.875$	619	64
				619	65
				3	66
			Mag. data unreliable	253, 305	67
			Antiferro.	158	68
	[0001]^v		Antiferro. ⇌ ferri. 158°K	3, 158, 712	69
			μ_s(max) $= 0.11\mu_B/\mathrm{Cr}$)^w		
( )^x	Trig.	2.9		131, 618	70
		⊥ [0001]^x			
( )^y				65	71
Ferro.		2.45	[0001] apparent easy axis	403	72
Hex. (I)	[0001]	2.7		277, 310, 403, 593, 662	73
				403	74
Hex. (I)	[0001]	2.4	Ferro. ⇌ antiferro. at 170–180°K	277, 519	75
Ferro.	⊥ [0001]	3.4		236, 336, 363a, 541, 557	76
Ferro.				236, 557	77
Ferro.	⊥ [0001]$T < T_s$		$T_s = 80°$K	236, 262	78
	[0001]$T > T_s$				
Hex. (I)	⊥ [0001]	5.0		165, 403	79
Hex. (I)	⊥ [0001] $> T_s$	4.0	$T_\alpha = 413°$K; $T_s = 433°$K)^{aa}	21, 50, 574, 575, 597	80
	[0001] $< T_s$				
Hex. (I)	⊥ [0001]	4.0	$0.06 \leq x \leq 0.09$	21, 574, 575, 597	81
				402	82
Ferri.	⊥ [0001]^{ac}		$\mu_s = 0.29\mu_B/\mathrm{Fe}$	402, 506	83
Ferri.	⊥ [0001] $> T_s$		$T_s \sim 150°$K depends on type	3, 490	84
	[0001] $< T_s$		order. $\mu_s = 0.20\mu_B/\mathrm{Fe}$		
Ferri.	⊥ [0001]		$\mu_s = 0.23\mu_B/\mathrm{Fe}$	3, 490	85
				622	86
				50	87
			$\theta_a = -1400°$K	3	88
				3	89
				619	90
			$\theta_a = -1110°$K	3	91
			Diamag.	3	92
Ferri.				3	93

(*continued*)

TABLE VIII (*continued*)

Row no.	Substance	Chem. structure	Crystal sym. $T > T_N$	Mag. cat. structure	n_{eff}	T_N, °K	$-\theta_a/T_N$
94	$Fe_{1.3}Sn$	Ni_2In	Hex.	two hex.		$T_c = 676$	
95	$Fe_{1.67}Ge$	Ni_2In	Hex.	two hex.	3.14	$T_c = 485$	-1.1
96	$Mn_{1.77}Sn$	Ni_2In	Hex.	two hex.	3.4	$T_c = 263$	
96a	Mn_3Ge_2				3.2	283–290	-1.1
97	CrAs	MnP	Ortho.	Dist. hex.		823	
98	MnP	MnP	Ortho.	Dist. hex.	2.9	$T_c = 298$	-1.1
99	FeP	MnP	Ortho.	Dist. hex.	3.42	$T_c = 215$	0.25
100	$MnSn_2$	Cu_2Al	Tet.	( )[ad]	4 53	86	( )[ae]
101	$FeGe_2$	Cu_2Al	Tet.	( )[ad]	2.43	190	-0.47
102	$FeSn_2$	Cu_2Al	Tet.	( )[ad]	3.36	380	0.6
103	$CoSn_2$	Cu_2Al	Tet.	( )[ad]			
104	$MnBr_2$	CdI_2	Trig.	s. hex.	5.84	2.16	1.0
105	MnI_2	CdI_2	Trig.	s. hex.	5.88	3.40	1.1
106	$FeBr_2$	CdI_2	Trig.	s. hex.	5.62	11	0.6
107	FeI_2	CdI_2	Trig.	s. hex.	5.88	10	2.3
108	$CoBr_2$	CdI_2	Trig.	s. hex.		19	
108a	$TiCl_3$	Vac. CdI_2	Trigonal	s. hex.[af]		217	
109	$CrBr_3$	Vac. CdI_2	Trig.	s. hex.[af]	3.85	$T_c = 37$	$\sim\!-1.0$
110	$FeCl_3$	Vac. CdI_2	Trig.	s. hex.[af]	5.73	16	0.7
111	$MnCl_2$	$CdCl_2$	Trig.	( )[ah]	5.73	1.96[aha]	1.7
112	$FeCl_2$	$CdCl_2$	Trig.	( )[ah]	5.36	24	-2.0
113	$CoCl_2$	$CdCl_2$	Trig.	( )[ah]	5.26	25	-1.5
114	$NiCl_2$	$CdCl_2$	Trig.	( )[ah]	3.3	50	-1.4
115	$NiBr_2$	$CdCl_2$	Trig.	( )[ah]	3 0	60	0.3
116	$CrCl_3$	Vac. $CdCl_2$	Trig.	( )[af]	3.9	17	-1.8
116a	CrI_3	Vac. $CdCl_2$	Trigonal	( )[af]	4.03	$\theta_p = 70$	
117	Ti_2O_3	Corund.	Trig.	( )[al]	( )[a]	470–520[am]	
118	V_2O_3	Corund.	Trig.	( )[al]	( )[a]	( )[an]	
119	α-Cr_2O_3	Corund.	Trig.	( )[al]	3.73	307	1.6
120	α-Fe_2O_3	Corund.	Trig.	( )[al]	5.92	953	2.1
121	$FeVO_3$	Corund.	Trig.	( )[al]		446	
122	$MnTiO_3$	Ilmen.[ao]	Trig.	( )[ao]	5.80	41	5.0
123	$FeTiO_3$	Ilmen.[ao]	Trig.	( )[ao]	5.62	55–68	-0.3
124	$NiTiO_3$	Ilmen.[ao]	Trig.	( )[ao]	3.24	23	$\sim\!0.0$
125	$CoMnO_3$	Ilmen.[ao]	Trig.	( )[ao]		391	
126	$NiMnO_3$	Ilmen.[ao]	Trig.	( )[ao]		437	
127	$Nb_2Mn_4O_9$	Ord. corund.	Trig.	( )[ap]	5.88	125	2.0

TABLE VIII (*continued*)

Mag. order	Spin axis	n_B^A	Remarks	Refs.	Row no.
Ferri. (?)			$\mu_s = 1.8\mu_B/Fe$	26	94
Ferro.		1.59	$n_B^A = \langle n_B^A \rangle$	703, 704	95
Ferri.			$\mu_s = 1.23\mu_B/Mn$	703, 704	96
			Parasitic ferro. $T_s < T < T_N$; first-order at $T_s = 113-150°K$	172a, 188a	96a
				3, 283	97
Ferro.	Short axis	1.29	Metamag. below 50°K	3, 283	98
			$\mu_s = 0.36\mu_B/Fe$	3, 437	99
( )ae			$c/2 = 2.72$ A, $a/\sqrt{2} = 4.70$ A,	154, 703, 704	100
			$c/2 = 2.48$ A, $a/\sqrt{2} = 4.18$ A, Paras. $\mu_s = 0.11\mu_B/Fe$, first-order change at 73°K	703, 704	101
			$c/2 = 2.66$ A, $a/\sqrt{2} = 4.60$ A	323	102
			Pauli paramag.	323	103
( )y	⊥ [0001]y	5.0	First-order trans. at T_N	146, 695	104
Spiral	In (307)	4.6	$\mathbf{k} \parallel [307]$ with $\theta = 2\pi/16$	114, 146	105
Hex. (I)	[0001]	4.4		76, 678	106
				76	107
Hex. (I)	⊥ [0001]	2.8		77, 678	108
			First-order at T_N (Fig. 76)	486	108a
Ferro.	∥ [0001]	3.0		620	109
Compl.ag				113, 599	110
Compl.			Antiferro. ⇌ antiferro. at 1.81°K	459a, 460, 599, 679	111
( )ai	[0001]	4.5	Metamag.)aj	599, 678	112
( )ai	⊥ [0001]	3.1	Metamag.)ak	599, 678	113
			Metamag.	599, 621	114
				619, 621	115
( )ai	⊥ [0001]	3.0		113, 392, 599	116
ferro. (?)			μ (16 Kgauss) $= 1\mu_B$ at 4.2°K is unsaturated	250a, 251	116a
( )k			Semicond. ⇌ met. at T_N)am	181, 510, 564	117
( )k			Semicond. ⇌ met.)an	116, 179, 184, 281, 500, 645	118
Corund. (I)	[0001]			69, 104, 300, 427	119
Corund. (II)	⊥ [0001] $> T_s$ [0001] $< T_s$	5.0	Paras. ferro. $T > T_s \approx 250°K$	75, 129, 168, 237, 446, 476, 570	120
Corund. (II)			Paras. $\mu_s = 0.15\mu_B$, $n_B = 2.5$	135, 691	121
Illmen. (III)	[0001]	5.0	$g = 2.1$; $(2H_wH_A)^{1/2} = 52$ Koe	292, 563, 217a, 600a	122
Ilmen. (I)	[0001]	4.0		74, 292, 565	123
Illmen. (I)	⊥ [0001]	2.25	$(2H_wH_A)^{1/2} = 67$ Koe; $\chi_\perp = 210 \times 10^{-6}$ cgs/gm	292, 563, 267a	124
Corund. (II)	⊥ [0001]		Ferri. $\mu_s = 0.72\mu_B$	97, 119, 303, 608	125
Corund. (II)	⊥ [0001]		Ferri. $\mu_s = 0.61-0.76\mu_B$	59, 97, 119, 303, 608	126
Compl.aq	[0001]	5.0		6, 61	127

(*continued*

TABLE VIII (*continued*)

Row no.	Substance	Chem. structure	Crystal sym. $T > T_N$	Mag. cat. structure	n_{eff}	T_N, °K	$-\theta_a/T_N$
128	$Nb_2Co_4O_9$	Ord. corund.	Trig.	( )^{ap}	4.91	$4.2 < T_N < 30$	>0
129	$MnCO_3$	Calc.	Trig.	b.c. trig.	6.26	$\sim$32	$\sim$2.0
130	$FeCO_3$	Calc.	Trig.	b.c. trig.	5.3	20–35	0.4–0.7
131	$CoCO_3$	Calc.	Trig.	b.c. trig.	4.34	17.5	3.9
132	Cu_2Sb	Cu_2Sb	Tet.	Fig. 18(j)	1.2	373	4.6
133	Cr_2As	Cu_2Sb	Tet.	Fig. 18(j)	1.8	393	5.2
134	Mn_2As	Cu_2Sb	Tet.	Fig. 18(j)	2.58	573	3.4
135	Mn_2Sb	Cu_2Sb	Tet.	Fig. 18(j)		550	
136	$Mn_{2-x}Cr_xSb$	Cu_2Sb	Tet.	Fig. 18(j)		T_c: 520–550 $T_N = T_s^{aa}$	
137	$Mn_2Sb_{0.8}As_{0.2}$	Cu_2Sb	Tet.	Fig. 18(j)			
138	β-MnS	Wurtz.	Hex.	c.p.h.	6.11	110	8.5
139	$CuFeS_2$	Chalcop.	Tet.	Ord. f.c. tet.		825	
140	CuO	CuO	Mono.	b.c. mono.	1.9	230	3.2
141	$CrVO_4$	$CrVO_4$	Ortho.	( )^{av}	$\sim$4	$\sim$50	
142	$FeSO_4$	$CrVO_4$	Ortho.	( )^{av}	5.20	21	1.5
143	$CoSO_4$	$CrVO_4$	Ortho.	( )^{av}	3.82	37	2.2
144	$NiSO_4$	$CrVO_4$	Ortho.	( )^{av}	5.65	15.5	3.0

[a] Curie-Weiss law not obeyed. Temperature independent χ_m below T_N.

[b] Antiferromagnetic $\rightleftharpoons$ ferromagnetic transition; μ(ferro.) $\approx 0.7\mu_B$ for $71°K < T < 77°K$.

[c] Assumes collinear spins. Multiple-axis structures may also be possible.

[d] Paramagnetic data unreliable because Fe^{2+} is un-table.

[e] From specific heat data. Susceptibility data does not give a sharp T_N.

[f] Ferromagnetic (111) planes are coupled antiferromagnetically.

[g] Combination of ordering of first and third kind. Magnetic unit cell is triple the chemical unit cell in [010] (magnetic [001]) direction.

[h] Antiferromagnetic order within c-axis chains at 40°K, between chains at 16°K.

[i] In direction of one or the other of longest Cr–Cl bonds of Jahn-Teller-distorted interstices.

[j] $\perp$ [001] (ref. (9)); $\leq 13°$ from [001] (ref. (171)). Parasitic ferromagnetism, nuclear magnetic resonance, and torque curves favor $\perp$ [001] and angle between sublattice magnetization of $\phi < \pi$ (see ref. (450)).

[k] No magnetic order observable down to 4.2°K. (Magnetic resolution insufficient to measure paramagnetic scattering from a single electron.) For Ti_2O_3, preliminary neutron diffraction results of Abrahams (2) indicate $\mu_{Ti} \approx 0.2\mu_B$ with Corund.-(II)-type order and spins in the basal plane.

[l] V–V pairing along c axis below T_N.

[m] Periodicity of screw is 3.5c.

[ma] T_N sensitive to impurities and marked by anomalies in χ_m, ρ, a_0, Y, ...

[n] Sensitive to impurities. Chromium samples appear to fall into two classes characterized by the two Néel temperatures indicated.

[o] Some samples exhibit a long-range modulation along the cube edge superimposed on the simple antiferromagnetic structure with a period of approximately 28 unit cells at room temperature. Modulation has been characterized as a sinusoidal variation in amplitude of resultant spin vector (no order perpendicular to this vector).

TABLE VIII (continued)

Mag. order	Spin axis	n_B^A	Remarks	Refs.	Row no.
Compl.[aq]	[0001]			6, 61	128
( )[ar]	$\sim \perp$ [0001]	5.0		8, 86, 516	129
( )[ar]	[0001]	5.0	Metamag.	8, 72, 515	130
( )[ar]	46° to [0001] 15° to [$2\bar{1}\bar{1}0$]			10, 86	131
				710	132
				710	133
				711	134
Cu₂Sb (I)	[001] $> T_s$ $\perp$ [001] $< T_s$	Mn₁: 2.13 Mn₁₁²: 3.87	$T_s = 240°K$. Curie-Weiss law not obeyed	235, 241, 557, 676	135
Cu₂Sb (I) $> T_s$ Cu₂Sb (II) $< T_s$	[001] $> T_s$	( )[as]	First-order trans. at T_s	70, 120, 122, 609	136
			$c_{crit} = 6.487$ A	29	137
Hex. (III)[asa]	$\perp$ (011)	5.0	orthohex. mag. cell	126	138
( )[at]	[001]	Fe: 3.9 Cu: 0.0		155, 615	139
( )[au]	[001]	0.6		105, 598	140
( )[aw]	( )[ax]	2.1	spin along **a** also possible ($\mu_V = 0\mu_B$)	191	141
( )[ay]	‖ **b**	4.1		191, 87a	142
( )[az]	( )[az]	3.3	metameg. $\mu_s = 1.4\mu_B$ for $H > 12$Koe	191, 87a	143
( )[ay]	‖ **b**	2.1		191, 87a	144

[p] Perpendicular to modulation axis at room temperature, parallel to modulation axis below a T_s, where $110°K < T_s < 155°K$.

[q] Excess Au, tet. $c/a < 1$; stoichiometric or excess Mn, tet. $c/a > 1$.

[r] For $T > T_t$, extrapolation to 0°K gives $n_B^{Fe} \approx 3.1$, $n_B^{Rh} \approx 0.7$. For $T < T_t$, $n_B^{Fe} \approx 3.3$ if $n_B^{Rh} = 0$. T_t varies from 150°K to 400°K as the Rh concentration increases from 50% to 55%. First-order transition at T_t.

[s] Estimated from paramagnetic neutron scattering.

[t] Reference (261a) reports uniaxial ([100] of pseudocell) antiferromagnetism $81.5°K < T < 88.3°K$, parasitic ferromagnetism due to canted spins $T < 81.5°K$ as a result of different single-ion anisotropies, thermal hysteresis in the canted-spin ⇌ uniaxial-spin transition, and an $H_c \approx 9000$ oe for field-induced spin canting in the intermediate temperature range.

[u] θ_a obtained from temperature interval $100°K < T < 700°K$, where the orthorhombic symmetry is $c/\sqrt{2} < a < b$.

[v] Room temperature.

[w] Magnetization is decreased by application of hydrostatic pressure and by quenching; T_t is unaffected. Thermal hysteresis of 5°C at T_t and T_t shifted to lower temperatures in increasing external fields.

[x] "Umbrella" spin arrangement with threefold symmetry about the c axis. The c-axis component orders as Hex. (I), the c-plane component spirals in the plane, taking six different directions along three crystallographic axes of the plane. It was difficult to determine the magnitude of the magnetic-moment component parallel to the c axis from powder data.

[y] Within each hexagonal layer, spins take on sequence ↑ ↑ ↓ ↓ ↑ along orthorhombic [100] (long axis) with the spin axis parallel to a hexagonal [1000], or orthorhombic [010] (short axis). Between hexagonal layers the linear Mn–Br–Br–Mn interactions are antiferromagnetic, which restricts antiferromagnetic domain growth to three of

(continued)

the possible six orthorhombic [100] directions that might be chosen. Order in Cr_3Se_4 qualitatively similar to that of $MnBr_2$.

[z] First-order phase change at T_c. Evidence for MnP structure in MnAs in the range $T_c < T < 400°K$. Also T_c for MnAs varies with external field.

[aa] χ_m anomaly and phase change at T_α. $T_s = T_\alpha$ (ref. (21)) and $T_s = T_\alpha + 20°C$ (ref. (597)) have been reported.

[ab] If slow cooled, antiferro. $\rightleftharpoons$ ferri. transition at $\sim480°K$, $T_c \sim 535°K$, paramag. $\rightleftharpoons$ antiferro. at $\sim580°K$, and $T_N \approx 600°K$. If annealed at $493°K$ and quenched to room temperature, the compound is ferrimagnetic for all $T < 300°K$.

[ac] Spins tilt increasingly out of basal plane as T is lowered from $\sim250°K$, reaching an angle of $\sim20°$ out of plane at lowest temperatures.

[ad] Close-packed layers registered directly above one another along the c axis. Mn–Mn separations are given by $c/2$ and $a/\sqrt{2}$. (Anions in between layers are somewhat displaced from the plane of their four near neighbors.)

[ae] Ferromagnetic chains along c axis coupled antiparallel within basal plane. Evidence of change to ferromagnetic coupling in all directions above $T_t = 324°K$. Curie-Weiss law for $T > T_t$ gives $\theta_p = +190°K$, and for $T < T_t$ a $\theta_a \approx 0°K$. Below $73°K$, χ_m is temperature independent, and there is evidence of spin-pairing below this first-order (hysteresis of $0.7°K$) transition.

[af] Close-packed layers have one-third of cations removed in a regular manner.

[ag] A spiral configuration with [230] screw axis, $\phi = 2\pi/15$, spins within (140), and antiferromagnetism along c axis is reported.

[ah] Layer structure formed by deleting alternate (111) planes of a f.c.c. lattice. ($CdCl_2$ corresponds to rock salt with every other (111) cation plane removed.)

[aha] T_N increases and antiferro. $\rightleftharpoons$ antiferro. transition decreases in an external field.

[ai] Ferromagnetic close-packed layers coupled antiferromagnetically. Analogous to Hex. (I).

[aj] If an external **H** is applied parallel to [0001], the system becomes ferromagnetic.

[ak] At small fields, spin axis in basal plane becomes perpendicular to **H**. At large fields there is a large component along **H** from both sublattices.

[al] Puckered layers, missing 1/3 the atoms of close-packed layers, have the sequence A–B–C–A–B–C.

[am] Noncooperative transition at T_N, so that apparent Néel temperature occurs over a temperature interval. The c/a ratio is smaller in low-temperature phase.

[an] Semiconductor $\rightleftharpoons$ metal transition occurs at $150°K$ (cooling), at $180°K$ (heating). The resistivity changes through the transition by a factor of 10^6. The low-temperature phase is monoclinic. A noncooperative, high temperature transition occurs over the temperature range $110°C < T < 260°C$.

[ao] Corundum with cations ordered into alternate (111), or (0001), cation planes.

[ap] Imagine a replacement in the Al_2O_3 structure of the Al(000) sublattice by Nb, the Al($\frac{1}{3},\frac{2}{3},\frac{1}{3}$) and Al($\frac{2}{3},\frac{1}{3},\frac{2}{3}$) sublattices by M_1 and M_2, where M = Mn or Co. Note that this gives Nb–Nb pairs across a common octahedral face which suggests Nb^{4+}, $M^{2.5+}$, $M_2^{2.5+}$.

[aq] Sublattices M_1 and M_2 are antiparallel to each other. (This gives parallel ordering between Mn^{2+} cations sharing a common face, which is compatible with one-electron (M = Mn) or three-electron (M = Co) bonding. (See eqs. 162, 163).

[ar] Moments alternate along [0001].

[as] An antiferromagnetic $\rightleftharpoons$ ferromagnetic (exchange-inversion) transition occurs at T_s, where T_s increases with increasing Cr content ($T_s \approx 120°K$ for $x = 0.03$, $T_s = 385°K$ for $x = 0.2$). For $x = 0.02$, the low-temperature phase has been reported to be a spiral along c axis with $120°$ turn angle between collinear II–I–II triple layers. However, a residual saturation moment one-third that of the high-temperature phase indicates either a more complex spin configuration or an ordered reversal of every third II–I–II triple layer. For $x = 0.03$, the complex configuration occurs in the intermediate temperature range $100°K < T < 130°K$. At $x = 0.1$, the average room-temperature atomic moments are:

$$\mu(\langle Mn(I)\rangle) = 1.4 \pm 0.15\mu_B, \; \mu(\langle Mn(II)\rangle) = 2.8 \pm 0.2\mu_B \text{ for antiferromagnetic state}$$
$$\mu(\langle Mn(I)\rangle) = 1.8 \pm 0.2\mu_B, \; \mu(\langle Mn(II)\rangle) = 2.3 \pm 0.2\mu_B \text{ for ferrimagnetic state}$$

where ferrimagnetic values are extrapolated from $50°C$. Thus the exchange-inversion transition, which changes an antiferromagnetic Mn(II)–Mn(II) interaction between successive (001) Mn(II) planes into a ferromagnetic interaction, is accompanied by a discontinuity in the atomic moments.

ᵃˢᵃ Keffer (341a) points out that the anisotropic superexchange of eq. 167 leads to a spiral ($\theta = 90°$) spin configuration, which would have the same powder diffraction pattern as Hex. (III), and that Hex. (III) does not minimize the dipolar energy.

ᵃᵗ Ferromagnetic (001) layers coupled antiferromagnetically. Equivalent to face-centered ordering of the third kind, but with one half of the atoms (the Cu atoms) having zero moment.

ᵃᵘ Ferromagnetic ($\bar{2}02$) planes coupled antiferromagnetically. Magnetic unit cell: $a = 2a_0$, $b = 2b_0$, $c = 2c_0$.

ᵃᵛ Face-centered sheets are stacked at d_{002} intervals in the c direction. (Magnetic cations occupy distorted octahedra of O^{2-} that share common edges to form chains parallel to c axis.)

ᵃʷ Ferromagnetic sheets stacked antiferromagnetically along c axis.

ᵃˣ Single spin direction inclined at angles $\phi_a = 27 \pm 15°$, $\phi_b = 64 \pm 10°$, $\phi_c = 85 \pm 15°$, with orthorhombic crystallographic axes.

ᵃʸ Antiferromagnetic sheets with ferromagnetic coupling between sheets along c axis.

ᵃᶻ Antiferromagnetic sheets, but coupling between sheets gives noncollinear, canted spin structure. The two spin directions alternate in successive sheets along the c axis. Spin vectors lie in y-z plane at alternately clockwise and counterclockwise angles of $25 \pm 2°$ from the b axis.

Antiferromagnetic-resonance (AFMR) experiments also provide information about the strength of these parameters. The theory of antiferromagnetic resonance has been given independently by Nagamiya (461), Kittel (342,348), and Keffer (341). Since the effective exchange fields of materials with high T_N are large, millimeter-wavelength microwaves and/or high ($>10^5$ oe) d. c. fields are generally required. Therefore early experimental work (141,207,227,623) was confined to such weak antiferromagnets as $CuCl_2 \cdot 2H_2O$ ($T_N = 4.3 - 4.7°K$) and $CuBr_2 \cdot 2H_2O$ ($T_N = 5 - 6.5°K$). Johnson and Nethercot (306) measured the AFMR in MnF_2 ($T_N = 68°K$) with millimeter waves and Foner (186) used pulsed high fields to observe AFMR in MnF_2 and Cr_2O_3 ($T_N = 308°K$). An earlier experiment (142) on Cr_2O_3 used lower fields and could not reveal the whole resonance behavior. Foner (188) has extended his techniques to examine the system $(Cr_2O_3)_{1-x}(Al_2O_3)_x$. With a far-infrared spectrometer, Tinkham (345,617) has measured AFMR in FeF_2 ($T_N = 79°K$) and in MnO ($T_N = 122°K$), and Kondoh (361) has measured NiO ($T_N = 523°K$). Interestingly, this phenomenon has already been incorporated into a practical device at millimeter wavelengths (267).

The exchange constants are also obtained from expressions like equation 94 that are derived with more sophisticated statistics (589).

3. Susceptibility of an Antiferromagnet below T_N

Below T_N, the two sublattices of a collinear antiferromagnet have their magnetic moments aligned antiparallel. Because of the axial symmetry of the configuration, it is meaningful to define $\chi_{||}$ and $\chi_{\perp}$, which refer to the susceptibilities for **H** parallel and perpendicular to the unique axis defined by $\mathbf{M}_1$ and $\mathbf{M}_2$. From equations 103, 105, and 109, the susceptibility at T_N is

$$\chi_m(T_N) = 1/n \tag{111}$$

For $\mathbf{H} \perp \mathbf{M}_1$, $\mathbf{M}_2$ below T_N, the sublattice moments are each turned by an angle ϕ from the original axis so that the magnitude of the net moment parallel to **H** is $M = (M_1 + M_2) \sin \phi \approx 2M_1\phi$ for small ϕ. Formation of the angle 2ϕ between $\mathbf{M}_1$ and $\mathbf{M}_2$ is resisted by the Weiss field. At equilibrium, the magnitude of the component of the Weiss field that opposes **H** is equal to **H**, so that for small ϕ

$$H \approx n2M_1\phi \approx nM$$

Therefore

$$\chi_{\perp} \approx \frac{1}{n} = \chi_m(T_N) \tag{112}$$

From these simple considerations, the susceptibility is expected to increase with decreasing temperature throughout the paramagnetic range, reaching a maximum of $1/n$ at T_N. Below T_N, $\chi_{\perp}$ remains constant whereas $\chi_{||}$ decreases smoothly to zero at $T = 0°$K. That $\chi_{||}(0) = 0$ follows from the fact that with perfect alignment, **H** can exert no torque on either $\mathbf{M}_1$ or $\mathbf{M}_2$. An analytic expression for the smooth transition from $\chi_{||}(0) = 0$ to $\chi_{||}(T_N) = \chi_m(T_N) = 1/n$ can be calculated by expanding $M^{\pm} = \frac{1}{2}Ng\mu_B J B_J(y'^{\pm})$ in powers of H and retaining the first-order term only. In this expression $y'^{\pm}$ refers to $\mathbf{H}_w^{\pm}$ taken, respectively, parallel and antiparallel to **H**. This gives

$$\chi_{||} = \frac{M^+ - M^-}{H} = \frac{C\Lambda}{T - \theta_a\Lambda} \qquad \Lambda = \frac{3JB_J'(y_0')}{J + 1} \tag{113}$$

where $y_0' = M_0 H_w/NkT$. Since [see eqs. 117, 117'] $B_J'(y_0')/T \to 0$ as $T \to 0$ and $B_J'(y_0') \to (J + 1)/3J$ as $y' \to 0$ (or for $T \geq T_N$), this susceptibility is seen to vanish at $T = 0$ and to reduce to the Curie-Weiss Law ($\Lambda = 1$) for $T \geq T_N$. This is known as the Néel (469,470)–Van Vleck (630) theory. Quantum mechanical calculations for $T < T_N$ have used the spin wave approach (18,67,287,376,463,616,718). Whereas some of these calculations suggest that $\chi_{\perp}$ should decrease slightly with temperature in the range $T < T_N$, Ziman (718) has concluded that $\chi_{\perp}$ should be temperature-independent, as predicted by the molecular field theory. Experimental data is not definitive

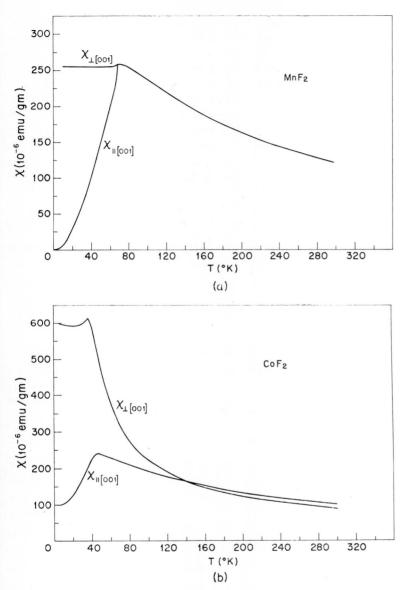

Fig. 19.   Magnetic susceptibility for single crystals of (a) MnF$_2$ and (b) CoF$_2$
(after S. Foner, private communication).

on this point since crystalline-anisotropy fields H_a, which are neglected in the present considerations, can introduce a small (since $H_a \ll H_w$) temperature dependence.

The paramagnetic susceptibilities of an ideal (MnF_2) and of a nonideal (CoF_2) antiferromagnet are shown in Figure 19. (Note that the simple theory has neglected, among other things, crystalline anisotropy. Octahedral Co^{2+}, unlike Mn^{2+}, exhibits a large crystalline anisotropy as a result of spin-orbit coupling.) The anisotropy in the susceptibility below T_N permits determination of the unique axis in single-crystal specimens. Since there always exists a magnetic anisotropy with respect to the structure, the measured susceptibility of a polycrystalline sample, χ_{mp}, is a mean value for all the crystallites. At $T = 0°K$

$$\chi_{mp}(0) = \tfrac{2}{3}\chi_{\perp}(0) + \tfrac{1}{3}\chi_{\|}(0) \approx \tfrac{2}{3}\chi_{mp}(T_N) \tag{114}$$

Polycrystalline antiferromagnets are characterized by a maximum at T_N in the χ_m vs. T curve, as indicated schematically in Figure 17. For a bibliography relating to experimental data on antiferromagnetic substances, see the review articles by Lidiard (393), and Nagamiya, Yosida, and Kubo (462). The experimental data is summarized by Alperin and Pickart (13).

4. *Temperature Dependence of the Magnetization in Ferrimagnets*

Below the Curie temperature of a collinear ferrimagnet, there is a spontaneous magnetization, just as in the ferromagnets. However, in this case the magnetization is the vector sum of the magnetizations of the two antiparallel sublattices and therefore has the magnitude

$$M_s = |M_1 - M_2| \tag{115}$$

To find the temperature dependence of M_s, it is necessary to consider the temperature dependences of M_1 and M_2 independently. Because M_1 and M_2 may have quite different temperature dependences, the M_s vs. T curves are not restricted to a Brillouin-type shape, as is the case for ferromagnets. This fact is illustrated schematically in Figure 20. From equations 14 and 100

$$M_i(T) = M_{0i}B_{Ji}(y_i'') \qquad y_i'' = M_{0i}(H + \textstyle\sum_j W_{ij}M_j)/N_i kT \tag{116}$$

where $M_{0i} = N_i J_i g_i \mu_B$.

In order to determine the principal characteristics of the M_s vs. T

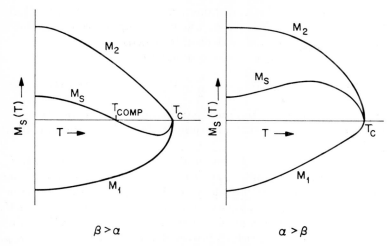

$$\beta > \alpha \qquad\qquad\qquad \alpha > \beta$$

Fig. 20. Schematic M_s vs. T curves according to the Néel theory (471).
$M_s = M_2 - M_1$ is the resultant magnetization.

curve to be anticipated for various values of α and β, Néel (471)
considered the temperature dependence in two temperature regions:
just above $0°$K and just below T_c. These regions are chosen because
at high temperatures (in the neighborhood of the Curie point) the
Brillouin function may be approximated by the expression

$$B_J(y'') = \frac{J+1}{3J}\, y'' - \frac{[(J+1)^2 + J^2](J+1)}{90J^2}\, y''^3 + \cdots$$

$$(y'' \ll 1) \quad (117)$$

and at low temperatures by the expression

$$B_J(y'') \approx 1 - J^{-1} \exp(-y''/J) \qquad (y'' \gg 1) \qquad (117')$$

Néel proceeded in three steps: First, he considered what regions in
the α-β plane give the various minimum-energy configurations that
are possible at $T = 0°$K. Second, he considered what regions in the
α-β plane have $M_1 > M_2$ just below T_c and in what regions $M_2 > M_1$.
This knowledge, together with that from step one, defines the region
in α-β space for which $M_s = M_1 - M_2$ changes sign at a *compensation
temperature* T_{comp}, where $0 < T_{comp} < T_c$ (see, for example, Fig. 20).
Third, the temperature dependencies of M_s just above $T = 0°$K are
considered for each of the regions of the α-β plane defined by step one.

The results of these investigations are displayed in Figure 21 for values of $M_{01}/M_{02} = \lambda/\mu = 2/3$, which is an appropriate possibility for ferrospinels (λ and μ were defined below eq. 101).

The interaction energy of a two-sublattice structure is

$$W = -\frac{1}{2} \sum_i M_i H_{wi} = -\frac{n}{2}(\alpha M_1^2 + \beta M_2^2 - 2\mathbf{M}_1 \cdot \mathbf{M}_2) \quad (118)$$

which is a minimum for $\mathbf{M}_1$ and $\mathbf{M}_2$ antiparallel. However, there are four possible situations that are compatible with a minimum W at $T = 0°\mathrm{K}$.

Case I. $T_c \leq 0$ so that the material is always paramagnetic: If T_c, as given by equation 108, is set equal to zero, the boundary line $\alpha\beta = 1$ is found for the boundary of this region in the α-β plane.

Case II. $M_{01} = \lambda M$ is its maximum possible value and $M_{02} < \mu M$, where μM is its maximum possible value: Then $M_{02} = -\lambda M/\beta$ minimizes W, and this is consistent provided $1 > -\lambda/\mu\beta$, or $\beta < -\lambda/\mu$. This defines the boundary CE in Figure 21.

Case III. $M_{02} = \mu M$ and $M_{01} < \lambda M$: Similar to Case II, this is compatible with a minimum W provided $\alpha < -\mu/\lambda$. This defines the boundary CF in Figure 21.

Case IV. $M_{01} = \lambda M$, $M_{02} = \mu M$. This solution minimizes W in the region bounded by FCE. Further, if the sublattices are so chosen that $\lambda < \mu$ and $M_s > 0$ for $\mathbf{M}_s \cdot \mathbf{M}_1 > 0$, then in region BCE (Case III)

$$M_s(0) = M_{01} - M_{02} = \lambda M(1 + 1/\beta)$$

From this it follows that $\mathbf{M}_s(0) \parallel \mathbf{M}_{01}$ in region HSB, $\mathbf{M}_s(0) \parallel \mathbf{M}_{02}$ in region HSA.

At a temperature slightly below T_c a combination of equations 115, 116, and 117 gives

$$M_s = F(J)M\left[\frac{T_c - T}{T_c}\right]^{1/2}\left(\lambda\sqrt{k} - \frac{\mu}{\sqrt{k}}\right)\left[\frac{\lambda k + \mu/k}{\lambda k^2 + \mu/k^2}\right]^{1/2} \quad (119)$$

where $F(J) > 0$ and k is the positive root of the equation

$$\lambda k^2 + (\beta\mu - \alpha\lambda)k - \mu = 0$$

From equation 119 it follows that M_s changes sign along the line defined by

$$(\lambda\sqrt{k} - \mu/\sqrt{k}) = 0$$

which is the line

$$\lambda(\alpha + 1) - \mu(\beta + 1) = 0 \quad (120)$$

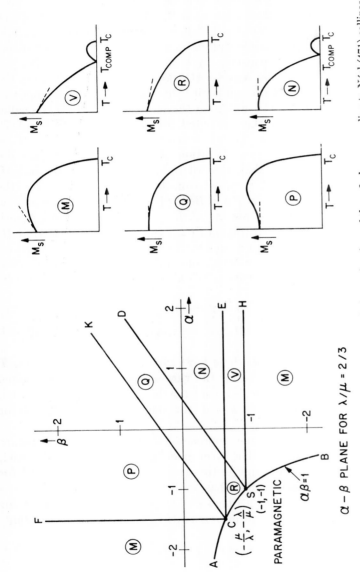

α – β PLANE FOR λ/μ = 2/3

Fig. 21. Types of magnetization curves corresponding to designated regions of the α-β plane, according to Néel (471) collinear, molecular field model.

For the case $\lambda + \mu = 1$, this is the line $\theta_b = 0$ [see eq. 107]. It is the line SD of Figure 21. Just below T_c, $\mathbf{M}_s \parallel \mathbf{M}_1$ in the region BSD, $\mathbf{M}_s \parallel \mathbf{M}_2$ in the region DSA. It follows that there should be a compensation point for samples falling in region DSH of the α-β plane.

It is convenient to consider the temperature variation of M_s just above $T = 0°K$ for the regions ACF and BCE separately from the region FCE. If only one sublattice is saturated, then it is apparent that the molecular field acting on the unsaturated atoms is smaller than that acting on the saturated atoms. From equation $117'$, $B_J(y'')$ can be shown to be less sensitive to changes in T if H_w is large. Therefore the magnetization of the unsaturated sites decreases with T faster than that of the saturated sites, so that M_s increases initially as T is raised from $0°K$ if M_s is parallel to the saturated sites (regions ACF and BSH), but decreases if M_s is parallel to the unsaturated sites (region $ECSH$). On the other hand, if both sublattices are saturated (region FCE), the variations of M_1 and M_2 at $T = 0°K$ are zero, just as in the case of ferromagnets. However, just above $0°K$ there is a small, but finite variation. Substitution of equation $117'$ into equation 115 gives the line CK of Figure 22 defined by

$$\lambda\alpha + \mu = \mu\beta + \lambda \tag{121}$$

as the boundary between $dM_s/dT > 0$ (region FCK) and $dM_s/dT < 0$ (region KCL).*

The combination of all these facts gives the schematic M_s vs. T curves shown in Figure 21 for the various regions of the α-β plane. In Figure 22 is shown the α-β plane for the special case $\lambda = \mu = 0.5$. For ideal antiferromagnets $\alpha = \beta$ (the line SD), so that $M_s = 0$ for all temperatures.

Those curves that do not approach $T = 0°K$ with zero slope are not realized in nature. The Néel model is a molecular field model, and is subject to the same criticisms as the Weiss field model for ferromagnets. Kaplan (325) has applied spin wave theory to ferrimagnets and worked out a Bloch $T^{3/2}$ law, similar to equation 98, for low temperatures. In this approximation M_1/M_2 remains constant,

---

* Use is made of the fact that for $p > q$ in $F(T) = A + B + C \exp(-p/T) + D \exp(-q/T)$,

$$\frac{dF(T)}{dT} = e^{-q/T} \left[\frac{pC}{T^2} e^{(q-p)/T} + \frac{qD}{T^2} \right] \approx \frac{qD}{T^2} e^{-q/T} \qquad \text{(small } T\text{)}$$

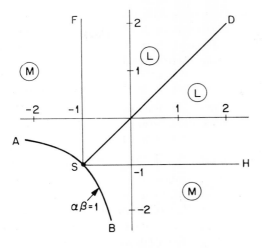

$\alpha-\beta$ PLANE FOR $\lambda=\mu=0.5$

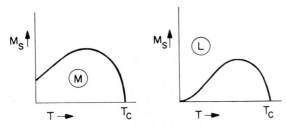

Fig. 22. Possible magnetization curves for $\lambda = \mu = 0.5$, according to Néel (471) collinear, molecular field model. (Along the line SD, $M_s = 0$ for all temperatures.)

so that M_s *can only decrease with increasing* T. Moreover Smart (588) has shown that as a result of short-range order, the slope of the $1/\chi_m$ vs. T curve above T_c is less steep than in the Weiss field approximation, just as for ferromagnets (see Fig. 28). The Néel model is also a two-sublattice model with collinear spins. It will be shown below that this model breaks down outside of a limited region in the α-β plane. However, the Néel model has proven highly successful in describing the $1/\chi_m$ and M_s vs. T curves of ferrospinels, magnetoplumbite-type oxides containing iron, and ferrogarnets, three classes of materials currently finding important technical applications.

Before consideration is given to the experimental data, it is of interest to consider the connection between the Weiss field constants used by Néel and the Heisenberg exchange integrals. In the non-collinear models, the Heisenberg formalism is generally used.

5. *Interaction Parameters and Exchange Integrals*

The energy of an atom of moment $\boldsymbol{\mu}_i$ in a Weiss field $\mathbf{H}_{wi}$ is equal to the sum of the exchange interactions with its near neighbors. Therefore from equation 90 it follows that

$$-\boldsymbol{\mu}_i \cdot \mathbf{H}_{wi} = -g_i \mu_B \mathbf{S}_i \cdot \sum_j W_{ij} \mathbf{M}_j = -2 \sum_j z_{ij} J_{ij} \mathbf{S}_i \cdot \mathbf{S}_j \quad (122)$$

where z_{ij} represents the number of nearest neighbors on the jth sublattice that interact with the ith atom. (Strictly speaking, this relation is only correct at $T = 0°\text{K}$ because of different averaging procedures for the Heisenberg and molecular field approaches.) Substitution of $M_j = N_j g \mu_B S_j$ into equation 122 gives

$$W_{ij} = (z_{ij}/N_j) 2J_{ij}/g_i g_j \mu_B^2 \quad (123)$$

For a two-sublattice structure,

$$z_{12}/N_2 = z_{21}/N_1 \quad \text{and} \quad J_{12} = J_{21}$$

so that

$$W_{12} = W_{21} \quad (124)$$

6. *Effective g Factors*

Since the two sublattices of a ferrimagnet have different g factors and different moments, it might be anticipated from equation 74 that each would resonate at a different frequency in a magnetic-resonance experiment. However, the strong coupling between sublattices causes them to resonate at the same frequency and in the same sense. Therefore in place of equation 74, it is necessary to consider the pair of coupled equations

$$\dot{\mathbf{M}}_i = \gamma_i (\mathbf{M}_i \times \mathbf{H}_i) \quad (125)$$

where

$$\mathbf{H}_i = (H \pm H_a)\mathbf{e}_z + W_{12}\mathbf{M}_j + \mathbf{h} \exp(j\omega t) \quad (126)$$

and H_a is the crystalline-anisotropy field for the crystallographic easy axis taken parallel to the applied field $\mathbf{H} = H\mathbf{e}_z$, $\mathbf{h} \exp(j\omega t)$ is the small a.c. field applied perpendicular to the unit vector $\mathbf{e}_z$. (Demagnetizing fields dependent on the shape of the sample are neglected for simplicity.) Wangsness (644) has solved this problem and shown that to first order in $(H \pm H_a)/W_{12}M_s$, there is a low-frequency mode in which the angle between $\mathbf{M}_1$ and $\mathbf{M}_2$ does not vary with time and that has the resonant frequency

$$\omega_r = \gamma_{\text{eff}}\left[H + \frac{M_1 + M_2}{M_1 - M_2}H_a\right] \tag{127}$$

where

$$(2mc/e)\gamma_{\text{eff}} = g_{\text{eff}} = M_s/NJ\mu_B = \frac{M_1 - M_2}{(M_1/g_1) - (M_2/g_2)} \tag{128}$$

There is also a high-frequency mode (infrared for ferrospinels with high T_c), known as the exchange mode, that has the resonant frequency

$$\omega_r \approx \gamma_1\gamma_2 W_{12}[(M_1/\gamma_1) + (M_2/\gamma_2)] \tag{129}$$

From equation 128 it follows that $g_{\text{eff}} = 0$ or ∞, depending upon whether $M_s = 0$ or $J = 0$. The compensation points for M_s and the angular momentum J need not be the same, in which case g_{eff} vs. T curves have the hyperbolic form indicated in Figure 25(b). Actually g_{eff} never reaches infinity as the neglected terms in higher powers of $(H \pm H_a)/W_{12}M_s$ become important as $J \to 0$.

B. EXPERIMENTAL EXAMPLES

The principal predictions of the Néel two-sublattice, collinear theory of ferrimagnetism are: (1) a nonlinear behavior of the $1/\chi_m$ vs. T curve that is specified by the parameters appearing in Figure 17; (2) a saturation magnetization at $T = 0°K$ given by $M_s(0) = |M_{10} - M_{20}|$, where $M_{i0} = N_ig_i\mu_BS_i$ (if there are more than one type of magnetic ion on a sublattice, it is of course necessary to replace N_iS_i by $\sum_m N_{im}S_{im}$); (3) the shape of the M_s vs. T curve, including the possibility of a compensation point; (4) the possibility of a large g_{eff} in the vicinity of a compensation point; (5) two magnetic-resonance modes; and (6) the chemical phases in which ferrimagnetism versus antiferromagnetism can be anticipated given a negative exchange interaction between the two sublattices. Aside from the approximations of the molecular field approach, the limitation of the model, as will be shown, is its inapplicability outside of specified zones in the interaction-parameter space (the α-β plane). The parameters of the theory may be directly related to the Heisenberg theory, which assumes localized atomic moments coupled through exchange integrals that depend on the overlap of nonorthogonal, atomic orbitals of neighboring atoms.   Evaluation of these parameters is considered in Chapter III.

The principal collinear, ferrimagnetic structures that have been investigated to date are ferrospinels, ferrogarnets, and magnetoplumbite-type structures containing iron.   The cation-excess, nickel arsenide $Mn_{2-\epsilon}Sn$ also is a ferrimagnetic, two-sublattice structure (705).   Ferrimagnetism has also been observed in ordered systems: The rock salt system (223) $Li_xNi_{1-x}O$, the perovskite system (225) $La(Ga,Mn)O_3$, several cation-deficient nickel arsenide systems like (,Fe)S (53,402,473), and (,Cr)S (253,305,650,713), interstitial alloys with perovskite structure like Mn_4N (610), and several corundum-ilmenite systems (4,59,97,99,119,292,293,565,608).

The four interpenetrating, simple-cubic cation sublattices of the rock salt structure and the simple-cubic sublattice of the perovskites usually exhibit intrasublattice antiferromagnetic order, so that ferrimagnetism requires preferential ordering of the nonmagnetic ion on one of the two antiparallel sublattices.   In the hexagonal, cation-deficient NiAs and corundum structures there must be preferential ordering into alternate (001) layers.   In addition, collinear ferrimagnetism has been observed in disordered structures whose majority magnetic atom couples ferromagnetically with its neighbor, but whose minority magnetic atom couples antiferromagnetically with itself. These systems, which cannot be described by a two-sublattice model, are exemplified by the disordered perovskite system (51,308) $La(Cr,Mn)O_3$ and the disordered, face-centered (f.c.c.) Ni–Mn and Co–Mn alloys (367,370,371).

The spinel structure consists of a f.c.c. anion sublattice that has half its octahedral interstices and one-eighth of its tetrahedral interstices (there are twice as many tetrahedral as octahedral interstices) occupied by cations.   For oxygen spinels, the chemical formula is usually written: $M^{2+}[N_2^{3+}]O_4$ for a *normal* 2–3 spinel, $N^{3+}[M^{2+}N^{3+}]O_4$ for an *inverse* 2–3 spinel, where the cations in brackets are in octahedral interstices, those outside of the brackets are in tetrahedral interstices.   The 2–4 spinels $M^{2+}[M^{2+}N^{4+}]O_4$ and $N^{4+}[M_2^{3+}]O_4$ are also common.   In most ferrospinels, $N^{3+} = Fe^{3+}$ or $(1 - x)Fe^{3+} + xN^{3+}$.   ($Fe^{2+}[Fe^{2+}N^{4+}]O_4$ is also a ferrospinel.)   Most ferrospinels are inverse; however, Mn^{2+}, Zn^{2+}, and Cd^{2+} displace Fe^{3+} from the tetrahedral interstices.   Therefore $Zn_x^{2+}M_{1-x}^{2+}Fe_2O_4$ has the partially inverse structure

$$Zn_x^{2+}Fe_{1-x}^{3+}[M_{1-x}^{2+}Fe_{1+x}^{3+}]O_4 \qquad (130)$$

In the ferrospinels, the tetrahedral-site and octahedral-site cations represent the two collinear, antiparallel sublattices. Therefore for $x = 0$, the magnetic moments on the iron atoms cancel one another out, and $\mathbf{M}_0 = N'g_M\mu_B S_M$, where N' is the number of molecules per unit volume. However, as the nonmagnetic Zn^{2+} ion is substituted for the magnetic ion M^{2+}, the magnetization *increases*:

$$\begin{aligned} M_0 &= N'[(1 - x)g_M\mu_B S_M + 2x(5\mu_B)] \\ &= N'\mu_B[g_M S_M + x(10 - g_M S_M)] \end{aligned} \qquad (131)$$

where $Fe^{3+}(3d^5)$ carries a spin-only moment of $5\mu_B$ since its $3d$ electrons are localized, HL electrons in the oxides.

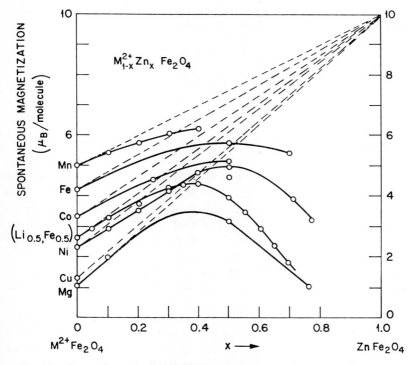

Fig. 23. Saturation moment in Bohr magnetons per molecule of various mixed-crystal ferrospinels $Zn_xM_{1-x}^{2+}Fe_2O_4$, where M = Mn, Fe, Co, ($Li_{0.5}^+Fe_{0.5}^{3+}$), Ni, Cu, Mg. (After Gorter (229). Also refer Guillaud (243).)

One of the striking successes of the Néel model was its ability to account for the magnetization curves of the zinc-substituted ferrospinels shown in Figure 23, where $n_B = M_0/N'\mu_B$ is the number of Bohr magnetons per molecule. From the intercept at $x = 0$, it is theoretically possible to obtain the spectroscopic splitting factor, as defined by equation 81. However, the discrepancies shown in Table IX between the original measurements by Guillaud et al. (243) and

TABLE IX

Saturation Moments of Single Ferrospinels

	Corter (228)	Guillaud (243)	Pauthenet (509)	Wickham (672)	$2S_M$	T_c, °C (590)
$MnFe_2O_4$	5.0	4.60	4.40	4.5[a]	5	300
$FeFe_2O_4$	4.2	4.03	4.08[b]		4	585
$CoFe_2O_4$	3.3	3.67, 3.70	3.94	3.57[c]	3	520
$NiFe_2O_4$	2.3	2.40	2.22	2.12	2	585
$CuFe_2O_4$	1.3		1.37		1	455
$MgFe_2O_4$	1.1	≥ 1.0	0.86	1.37	0	440
$(Li_{0.5}Fe_{0.5})Fe_2O_4$	2.6				(2.5)	670

[a] Quenched in N_2. Contains 0.12% by weight excessive active oxygen.
[b] Natural magnetite.
[c] Not saturated at 10,000 oe.

by Pauthenet et al. (509) and those by Gorter (228,229) and by Wickham et al. (672) indicate differences in the number of M^{2+} ions on octahedral versus tetrahedral sites as a result of different preparation procedures. In $MgFe_2O_4$ and $CuFe_2O_4$ the number of M^{2+} on tetrahedral sites are particularly sensitive to the quenching temperature, and a completely inverse spinel is never obtained (52,128). $MnFe_2O_4$ is sensitive to atmosphere as well as heat treatment. One sample investigated by neutron diffraction techniques proved to be 81% normal (258).

The ideal mineral garnet has the chemical formula $Mn_3Al_2Si_3O_{12}$. It is a three-sublattice structure in which the large Mn^{2+} ion has twelvefold anion coordination, the smaller Al^{3+} and Si^{4+} ions are in octahedral and tetrahedral interstices of the anion sublattice. Bertaut and Forrat (58) reported the preparation and magnetic properties of $Y_3Fe_2Fe_3O_{12}$ and Geller and Gilleo (205) prepared and investigated $Gd_3Fe_2Fe_3O_{12}$. Subsequently Bertaut and Pauthenet (60) succeeded in substituting for Y the rare earth ions of comparable radius: Pm, Sm, Eu, Gd, Tb, Dy, Ho, Er, Tm, Yb, or Lu. In these ferrogarnets, the strong antiferromagnetic interactions are between the two iron sublattices, and if the large ions are nonmagnetic, as in the case of $Y_3Fe_5O_{12}$, the two-sublattice model is applicable. Magnetization curves for $Y_3Fe_5O_{12}$, $Er_3Fe_5O_{12}$ and $Gd_3Fe_5O_{12}$ are shown in Figure 24. If rare earth ions (with $4f$ shell half or more filled so that $\mathbf{J} = \mathbf{L} + \mathbf{S}$) are present, their moments are more weakly (the Curie point is determined by the Fe–Fe interactions so that it is nearly the same for all the rare earth ferrogarnets) coupled parallel

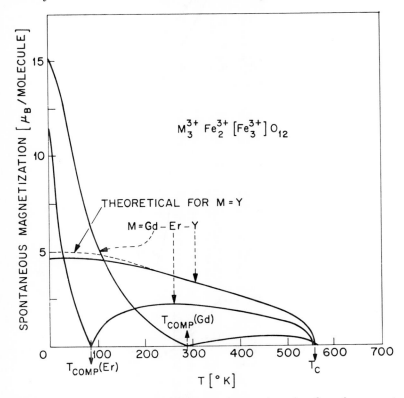

Fig. 24. Spontaneous magnetization vs. temperature for three ferrogarnets. (After Bertaut and Pauthenet (60). Theoretical curve is based on molecular field parameters obtained by Aléonard (5).)

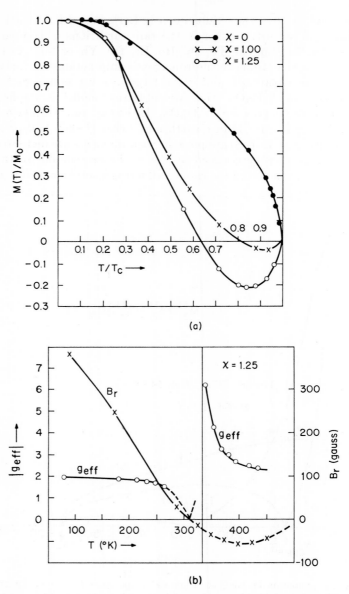

Fig. 25.   Magnetic data for the system $Li_{0.5}Fe_{2.5-x}Cr_xO_4$.   (a) Reduced magnetization vs. temperature.   (Although only $|M(T)/M_0|$ is measured, $M(T)/M_0$ is displayed with a sign reversal at $T_{comp.}$.)   (b) Remanent induction and effective gyromagnetic ratio for $Li_{0.5}Cr_{1.25}Fe_{1.25}O_4$.   (See following page for Fig. 25(c).)

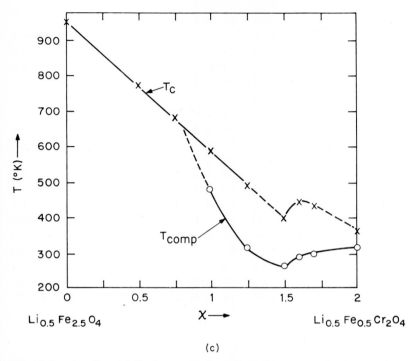

Fig. 25 (*continued*).   (c) Curie temperatures T_C and compensation temperatures T_{comp}.   (After Gorter (229) and van Wieringen (635).)

to the octahedral-site moments, antiparallel to the net iron moment.*
Since $Gd^{3+}(4f^7)$ has an atomic moment of $7\mu_B$ at low temperatures,
the net magnetization is parallel to the rare earth moment.   Because
of the weak coupling of the rare earth ions, the magnetization of the
rare earth sublattice falls off rapidly with temperature, so that just
below the Curie temperature the net magnetization is parallel to
the net iron moment.   This gives rise to the compensation point of

---

* If Nd^{3+}, with $4f$ shell less than half filled, is substituted for Y^{3+} in $Y_3Fe_5O_{12}$,
the net moment *increases* (210) since $\mathbf{J} = \mathbf{L} - \mathbf{S}$ (666). Pr^{3+} should also have
$\mathbf{J} = \mathbf{L} - \mathbf{S}$. Eu^{3+}, with $\mathbf{J} = 0$, has an excited state with $\mathbf{J} = \mathbf{S} - \mathbf{L}$ that determines the sign of the coupling. Sm^{3+} has $g = 0$, and it is necessary to go to
second order Zeeman splitting (Van Vleck temperature-independent paramagnetism of eq. 17) to determine the sign of the moment.   It changes sign, from
hat of Nd^{3+} to that of Gd^{3+}, with increasing temperature.

Figure 24. $Er^{3+}(4f^{11})$ has a smaller atomic moment, and T_{comp} is lower for $Er_3Fe_5O_{12}$ than for $Gd_3Fe_5O_{12}$. The rare earth iron garnets are ideal for observation of two resonant-frequency modes since H_w is small, compensation points occur near or below 300°K, and single crystals are obtainable. Foner (187) has observed both high- and low-field resonances in single-crystal gadolinium and erbium ferrogarnets. The compound $Y_3Fe_5O_{12}$ has proven useful in microwave devices since the structure does not tolerate much variation from stoichiometry, and magnetic-resonance losses are, among other things, sensitive to chemical homogeneity and Fe^{2+} content. Limited substitutions for iron by other cations have been made with quite predictable results (15,47,95,204,411,641).

Compensation points have also been observed in spinels. Gorter and Schulkes (230) reported the first such compound, $Li_{0.5}Cr_{1.25}Fe_{1.25}O_4$. Since the compensation point of this substance is a little above room temperature, it provides an interesting demonstration of the effect: A small bar suspended by a string in the presence of a magnetic field rotates 180° as it is heated by a lighted match through the compensation point. Data for the system are shown in Figure 25 and Table X.

TABLE X

Cation Distributions, Cell Edges, Curie Temperatures, Compensation
Temperatures and Saturation Moments for the System
$Fe_{1-\delta}Li_\delta[Li_{0.5-\delta}Fe_{1.5+\delta-x}Cr_x]O_4$
(After Gorter (229))

x	δ	Cell edge, A	T_c, °C	T_{comp}, °C	$n_B = M_s(0)/Ng\mu_B$
0	0	8.331	680		2.47; 2.60
0.50	0	8.306	500		1.62; 1.50
0.75	0.02	8.296	410		1.35
1.00	0.06	8.292	315	+205	0.84
1.25	0.09	8.290	214	+38	0.61
1.50	0.20	8.287	119	−16	0.55
1.60	0.36	8.288	167	+11	0.42
1.70	0.46	8.290	155	+20	0.22
2.00	0.50	8.288	80 ± 16	+37 ± 15[a]	0.10

[a] Obtained from measurements of the remanent magnetization.

However, most ferrites have more conventional M_s vs. T curves (see Fig. 26). The excellent agreement between Néel's M_s vs. T curve

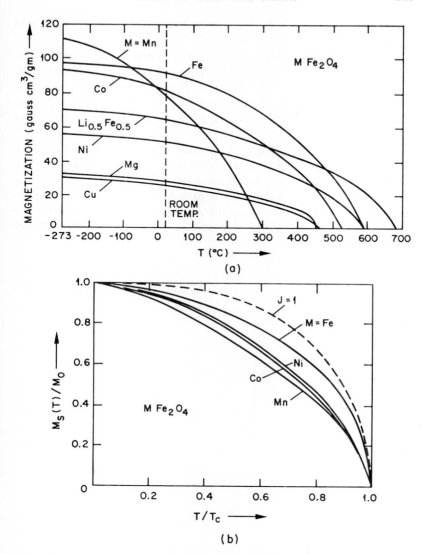

Fig. 26. Spontaneous magnetization for several ferrospinels. (From J. Smit and H. P. J. Wijn, *Ferrites*, John Wiley & Sons, Inc., New York, 1959; data from Pauthenet (509).)

and the measured curve for the case of $MgFe_2O_4$ has been emphasized by Rado and Folen (536).

$NiFe_{2-x}Al_xO_4$ is another spinel exhibiting a compensation point that has been studied. McGuire (423) has measured g_{eff} as a function of x at $T = -196°C$ and 10 kMc/sec. The anomalous increase in g_{eff} for compositions with $T_{comp} \approx -196°C$ is shown in Figure 27. McGuire has also observed the high-frequency resonance mode in this system.

In Figure 28 are shown the $1/\chi_m$ vs. T curves of Aléonard (5) for $Y_3Fe_5O_{12}$ and $Gd_3Fe_5O_{12}$. The theoretical curve contains the five molecular field constants and their temperature parameter given in Section II-A-1. The calculated α and β are probably too high to be representative of the actual intrasublattice interactions since, as mentioned before, the theory neglects the effects of short-range order above T_c.

The compounds loosely referred to as magnetoplumbite-type are a group of oxides having the general formulae $xBaO \cdot yFe_2O_3 \cdot zM^{2+}O$. Four closely related, hexagonal structures have been identified

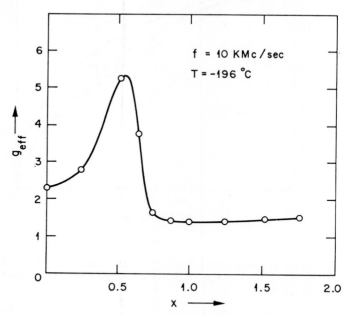

Fig. 27.   Effective gyromagnetic ratio vs. aluminum content x in $NiFe_{2-x}Al_xO_4$. (After McGuire (423).)

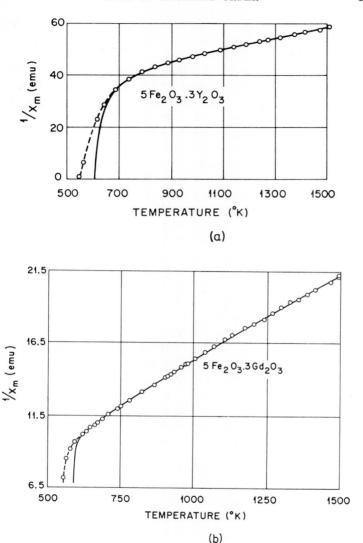

Fig. 28. Paramagnetic susceptibilities of (a) yttrium and (b) gadolinium ferrogarnets. Solid lines are theoretical curves based on molecular field model and empirically determined molecular field constants. Dashed lines are experimental curves indicating effects of short-range order in the neighborhood of the Curie temperature. (After Aléonard (5).)

(312,663).   Because of their hexagonal symmetry, their magnetic anisotropy has properties that are useful for some technical applications.   The chemical formulas are $BaFe_{12}O_{94}$, $BaM_2^{2+}Fe_{16}O_{27}$, $Ba_2M_2^{2+}Fe_{12}O_{22}$, and $Ba_3M_2^{2+}Fe_{24}O_{41}$.   In most cases the Ba ion can be partly or completely replaced by Ca, Sr, or Pb, or by La^{3+} (in which case an equivalent amount of $Fe^{3+} \rightarrow Fe^{2+}$).   The Fe^{3+} ions may be replaced by Al^{3+}, Ga^{3+}, or $(M^{2+} + N^{4+})/2$ provided the M^{2+}, N^{4+} ions have comparable radii.   The structures consist of closely packed oxygen ions built up of sections having alternately a cubic and a hexagonal symmetry (102).   In certain layers some oxygens are replaced by barium ions.   The structures consist of cubic spinel blocks ([111] axis parallel to c axis) coupled by either one or two layers (hexagonal with respect to cubic blocks) containing both oxygen and barium ions.   In the single-layer coupling block (characteristic of $BaFe_{12}O_{19}$), Fe^{3+} ions occupy a five-coordinated site (in the hexagonal layers, two adjacent tetrahedral sites share a common face).   Since this atom essentially shares a tetrahedral site in common with the two cubic blocks, it serves to couple the net magnetizations of the spinel blocks parallel to one another to give rise to ferrimagnetism.   This is in contrast to the compound $KFe_{11}O_{17}$, which contains identical spinel blocks, but has no Fe^{3+} ion in the coupling layer.   Instead it has an O^{2-} ion between tetrahedral-site cations of neighboring blocks so that the net magnetizations of the ferrimagnetic blocks are coupled antiparallel, and antiferromagnetism results (229).   Between the layers of the double-hexagonal-layer coupling blocks, octahedral-site cations occur that share a common face along the c axis with cations (would-be tetrahedral made octahedral by hexagonal stacking of barium-oxygen layers) of adjacent spinel blocks.   Therefore they couple the net ferrimagnetic moments of the neighboring spinel blocks parallel to one another.

These substances illustrate quite complicated structures for which it is possible, given a knowledge of the sign and relative magnitudes of the basic intercation coupling interactions, to predict the magnetic order, and hence the saturation magnetization at $T = 0°K$.   Kaplan (326) has examined the spin wave problem and shown that the zero-point excitation so contributes to the z component of the total spin that the magnetization predicted from the above classical arguments is indeed correct.   However, a knowledge of the cation distributions over the occupied interstices, and hence a knowledge of site-preference energies, as well as a knowledge of the ionic moments in the presence of crystalline fields, is essential for any accurate predictions.

III. Noncollinear Configurations

A. GENERALIZED LUTTINGER-TISZA METHOD

In the previous discussion, collinear spins were taken *a priori*. This means that for antiferromagnets and ferrimagnets the antiferromagnetic coupling between sublattices is simply assumed to dominate all others. This of course cannot be true if α and/or β approach, or exceed, one. This fact means that the Néel spin configurations and magnetization curves for most regions of the α-β plane of Figures 21 and 22 are irrelevant. A problem of considerable interest, therefore, is a rigorous (all 10^{21} spins permitted to have variable orientations) determination of ground-state spin configurations at $T = 0°\mathrm{K}$ given the Heisenberg exchange Hamiltonian of equation 90. Although this problem has not been solved in general, a generalized Luttinger-Tisza (407) method has provided rigorous solutions for a large class of compounds (331,408).

Let $\mathbf{R}_n$ be a vector of the direct lattice such that

$$\mathbf{R}_{n\nu} = \mathbf{R}_n + \rho_\nu \qquad \nu = 1, 2, \ldots, p \qquad n = 1, 2, \ldots, N \quad (132)$$

is the position of a magnetic atom. There are p spins per primitive unit cell and N_p spins in the lattice. If $\mathbf{S}_{n\nu}$ is the spin at position $\mathbf{R}_{n\nu}$, the exchange energy of equation 90 is

$$H_{\mathrm{ex}} = - \sum_{n\nu, m\mu} J_{n\nu, m\mu} \mathbf{S}_{n\nu} \cdot \mathbf{S}_{m\mu} \quad (133)$$

The problem is to find the set of spins that minimize H_{ex} subject to the constraints

$$\mathbf{S}_{n\nu} \cdot \mathbf{S}_{n\nu} = S_\nu^2 \quad (134)$$

that fix the magnitude of each spin vector. These are known as the "strong constraints." It is noted that a necessary, but not sufficient condition for the validity of equation 134 is

$$\sum_{n,\nu} \alpha_{n\nu}^2 \mathbf{S}_{n\nu} \cdot \mathbf{S}_{n\nu} = \sum_{n,\nu} \alpha_{n\nu}^2 S_\nu^2 \quad (135)$$

where the $\alpha_{n\nu}$ are any real, non-zero numbers. (The restrictions on $\alpha_{n\nu}$ keep bounded the minimum of H_{ex} subject to equation 135.) This is called the "weak constraint." The generalized Luttinger-

Tisza theorem states: *If the solution of equation 133 subject to the single weak constraint, equation 135, also satisfies the strong constraints of equation 134, then the solution of the simpler weak constraint problem is a rigorous solution of the strong constraint problem.* With simple choices of the $\alpha_{n\nu}$, it happens that rigorous solutions of many physically interesting problems can be solved.

To take advantage of the translational symmetry, the variables $S_{n\nu}$ and $\alpha_{n\nu}^2$ are transformed as

$$S_{n\nu} = \sum_{\mathbf{k}} \exp(i\mathbf{k}\cdot\mathbf{R}_{n\nu})\mathbf{Q}_{\mathbf{k}\nu} \tag{136}$$

$$\alpha_{n\nu}^2 = \sum_{\mathbf{k}} \exp(i\mathbf{k}\cdot\mathbf{R}_{n\nu})A_\nu(\mathbf{k}) \tag{137}$$

where the $\mathbf{k}$ are the rationalized, reduced reciprocal vectors of the first Brillouin zone. Further,

$$J_{n\nu,m\mu} = J_{\nu\mu}(\mathbf{R}_m - \mathbf{R}_n) = J_{\mu\nu}(\mathbf{R}_n - \mathbf{R}_m)$$

so that, given periodic boundary conditions, the energy per primitive unit cell is

$$\epsilon = E/N = \sum_{\mathbf{k}} \sum_{\nu\mu} L_{\nu\mu}(\mathbf{k})\mathbf{Q}_{\mathbf{k}\nu}^* \cdot \mathbf{Q}_{\mathbf{k}\mu} \tag{138}$$

where

$$L_{\nu\mu}(\mathbf{k}) = - \sum_{\mathbf{R}_m - \mathbf{R}_n} \exp[i\mathbf{k}\cdot(\mathbf{R}_{m\mu} - \mathbf{R}_{n\nu})]J_{\nu\mu}(\mathbf{R}_m - \mathbf{R}_n)$$
$$= [L_{\mu\nu}(\mathbf{k})]^* \tag{139}$$

and the weak constraint is

$$\sum_{\mathbf{k},\mathbf{k}'} \sum_\nu A_\nu(\mathbf{k} - \mathbf{k}')\mathbf{Q}_{\mathbf{k}\nu}^* \cdot \mathbf{Q}_{\mathbf{k}'\nu} = \sum_\nu A_\nu(0)S_\nu^2 \tag{140}$$

With the method of Lagrange multipliers, it can be shown that ϵ is minimized subject to equation 140 provided for all $\mathbf{k}$

$$\sum_\mu L_{\nu\mu}(\mathbf{k})\mathbf{Q}_{\mathbf{k}\mu} = \lambda \sum_{\mathbf{k}'} A_\nu(\mathbf{k} - \mathbf{k}')\mathbf{Q}_{\mathbf{k}'\nu} \tag{141}$$

where λ is a constant independent of $\mathbf{k}$. Substitution of equations 141 and 140 into equation 138 gives

$$\epsilon = \lambda \sum_\nu A_\nu(0)S_\nu^2 \tag{142}$$

Therefore the minimum ϵ corresponds to the minimum λ for which solutions of equation 141 exist.

In all applications attempted thus far, $\alpha_{n\nu} = \alpha_\nu$ independent of n has been chosen, so that $A_\nu(\mathbf{k} - \mathbf{k}') = \alpha_\nu^2\delta_{\mathbf{k},\mathbf{k}'}$, where $\delta_{\mathbf{k},\mathbf{k}'}$ is the Kroeniger delta function. Then equations 140, 141, and 142 become

$$\sum_{\nu \mathbf{k}} \mathbf{P}_{\mathbf{k}\nu}^* \cdot \mathbf{P}_{\mathbf{k}\nu} = \sum_{\nu} \alpha_{\nu}^2 S_{\nu}^2 \tag{140'}$$

$$\sum_{\mu} \mathcal{L}_{\nu\mu}(\mathbf{k}) \mathbf{P}_{\mathbf{k}\mu} = \lambda \mathbf{P}_{\mathbf{k}\nu} \tag{141'}$$

$$\epsilon = \lambda \sum_{\nu} \alpha_{\nu}^2 S_{\nu}^2 \tag{142'}$$

where $\mathbf{P}_{\mathbf{k}\nu} \equiv \alpha_{\nu} \mathbf{Q}_{\mathbf{k}\nu}$ and $\mathcal{L}_{\nu\mu}(\mathbf{k}) = \beta_{\nu}\beta_{\mu}L_{\nu\mu}(\mathbf{k})$, $\beta_{\nu} = \alpha_{\nu}^{-1}$. The procedure is to find the lowest eigenvalue λ of the matrices $\mathcal{L}_{\nu\mu}(\mathbf{k})$. For a given crystal, $\lambda = \lambda(\beta, \ldots, \beta_p)$ only. However, it should be noted that there is one matrix for each $\mathbf{k}$ in the first Brillouin zone. Therefore it may be necessary to compare the minimum configurations for each of the different $\mathbf{k}$ vectors.

Let $\mathbf{k}_0$ and $-\mathbf{k}_0$ be values of $\mathbf{k}$ for which λ is a minimum, with corresponding normalized eigenstates $\psi = \{\psi_1 \ldots \psi_p\}$ and ψ^*, respectively. Then

$$\mathbf{P}_{\mathbf{k}\nu}^i = \begin{cases} 0, & \mathbf{k} \neq \pm\mathbf{k}_0 \\ c_i\psi_{\nu}, & \mathbf{k} = \mathbf{k}_0 \\ c_i^*\psi_{\nu}^*, & \mathbf{k} = -\mathbf{k}_0 \end{cases} \tag{143}$$

are the cartesian components of $\mathbf{P}_{\mathbf{k}\nu}$, and the c_i satisfy

$$2 \sum_i |c_i|^2 = \sum_{\nu} \alpha_{\nu}^2 S_{\nu}^2 \tag{144}$$

but are otherwise arbitrary. From equations 136, 144, and the definition of $\mathbf{P}_{\mathbf{k}\nu}$, it follows that

$$\mathbf{S}_{n\nu} = \beta_{\nu} \sum_i \hat{\mathbf{x}}_i [c_i\psi_{\nu} \exp\,(i\mathbf{k}_0 \cdot \mathbf{R}_{n\nu}) + c_i^*\psi_{\nu}^* \exp\,(-i\mathbf{k}_0 \cdot \mathbf{R}_{n\nu})] \tag{145}$$

where the $\hat{\mathbf{x}}_i$ are the cartesian unit vectors. For different choices of the c_i consistent with equation 144, this gives various minimum-energy spin configurations for the weak constraint problem. There remains to see whether there is any choice of the β_{ν} (real) and c_i such that equation 145 also satisfies the strong constraints, equation 134.

If $c_x = c/2i$, $c_y = c/2$, $c_z = 0$, $c = c^*$, and $\psi_{\nu} = |\psi_{\nu}| \exp\,(i\phi_{\nu})$, the weak constraints are satisfied and equation 145 becomes

$$\mathbf{S}_{n\nu} = c\beta_{\nu}|\psi_{\nu}| \{\hat{\mathbf{x}} \sin\,(\mathbf{k}_0 \cdot \mathbf{R}_n + \phi_{\nu}) + \hat{\mathbf{y}} \cos\,(\mathbf{k}_0 \cdot \mathbf{R}_n + \phi_{\nu})\} \tag{146}$$

This represents a set of p spirals, one on each sublattice ν, having respective phases ϕ_{ν}. It is the only configuration derivable from equation 145 that has, to within rotations of the plane of the spins, $S_{n\nu}^2$ independent of n. With this equation, the strong constraints of equation 134 become p equations in the p unknowns $\beta_1 \ldots \beta_p$:

$$c\beta_{\nu}f_{\nu}(\beta_1 \ldots \beta_p) = S_{\nu} \qquad \nu = 1 \ldots p \tag{147}$$

where $f_{\nu}(\beta_1 \ldots \beta_p) \equiv |\psi_{\nu}|$. If these equations have finite, real β_{ν} as their solution, then the original strong constraint problem is solved. Unfortunately such solutions do not always exist. In such cases it is sometimes possible to obtain a rigorous solution by forcing, via the β_ν, additional degeneracy of the lowest eigenvalue, and hence additional freedom for the construction of a solution to the weak constraint problem.

B. THE BRAVAIS LATTICE

The Bravais lattice corresponds to the simplest case, $p = 1$. In this case, all spins are equivalent. To determine whether the spins are equivalent in any physical problem, first identify the exchange parameters J_{nm} (which may be due to indirect exchange via nonmagnetic ions). Then imagine (or construct) the lattice with all nonmagnetic atoms removed and assign the number S_ν to an appropriate magnetic site, J_{nm} to the line connecting magnetic sites n and m. If the resulting picture is invariant to any translation $n \rightarrow m$, then the spins are equivalent.

If $p = 1$, then β_1 adds nothing since ψ_1 is arbitrary, the matrix $L_{\nu\mu}$ being 1×1. In this case equation 146 satisfies the strong constraints for any **k** provided $c\beta_1|\psi_1| = S_1$. Therefore it follows that: *For any Bravais lattice, the ground-state spin configuration is always a spiral defined by the* **k** *that minimizes* $L(\mathbf{k})$. This conclusion can be generalized to include hexagonal-close-packed elements (408).* Spiral ground-state spin configurations were discovered theoretically by three independent workers (327,640,706). *This result implies that whenever the spins are equivalent, the only state with non-zero total spin is the ferromagnetic state, which is a* **k** $= 0$ *"spiral," and that, except*

---

* In the h.c.p. structure there are two atoms per primitive unit cell, and ν, μ each run over two values, referring to the two different sublattices A_1 and A_2. Since the A_1 sublattice can be obtained by a translation of the A_2 sublattice, $J_{n1,m1} = J_{n2,m2}$ so that $L_{11}(\mathbf{k}) = L_{22}(\mathbf{k})$, from equation 139. Therefore the Hermitian matrices $L(\mathbf{k})$ are all of the form

$$\begin{pmatrix} a & b \\ b^* & a \end{pmatrix}$$

which have normalized eigenvectors of the form

$$\begin{pmatrix} \exp i\phi_1 \\ \exp i\phi_2 \end{pmatrix}$$

and $\phi_2 - \phi_1 = -\gamma$ or $\pi - \gamma$, where γ is the phase of b. Since this only influences the phase angles ϕ_ν of equation 146, it follows that for the h.c.p. structure the ground-state spin configuration is always a spiral.

for quite special degenerate cases, the spins are necessarily all parallel to one plane. An antiferromagnetic with collinear spins corresponds to $\mathbf{a} \cdot \mathbf{k} = \pi$, where $\mathbf{a}$ is a translation vector between nearest neighbors. It is impossible to have a ferrimagnetic ground state. Any experimental deviations from this rule, such as parasitic ferromagnetism, must be due to deficiencies in the energy expression. For at least some parasitic ferromagnets, these deficiencies can be attributed to anisotropic-exchange terms arising from spin-orbit coupling that must be added to the pure-spin exchange Hamiltonian of equation 90. (See Chapter III, Section I-B-6.)

For the b.c.tet. magnetic lattice of Figure 29(a), all spins are equivalent, and the ground-state spin configuration is a spiral defined by the $\mathbf{k}$ that minimizes $L(\mathbf{k})$ as given by its definition plus equation 139. This leads to the following ground-state spin configurations for the four regions of interaction-parameter space shown in Figure 29(b). (Interactions J_1 and J_2 are assumed negative.) In Region I, the corner cation moments are antiparallel to the body-center cation moments. In Region II, each simple-tetragonal sublattice is collinear, antiferromagnetic within itself, the spin axes of the two sublattices being uncorrelated. In Region III, the positive spins on the corner sites and the negative spins on the body-center sites spiral along the c axis, the wavelength of the spiral decreasing continuously with increasing J_2/J_1. The spiral configuration persists if anisotropy energy is included. Yoshimori (706) has found that if dipolar interactions are included (other anisotropy terms neglected) for the case of MnO_2 (in the rutile structure the Mn^{4+} atoms form a b.c.tet. array such as shown in Figure 29(a)), the boundary between Regions I and III is shifted to $J_2/J_1 = 1.19$, and the wavelength corresponding to the new boundary is about $5c$. In the range $1.19 \leq J_2/J_1 \leq 1.56$, the spins spiral in a plane that contains the c axis, and for $J_2/J_1 > 1.56$ they are parallel to the c plane and spiral about the c axis. A spiral structure of wavelength $3.5c$, which occurs at $J_2/J_1 = 1.60$, accounts for the neutron diffraction lines (170) of MnO_2. Villain (640) has pointed out that a spiral structure of wavelength $3.5c$ fits the neutron data of Herpin and Mériel (269) for $MnAu_2$, an ordered alloy in which the Mn atoms form a b.c.tet. array.

Similarly Kaplan (327) has shown that a b.c.c. magnetic lattice, with J_1, J_2, J_3 (all negative) interaction constants corresponding to nearest, next-nearest, and next-next-nearest neighbors, consists of

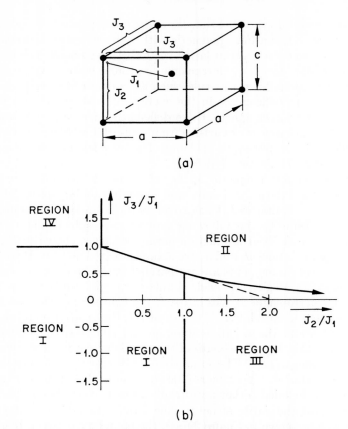

(a)

(b)

Fig. 29.   Ground-state spin configuration for b.c. tet. magnetic lattice having $J_1 < 0$ (data from Yoshimori (706) and Villain (640)).   Region I: Ferromagnetic sublattices antiparallel.   Region II: Antiferromagnetic sublattices uncorrelated. Region III: Spiral sublattices antiferromagnetic.   Region IV: Ferromagnetic along c axis, antiferromagnetic within c planes.

ferromagnetic simple-cubic sublattices aligned antiparallel to one another provided $(1 - J_2/J_1 - 4J_3/J_1) \geq 0$, but of spiral sublattices otherwise.   However, application of the spiral configuration to the present neutron results for b.c.c. chromium, though suggestive, is not conclusively successful (33,255,424,563).   Kaplan pointed out that the relative reduction in energy due to spiral formation was only $\Delta E/E_0 \approx 10^{-4}$, so that consideration of exchange forces alone may not be adequate.   It is also possible that the Heisenberg formalism is not appropriate to this case since the atomic moment is only ⌣0.4μ_B.   Overhauser (497) has recently suggested that conduction-electron spin-density waves introduce a spin correlation capable of accounting for the "apparent" antiphase-domain structure (255). Further experimental and theoretical work is required in this case.

Discussion of the rare earth metals and compounds is neglected in this review.   However, attention is called to the fact that spiral-spin configurations have also been found in the rare earth metals.   There is also a peculiar spin configuration just below T_N in metallic Er: The x-y components of the spin are uncorrelated, and the amplitude of the correlated z components varies sinusoidally along the c axis. This latter configuration can be derived from the molecular field model if crystalline anisotropy is included in the Hamiltonian.   Even though the crystalline anisotropy is only about 10% of the exchange fields, it has a profound effect because it is compared to the difference in energy of two exchange-determined spin configurations of nearly the same energy.   The theoretical work for these materials has been developed independently by Kaplan (329,330) and Elliott (166) and later by Yosida and Miwa (709).

C. THE SPINEL LATTICE

1. Cubic Spinels

Néel's model for ferrospinels, which has the cation spins on the tetrahedral (A) interstices of the anion sublattice parallel to one another and antiparallel to all the cation spins on the octahedral (B) interstices, is obviously correct if only a negative J_{AB} interaction exists.   However, the introduction of "competing" interactions removes the simplicity of the problem.   For illustration, consider the case of cubic symmetry with only nearest-neighbor A-B and B-B antiferromagnetic interactions.   This problem can be parametrized by the single quantity $u = 4J_{BB}S_B/3J_{AB}S_A$, the energy of equation 90 becoming

$$H_{ex} = \overline{J}_{AB}\left\{ \sum_{i,j} \mathbf{s}_i^A \cdot \mathbf{s}_j^B + \frac{3}{4} u \sum_{i,j} \mathbf{s}_i^B \cdot \mathbf{s}_j^B \right\} \tag{148}$$

where $\overline{J}_{AB} = -J_{AB}S_A S_B > 0$, $\mathbf{s}^A$ and $\mathbf{s}^B$ are unit vectors in the spin directions on the A and B sites, respectively, and the sums are over

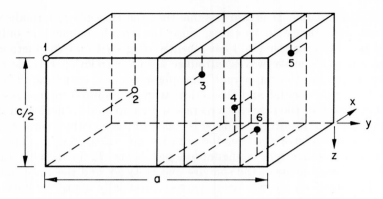

Fig. 30. The cation sites in a primitive unit cell of the spinel structure. If cubic, $c = a$. $\circ$ = A sites; $\bullet$ = B sites. (Oxygen not shown.)

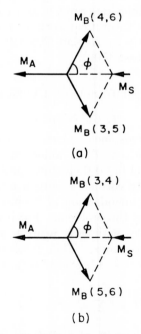

Fig. 31. Possible Yafet-Kittel triangular configurations for spinels with (a) $c/a < 1$ and (b) $c/a > 1$.

the pertinent nearest-neighbor pairs.   In the Néel configuration, each $\mathbf{s}_i^A \cdot \mathbf{s}_j^B = -1$ gives a minimum energy contribution, but each $\mathbf{s}_i^B \cdot \mathbf{s}_j^B = +1$ a maximum, so that the character of the ground-state spin configuration is not obvious if $u > 0$.

The normalized energy for the Néel state of a ferrospinel is

$$\epsilon(\text{Néel}) = H_{\text{ex}}(\text{Néel})/N\bar{J}_{AB} = 48(\tfrac{3}{8}u - 1) \qquad (149)$$

where N is the number of primitive unit cells, each containing two A and four B sites (see Fig. 30).   Since zero energy corresponds to a completely disordered state, the Néel configuration cannot be the ground state for $u > 8/3$.   In 1952 Yafet and Kittel (698) pointed out that a "triangular" configuration becomes more stable than the Néel configuration for $u \geq 1$.   The Yafet-Kittel (YK) theory is based on the assumption that the spin configuration can be divided into six sublattices instead of two, so that there are six (not 10^{21}) independent spin directions allowed in the crystal, one for each set

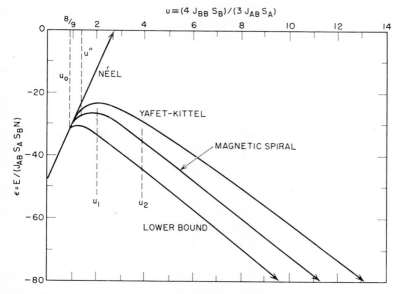

Fig. 32.   Normalized energy vs. relative interaction strengths for three spin configurations in cubic spinels.   (A-A interactions neglected.)   The lower bound represents the minimum energy over the weak constraint.   (After Kaplan, Dwight, Lyons and Menyuk (331).)

of equivalent magnetic sites. Possible triangular configurations are shown in Figure 31. Each B-site spin is seen to make an angle ϕ with the A-spin axis so that the normalized energy becomes

$$\epsilon(\text{YK}) = 48((u/4)\cos 2\phi + (u/8) - \cos \phi) = -24/u - 6u \quad (150)$$

since $\cos \phi = 1/u$ minimizes $\epsilon(\text{YK})$. For $u \geq 0$, $\epsilon(\text{YK}) < \epsilon(\text{Néel})$ if $u > 1$, as is shown in Figure 32. The Yafet-Kittel solution for $u < 1$ is the Néel configuration since $\cos \phi \leq 1$.

Subsequently Anderson (19) removed the six-sublattice assumption in a consideration of the case $\overline{J}_{AB} = 0$. He showed that in this case there is no long-range ordering of the B-cation spins as a result of exchange forces alone. He then reasoned that if $\overline{J}_{AB} \neq 0$, there should be a short-range "triangular" ordering, but no long-range order of the spin components perpendicular to the net spin. However, Kaplan (327,328) has recently shown that the YK configuration does not minimize equation 148 for any value of u if $\overline{J}_{AB} > 0$. From a consideration of local stability of the configuration, he was able to show that the Néel configuration is locally stable for $u \leq u_0 = 8/9$, and unstable for $u > u_0$. He was later able to show (408) rigorously, with the aid of the generalized Luttinger-Tisza (GLT) formalism, that the Néel configuration is the true ground state whenever it is locally stable. Although the convergence of his perturbation series for $u > u_0$ is still in doubt, his calculations (328) strongly suggest that in the ground state all the components of the spin have a definite long-range order, at least for small $u - u_0$. With the aid of the GLT formalism, he has been able to show (408) that there exists a class of spin configurations described by

$$\mathbf{S}_{n\nu} = \sin \phi_\nu \{\hat{\mathbf{x}} \sin (\mathbf{k} \cdot \mathbf{R}_{n\nu} + \gamma_\nu) + \hat{\mathbf{y}} \cos (\mathbf{k} \cdot \mathbf{R}_{n\nu} + \gamma_\nu)\}$$
$$+ \cos \phi_\nu \hat{\mathbf{z}} \quad (151)$$

where ϕ_ν, γ_ν, and $\mathbf{k} = \mathbf{k}_1$ are cone angles, phase angles, and wave numbers that are given by Figure 33, that these configurations approach the Néel configuration (i.e. $\mathbf{k}_1 \rightarrow \mathbf{k}_0$) as $u \rightarrow u_0$ from $u > u_0$, and that the values of γ_ν and ϕ_ν for small $u - u_0$ agree with the perturbation results. The normalized energy of this "magnetic-spiral" configuration is also shown in Figure 32. Although it has not yet been possible to prove that the magnetic spiral configuration is the true ground state for cubic spinels with $u > u_0$, these results suggest that it may be for $u_0 < u < u_1$, where $u_1 \approx 1.3$. At least the configuration has been found to be *locally stable* for $u_0 < u < u_1$, and unstable for $u > u_1$. Unfortunately no experimental example of such a magnetic spiral has yet been found. The compound $MnCr_2O_4$ represents a cubic spinel with $u > u_0$, but the value of the magnetization implies that $u > u_1$ in $MnCr_2O_4$. The neutron diffraction pattern (125) has principal peaks that can be accounted for

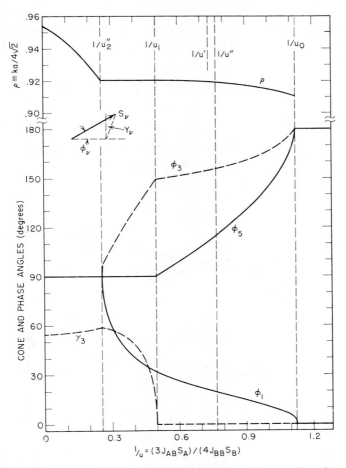

Fig. 33.   Parameters of the magnetic-spiral configuration as a function of the relative interaction strengths for cubic spinels.   (*A-A* interactions neglected and $J_{AB} < 0$).   (After Kaplan, Dwight, Lyons, and Menyuk (331).)

by equation 151, which is indicative that this is the ground state for
$u \leq u_1$ and that this configuration is not strongly modified for
$(u - u_1) > 0$ small.   These results are also significant for much of
the available magnetization data on cubic spinels containing little
or no iron as they demonstrate that the several previous attempts to
correlate the data with YK angles are not applicable even though
differential susceptibility at high magnetic fields and low temperatures (295) indicates noncollinear, ferrimagnetic spin configurations
(see Fig. 34).   Since the most favorable spiral configuration possible
has been obtained, the results also indicate that the true ground state
is quite complex.

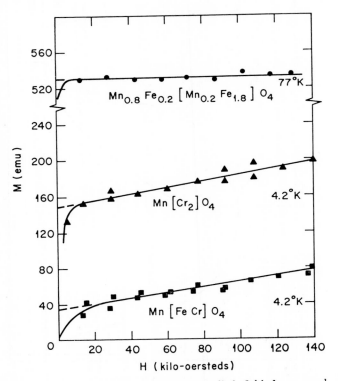

Fig. 34. Spontaneous magnetization vs. applied field for several spinels.
Saturation attained by $H = 20$ kilo-oersteds for sample with collinear spins,
top curve, but not attained by 140 kilo-oersteds for samples with noncollinear
spins. (After pulsed-field data of Jacobs (295).)

At temperatures just below T_c, the molecular field energy

$$E = - \sum_{n\nu} \mathbf{S}_\nu \cdot \sum_{m\mu} J_{n\nu,m\mu} \mathbf{S}_\mu$$

is used in place of equation 133. Thus the Weiss molecular field to be used in equation 91 is $H_w \propto \sum_{m\mu} J_{n\nu,m\mu} \mathbf{S}_\mu$, so that for $\mathbf{H} = 0$ and high temperatures

$$\lambda \mathbf{S}_\nu = \sum_{m\mu} J_{n\nu,m\mu} \mathbf{S}_\mu$$

where the parameter $\lambda \propto T_c$. The Fourier transformation (eq. 136) together with equation 139 reduces this eigenvalue equation to

$$\lambda \mathbf{Q}_{k\nu} = \sum_{k\mu} L_{\nu\mu}(\mathbf{k}) \mathbf{Q}_{k\mu}$$

For a cubic spinel, the lowest eigenvalue λ corresponds to a Néel configuration if $u < 2.2$, to a simple antiferromagnetic spiral if $u > 2.2$ (331,409). This means that even though the ground state at $T = 0°K$ may be complex, the configuration just below the magnetic-ordering temperature is collinear (provided $u < 2.2$). This has been directly verified for $MnCr_2O_4$ ($1.4 < u < 1.7$) (see Table XI) (125), and there is evidence for an antiferromagnetic region above T_c in Mn_3O_4 (similar results are obtained for tetragonal spinels).

2. Tetragonal Spinels

Distortions from cubic to tetragonal symmetry are commonly encountered in spinels. These distortions require the introduction of

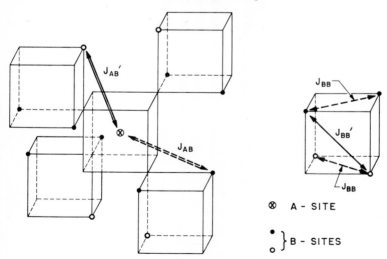

Fig. 35.   Exchange interactions in the spinel structure.

TABLE XI

Low-Temperature Magnetic Structures for Several Ferromagnetic and Ferrimagnetic Compounds[a]

Compound	Chem. structure	Mag. cat. structure	Mag. order	n_B^A	T_c, °K	Remarks	Refs.
V, Nb, Mo, W	b.c.c.	b.c.c.	None	0		No observable moment to 4°K.	567
Fe	b.c.c.	b.c.c.	Ferro.	2.22	1043	Form factors slightly favor e_g.	569, 571
Co	c.p.h.	c.p.h.	Ferro.	1.7	1403	e_g/t_{2g} hole ratio ~3/1.	464, 567, 568
Ni	f.c.c.	f.c.c.	Ferro.	0.6	631	e_g/t_{2g} hole ratio ~1/3.	520, 567
Eu	b.c.c.	b.c.c.	Spiral, **k** ‖ [100]		$T_N = 87$	Spiral period = 3.60 a_0 is T independent.	493a
Gd	c.p.h.	c.p.h.	Ferro. ($H > H_{crit}$)	7.12	289	Metamag. with $H_{crit} \approx 0.2[T - 220°K]$ oe for 220°K < $T \leq$ 270°K, appears greater for 270°K < $T < T_c$.	48, 93
Dy	c.p.h.	c.p.h.	Spiral, **k** ‖ [0001] Ferro. $T < T_c$	~10	$T_N = 179$ $T_c = 87$	Spiral period T-dependent. 140 < $T < T_N$. Higher harmonics present for $T_c < T < 140$ (°K). First order change at T_c.	680
Ho	c.p.h.	c.p.h.	Spiral, **k** ‖ [0001], Ferro. spiral, **k** ‖ [0001] if $T < T_c$	2 ‖ c 4.5 ⊥ c	$T_N = 132$ $T_c = 20$	Turn angle 36° per layer at 35°K, 50° per layer at T_N. For $T < T_c$, external $H \perp$ [0001] destroys spiral to give large M_s.	353
Er	c.p.h.	c.p.h.	Sinusoidal S_z, no order (0001) Ferro. spiral if $T < T_c$	7.2 ‖ c	$T_N = 80$ $T_c = 20$	c-axis period 3.5c_0 if 52 < $T < T_N$, increases to 4.0c_0 in $T_c < T < 52$ (°K).	115
Tm	c.p.h.	c.p.h.	Sinusoidal $S_z T_c < T < T_N$ Antiphase $T < T_c$	7	$T_N = 56$ $T_c = 22$	c axis period 3.5c_0 40°K < $T < T_N$. Ferrimag. antiphase harmonics appear $T < 40$°K, but $T_c = 22$°K. At 4.2°K, spins ‖ c_0, ferromag. (0001) have layer sequence +4, −3; +4, −3; $\mu_0 = 1\mu_B$, $\mu_{eff} = 7.56\mu_B$, $\mu_0 = 3.4\mu_B$ in $H = 70$ koe.	141a, 267b 355a
FeAl	CsCl	s.c.	None	0		No observable moment to 4°K.	522

FeAl	b.c.c. with s.c. Fe$_I$, Fe$_I$Al rock salt	Fe$_I$ has 4 n. n. Fe$_{II}$, Fe$_{II}$ has 8 n. n. Fe$_I$	Ferro.	773	Fe$_I$: 1.46, Fe$_{II}$: 2.14	Room-temperature n_B^A. 5 ± 1 outer $3d$ els. on Fe$_{II}$. Fe$_I$ 90% t_{2g}, Fe$_{II}$ 70% e_g.	359, 466, 520
Mn$_{1+\epsilon}$Al	CuAu	c.p. layers	Ferro. (Excess Mn ↑↓?)	646 ($\epsilon = 0.08$)	Mn: 1.40 ($\epsilon = 0.08$)	$0 < \epsilon < 0.08$. Metastable. Only $\epsilon = 0.08$ single phase. $\theta_a/T_c \approx 1.0$, but $n_{eff} = 3.17$.	362a
FeV	CsCl	s.c.	Ferro.	566	Fe: ~1, V: 0		566
FeTi	CsCl	s.c.	Para.		Fe: <0.061, Ti: 0	No evidence of a T_c below 300°K.	480a
Co–Cr	c.p.h.	c.p.h.	Ferro. but Cr–Cr ↑↓	567	Co: *, Cr: ~2	*Decreases to 1.0 by 12% Cr.	567
Fe–Cr	b.c.c.	b.c.c.	Ferri.	567	Fe: ~2.2, Cr: ~0.5	No long-range ferrimag. order. Initial Cr antiferro.	567
Ni–Fe	f.c.c.	f.c.c.	Ferro.		Table XXI	n_B^A not noticeably changed by order.	567
Ni$_3$Mn	CuAu	f.c.c.	Ferro.	743	Mn: 3.2, Ni: 0.3	Disordered alloy is ferri. without long-range mag. order.	567
FePd$_3$	CuAu	s.c. Face centers	Ferro.	705	Fe: 2.4, Pd: 0.3	n_B^A at 300°K. Disordered alloy is ferro.	173, 521
MnPt$_3$	CuAu	s.c. Face centers	Ferro.	350	Mn: 4.0, Pt: 0.0	n_B^A at 300°K. Disordered alloy is antiferro.	30, 521
CrPt$_3$	CuAu	s.c. Face centers	Ferri.	580	Cr: 2.22, Pt: ~0.0	n_B^A at 300°K. Disordered alloy is antiferro.	195, 521
Mn$_4$N	Perov.	f.c.c.	Mn^e ↑↓ Mn^f	738	Mn^e: 3.85, Mn^f: 0.9		610a, 610a
Fe$_4$N	Perov.	f.c.c.	Ferro.	761	Fe^e: 3.0, Fe^f: 2.0		190
ZnCMn$_3$	Perov. ($c/a < 1$)	Face centers	Ferro. Fig. 88(c)	353, $T_t = 231$	1.57, Fig. 88(c)	Tet. ⇌ cubic at 231°K.	106, 282
AlCMn$_3$	Perov.	Face centers	Ferro.	275	1.25	See Fig. 89.	106, 282
TbN	Rock salt	f.c.c.	Ferro.	43	7.0	Spin axis [111].	682, 683
DyN	Rock salt	f.c.c.	Ferro.	26	7.4		682

(continued)

TABLE XI (*continued*)

Compound	Chem. structure	Mag. cat. structure	Mag. order	n_B^A	T_c, °K	Remarks	Refs.
HoN	Rock salt	f.c.c.	Ferro.	8.9	18	Spin axis [100]. $\mu \parallel$ [111]. Ferromag. bands seven (111) layers thick alternately $\parallel$ three [100] axes.	682, 683
EuO[b]	Rocksalt	f.c.c.	Ferro.	6.9	77	Insulator.	416a, 476a
ErN	Rock salt	f.c.c.	Ferro.	3.5, 6.0	6	Large variation in diffuse scattering causes uncertainty in n_B^A.	683
TmN	Rock salt	f.c.c.	None			No mag. order to 1.3°K.	683
HoP	Rock salt	f.c.c.	Ferri.		5.5		682
Mn₅Ge₃		3-membered rings	Ferro.	1.85	293	$n_{eff} = 3.42$ per/Mn or n_B^{Mn}(para) ≈ 2.56.	116a, 188a
CrB	FeB	M I,II has 8 n. n. M I,I and 2 n. n. M I,II	Antiferro. (?)			$\mu = 0\mu_B$ at 78°K.	405a
MnB	FeB	M I,II has 8 n. n. M I,I and 2 n. n. M I,II	Ferro. (?)	1.92	578		405a
FeB	FeB	M I,II has 8 n. n. M I,I and 2 n. n. M I,II	Ferro. (?)	1.12	594		405a
CoB	FeB	M I,II has 8 n. n. M I,I and 2 n. n. M I,II	Ferro. (?)	0.28	477		405a
NiB	FeB	M I,II has 8 n. n. M I,I and 2 n. n. M I,II	Pauli para. (?)			$\mu = 0\mu_B$ at 78°K.	405a
Cr₁₋ₓMnₓB	FeB	M I,II has 8 n. n. M I,I and 2 n. n. M I,II	Ferri. (?)			$d\bar{n}_B/dx = +3.4$.	405a
Mn₁₋ₓFeₓB	FeB	M I,II has 8 n. n. M I,I and 2 n. n. M I,II	Ferro. (?)			$d\bar{n}_B/dx = -0.8$.	405a
Fe₃C	Cementite	Orthorhombic	Ferro.	1.78	485	$n_{eff} = 3.89$.	277a
Fe₂C	χ-phase	Orthorhombic (?)	Ferro.	1.75	520	$n_{eff} = 5.55$.	277a
	ε-phase	Hexagonal	Ferro.	1.72	653		277a
Fe₂P		Trigonal	Ferro.	1.32	266	$n_{eff} = 1.98$ per Fe and easy c axis $K_1 \sim 10^7$ ergs/cm³.	115b

FeP	NiP	Tetragonal	Ferro.	1.84	716	Spin in basal plane at 18°C, n_{eff} = 1.94.	115b
CrAs2	Tetragonal (c/a = 1.18)		Ferri.		213	n_{eff} = 2.0.	710
CeFe2	MgCu2	Normal spinel	Néel		878		684a
SmFe2	MgCu2	Normal spinel	Néel		674	n_{mol} = 6.97.	684a
GdFe2	MgCu2	Normal spinel	Néel		813		684a
DyFe2	MgCu2	Normal spinel	Néel		663		684a
HoFe2	MgCu2	Normal spinel	Néel		608	n_{mol} = 5.44.	684a
ErFe2	MgCu2	Normal spinel	Néel		473	n_{mol} = 6.02.	684a
TmFe2	MgCu2	Normal spinel	Néel		613	n_{mol} = 5.02.	684a
UFe2	MgCu2	Normal spinel	Néel		195	n_{mol} = 2.92.	357a
UMn2	MgCu2	Normal spinel	Antiferro.		260	n_{mol} = 1.13. Parasitic μ_a T < 230°K.	395a
Fe2Zr	MgCu2	Normal spinel	Ferro.	Fe: 1.56			352a
FeTi	MgZn2	Hexagonal	Ferro.	Fe$_I$: 0.1, Fe$_{II}$: 0.2			352a
MnAs2	Unknown	Unknown	Ferro.	0.31	273	n_B^A for 300°K. At 4.2°K, μ = 0.92μ_B/mol.	711
SrO·6Fe2O3	Magnetoplumbite	Subl. I = 2a, 2b, 12k; Subl. II = 4f$_1$, 4f$_2$	Néel	spin-only			63
Fe3O4	Spinel	Fe^{3+}[Fe^{2+}Fe^{3+}]	Néel	~spin-only	858	Ortho. ⇌ cubic at 119°K. Ortho. has spins ∥ c; Fe^{2+} ordered in rows ∥ b axis, where b < a.	248, 571
γFe2O3	Spinel	Fe^{3+}[Fe$^{3+}_{5/3}\square_{1/3}$]	Néel	spin-only	~856	Vacancies ordered.	418a, 623a
MgFe2O4	Spinel	Fe$^{3+}_{0.88}$Mg$^{2+}_{0.12}$[Fe$^{3+}_{1.12}$Mg$^{2+}_{0.88}$]	Néel	spin-only	713	Spin axis [111]. Sintered 1315°C; cooling program not given.	128
NiFe2O4	Spinel	Fe^{3+}[Ni^{2+}Fe^{3+}]	Néel	~spin-only	858	Spin axis [111].	256
NiCrFeO4	Spine	Fe^{3+}[Ni^{2+}Cr^{3+}]	Néel	~spin-only	570		517
NiCr1.5Fe0.5O4	Spinel	Fe$^{3+}_{0.5}$Ni$^{2+}_{0.5}$[Ni$^{2+}_{0.5}$Cr$^{3+}_{1.5}$]	Néel	$\bar{A}$: ~3.5, $\bar{B}$: ~4.0	378	$n_B^{\bar{A}}$ ($\bar{B}$) < spin-only.	517
NiCr2O4	Spinel (c/a > 1)	Ni^{2+}[Cr$^{3+}_2$]	Unresolved 77°K		70	Tet. ⇌ cubic 310°K. A-sites distorted.	533

(continued)

TABLE XI (continued)

Compound	Chem. structure	Mag. cat. structure	Mag. order	n_B^A	T_c, °K	Remarks	Rels.
MnFe₂O₄	Spinel	$Mn^{2+}_{0.81}Fe^{3+}_{0.19}[Mn^{3+}_{0.19}Fe^{3+}_{0.19}Fe^{3+}_{1.62}]$	Néel	~4.6	573	$n_B^A \sim 4.6$ for both sublattices.	258
MnFe₁.₈Cr₀.₂O₄	Spinel	$Mn^{2+}_{0.8}Fe^{3+}_{0.2}[Mn_{0.2}Fe_{1.8}Cr^{3+}_{0.5}]$	Néel	$\bar{A}$: 5.2 ± 0.3 $\bar{B}$: 7.0 ± 0.3	485	$n_B = 1.88$. $n_B^A(\bar{B}) <$ spin only.	518
MnFeCrO₄	Spinel	$Mn^{2+}_{0.9}Fe^{3+}_{0.1}[Mn_{0.1}Fe_{0.9}Cr^{3+}]$	Néel	$\bar{A}$: 4.5 ± 0.2 $\bar{B}$: 4.3 ± 0.2	375	$n_B = 0.21$. $n_B^A(\bar{B}) <$ spin only.	518
MnFe₀.₅Cr₁.₅O₄	Spinel	$Mn^{2+}[Fe^{3+}_{0.5}Cr^{3+}_{1.5}]$	Néel	$\bar{A}$: 4.6 ± 0.2 $\bar{B}$: 5.2 ± 0.3	240	$n_B = 0.80$. $n_B^A(\bar{B}) <$ spin only.	518
MnCr₂O₄	Spinel	$Mn^{2+}[Cr^{3+}_2]$	Ferri. spiral. T < 20°K Néel 20°K < T < 50°K		$T_N = 50$	$n_B = 1.20$. Below 20°K extra peaks appear. Details of structure not known.	125
ZnFe₂O₄	Spinel	$Zn^{2+}[Fe^{3+}_2]$	Ferro. layers > 2 casts. thick ↑↓	~ spin only	$T_N = 9$	Mag. order ambiguous.	256, 257
ZnCr₂O₄	Spinel	$Zn^{2+}[Cr^{3+}_2]$	Complex*		$T_N = 15$	*Order ambiguous, but different from Zn[Fe₂]O₄.	259
CoMn₂O₄	Spinel (c/a > 1)	$Co^{2+}[Mn^{3+}_2]$	Yafet-Kittel	~ spin only	85	Details of order still ambiguous.	333
Mn₃O₄	Spinel (c/a > 1)	$Mn^{2+}[Mn^{3+}_2]$	Yafet-Kittel	~ spin only	43	Ortho. doubling along tet. [100]. $T_N \sim 80°K$.	332
NiMn₂O₄	Spinel	$Mn[Ni^{2+}Mn]$	Pyramidal	?		Resultant of disordered B-site angles antiparallel to A-site spin.	88
CuFe₂O₄	Spinel (c/a > 1)	$Fe^{3+}_{1-\delta}Cu^{2+}_{\delta}[Cu^{2+}_{1-\delta}Fe^{3+}_{1+\delta}]$	Néel	~ spin only	763	$\delta \ll 1$. B sites distorted.	534
CuCr₂O₄	Spinel (c/a < 1)	$Cu^{2+}[Cr^{3+}_2]$	Yafet-Kittel	~ spin only		$n_B \approx 0.5$. A sites distorted.	531
Ni₀.₈Zn₀.₂Fe₂O₄	Spinel	$Zn_{0.2}Fe^{3+}_{0.5}[Ni^{2+}_{0.5}Fe^{3+}_{1.5}]$	Complex (unresolved)	?	560	$n_B (300°K) = 3.0$.	686
Mg_yMn₁₋_yFe₂O₄	Spinel	90% Mn^{2+} on A	Néel	~ spin only		O²⁻ positions indicate A-site. Mn²⁺ considerably covalent.	467
Zn_xMn₁₋_xFe₂O₄	Spinel	$\sim Zn^{2+}_x Mn^{2+}_{1-x}[Fe^{3+}_2]$	Néel	?		x = 0.1, 0.3, 0.5.	697
Mn₀.₆Fe₂.₄O₄	Spinel	$Mn^{2+}_{0.54}Fe^{3+}_{0.46}[Mn_{0.06}Fe_{0.06}Fe^{3+}_{1.88}]$	Néel	$\bar{A}$: 4.8 ± 0.4 B: 4.0 ± 0.4			12

$(1-x)FeTiO_3-xFe_2O_3$	Corundum	Hex.	~ spin only	60–950	Corund. II	Ordering of Ti^{4+} into alternate (111) gives ferri. for $0.15 < x < 0.5$ (quenched)	99, 565
$Y_3Fe_5O_{12}$	Garnet	Subl. I = tet. Fe Subl. II = oct. Fe	spin-only	555	Néel	Two sublattices saturate at different rates.	64, 532
$Ho_3Fe_5O_{12}$	Garnet	Subl. I = tet. Fe Subl. II = oct. Fe Subl. III = Ho	Fe: 5 Ho: 8	560	Subl. I and II ↑↓ Subl. III composed of 6 subls.		270
YCo_5	$CaZn_5$	Ord. c.p.h.	1.74	975	Ferro.	Spins ∥ c axis	302a′, 463a, 480a′
$HoCo_5{}^c$	$CaZn_5$	Ord. c.p.h.	Co: 1.74 Ho: 9.0	1025	Ferri.	Spins ⊥ c axis $T_{comp} = 345°K$	302a′, 463a, 480a′

a For abbreviations see key to Table VIII. The cation–cation interactions in this series of compounds are ferromagnetic and decrease with increasing cation separation; the cation–anion–cation interactions are antiferromagnetic and increase with increasing weight of the anion (626a′). [Although Eu(4f) has a half-filled 4f shell, there is little direct overlap of 4f states, so that cation–-cation superexchange presumably occurs via an overlapping, empty 5d state on one atom, a half-filled 4f state on the other. Promotion from a half-filled 4f state on one atom to a 5d state on its neighbor would give rise to ferromagnetic coupling, as it corresponds to eq. 162.]

b EuS and EuSe are also ferromagnetic, but EuTe is antiferromagnetic.

c Other MCo_5 compounds, where M is a rare-earth atom, also appear to have the spins of the Co and M atoms coupled antiparallel (480a′).

four exchange parameters (A-A interactions neglected as before) as indicated in Figure 35. If the average A-B interaction $(2J_{AB} + J'_{AB})/3$ is negative (i.e. antiferromagnetic), the ground state problem is completely parametrized by the quantities

$$u \equiv 2(J_{BB} + J'_{BB})S_B/(2J_{AB} + J'_{AB})S_A \qquad v \equiv J'_{BB}/(J_{BB} + J'_{BB})$$

$$w \equiv J'_{AB}/(2J_{AB} + J'_{AB}) \tag{152}$$

It is convenient to consider the ground-state spin configurations for various regions of u-v-w space, just as was done for the α-β plane in the Néel, collinear model. The region $u \geq 0$ and $0 \leq v \leq 1$ represents negative (antiferromagnetic) B-B interactions. The region $0 \leq w \leq 1$ represents negative J'_{AB} and $w > 1$ represents ferromagnetic coupling roughly parallel to the unique axis. Cubic spinels lie on the line $v = 1/2$, $w = 1/3$.

In Figure 36 are shown the regions in u-v-w space for which various

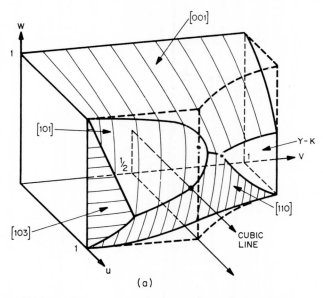

(a)

Fig. 36. Regions of u-v-w space (see equation 152) in which (a) Néel and (b) Yafet-Kittel configurations are stable. Region of (a) enclosed by dashed lines represents Néel region according to six-sublattice theory of Yafet and Kittel. Numbers in brackets indicate directions in **k** space for which Néel configuration becomes unstable. (After Kaplan, Dwight, Lyons and Menyuk (331).)

spin configurations are known to be stable. In the Néel and YK regions, the Néel and YK configurations have been shown to be locally stable. As in the case of the Néel configuration, Lyons and Kaplan (408) have shown that if the YK configurations of Figure 31 are locally stable, then by the GLT method they are rigorously the ground state. An interesting feature of the calculations is that as one moves up along the boundary of the Néel region in the $v = 1/2$ plane (see Fig. 37) from the point $u = 8/9$, $w = 1/3$, the direction of the destabilizing $\mathbf{k}$ vector changes continuously from that of $\mathbf{k}_0$ for the cubic case. This means that $\mathbf{k}$ vectors in directions possessing no particular symmetry may be those for which the Néel configuration first breaks down. The YK region to the right of the cubic line corresponds to a distortion with $c/a < 1$ and a spin configuration as shown in Figure 31(a) with $\cos \phi = (2uv)^{-1}$. The tetragonal symmetry of the configuration is obvious. The triangular configuration for the YK region on the plane $v = 0$ corresponding to $c/a > 1$ is shown in Figure 31(b). It has $\cos \phi = u^{-1}$.

Outside of the Néel and YK regions, the ground-state spin configuration has been obtained rigorously, by means of the GLT method,

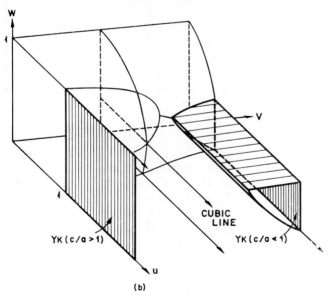

(b)

Fig. 36 (*continued*)

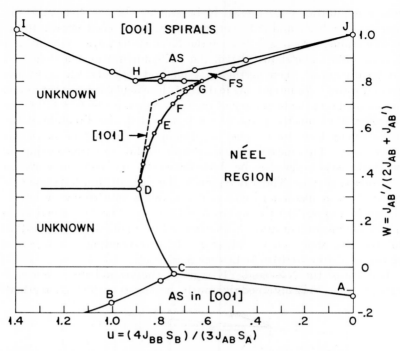

Fig. 37.   Boundary curves for $v = 1/2$; **k** in [001] for AC and GJ, [110] for BCD, [111] for GHI, [201] for EF, and continuously varying in direction for DE and FG. The circled points represent all-**k** calculations. (After Kaplan, Dwight, Lyons, and Menyuk (331).)

for only a limited region of the parameter space. In the region labeled FS, the ground state is a ferrimagnetic spiral, defined by equation 151 with **k** along the c axis. The ground state in the region AS is an antiferromagnetic spiral with $\cos \phi_\nu = 0$, **k** again being in the [001] direction. The spiral parameters ϕ_ν, γ_ν, and $|\mathbf{k}|$ are definite functions of u, v, w in these regions.

For the purpose of illustration, consider the particular spiral shown in Figure 38. The cone angles are all $\pi/2$, so that there is no net atomic moment (antiferromagnetic spiral). The phases are $\gamma_1 = 0$, $\gamma_2 = \pi$, $\gamma_3 = \gamma_4 = \pi/2$, $\gamma_5 = \gamma_6 = -\pi/2$, and the **k** vector is in the [001] direction with wavelength $\lambda = 2\pi/|\mathbf{k}| = 3c/2$, where c is the dimension along the c axis of the tetragonal unit cell. Each A-cation spin is exactly antiparallel to every one of its vertical B neighbors, so that at $u = 0$ and $w = 1$, ϵ(spiral) $= \epsilon$(Néel). If $u = 0$ and $w > 1$, so that J_{AB} becomes ferromagnetic, the horizontal A-B interactions favor the spiral over the Néel configuration. Similarly, if u is increased in the $w = 1$ plane and $v > 0$, the vertical A-B interactions and the horizontal B-B interactions contribute equally to ϵ(spiral) and ϵ(Néel), but the vertical B-B interactions favor the spiral over the Néel configuration. Thus the "roof" of the Néel region must slope down with increasing u and $v > 0$, as shown in Figure 36(a). The rigorous ground state in the region AS is different from this spiral, but approaches it continuously as the boundary line $u = 0$, $w = 1$ is approached.

Experimentally a YK configuration of the type shown in Figure 31(a) has been found by Prince (531) and unambiguously verified by Nathans, Pickart, and Miller (465) in neutron diffraction experiments on tetragonal $(c/a < 1)$ $CuCr_2O_4$. The fact that the YK region is confined to $w \leq 1/2$ indicates that in $CuCr_2O_4$ both J_{AB} and J'_{AB} are negative and that $|J_{AB}| \geq |J'_{AB}|/2$. The significance of this fact is discussed in Chapter III where an attempt is made to correlate the

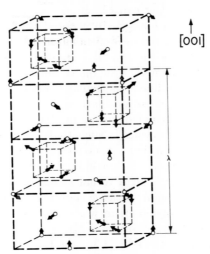

[00ī]

ANTIFERROMAGNETIC SPIN CONFIGURATION [00ī]

Fig. 38.   Antiferromagnetic-spiral configuration with **k** ∥ [001].   (After Kaplan, Dwight, Lyons, and Menyuk (331).)

origins of the tetragonal distortions and the sign and relative magnitudes of the exchange parameters with ordering of the Cu^{2+} outer electrons.

This work is being extended to include effects of A-A interactions. Since these interactions are small, the general conclusions presented above are not significantly altered. However, it might be noted that the A-A interactions do not increase the roof $w = 1/2$ of the YK region found where $v > 1/2$.

D. PARASITIC FERROMAGNETISM

Many antiferromagnetic materials at $T < T_N$ display a magnetization σ in high external fields H that varies as

$$\sigma = \sigma_0 + \chi_a H \tag{153}$$

where χ_a is the antiferromagnetic susceptibility. The constant σ_0 is weak (10^{-1} to 10^{-5} times the sublattice magnetization). It is called parasitic ferromagnetism. Such ferromagnetism could be due to ferromagnetic impurities or to preferential vacancy ordering, but such mechanisms are not capable of accounting for all of the experimental data. Dzialoshinsky (162) noted that for several of these substances there is a strong dependence of their properties on the magnetic symmetry of the crystal. He then proceeded to show how the parasitic ferromagnetism of many antiferromagnets can be accounted for by noncollinear molecular fields that cant the two antiparallel sublattices. If both sublattices are canted in the same direction, a net magnetization develops in that direction. However, if the symmetry of the crystal is such that the canting of the atomic moments cancel one another out, no parasitic magnetization develops. Such a concept suggests the possibility of piezomagnetism (161) in some antiferromagnets, an external stress introducing noncollinear molecular fields via magnetoelastic coupling. The first experimental confirmation of piezomagnetism was reported by Boravik-Romanov (87) in single crystals of CoF_2 and MnF_2. The origin of anisotropic exchange forces is discussed in Chapter III, Section I-B-6. Canted spin arrangements may also reflect noncollinear, crystalline-anisotropy fields such as may be encountered in orthorhombic perovskites, where the octahedral interstices are "puckered." (See Chapter III, Section I-F-2(e).)

IV. Neutron Diffraction Data

An important modern tool for the direct observation of spin configurations is neutron diffraction. Because the neutron is a neutral particle that carries a magnetic moment, it is primarily scattered by only the atomic nucleus and electrons with unpaired spins. Halpern and Johnson (247) have shown that the differential scattering cross section of an atom, including both nuclear and magnetic scattering, is

$$d\sigma = b^2 + 2bp\mathbf{q}\cdot\boldsymbol{\lambda} + p^2q^2 \qquad (154)$$

where $\boldsymbol{\lambda}$ is a unit vector in the direction of polarization of the incident neutron, b and p are the nuclear and magnetic scattering amplitudes, and $\mathbf{q}$ is the magnetic interaction vector defined by

$$\mathbf{q} = \boldsymbol{\epsilon}(\boldsymbol{\epsilon}\cdot\mathbf{K}) - \mathbf{K} \qquad q^2 = 1 - (\boldsymbol{\epsilon}\cdot\mathbf{K})^2 \qquad (155)$$

where $\mathbf{K}$ is a unit vector in the direction of the atomic magnetic moment and $\boldsymbol{\epsilon}$ is a unit vector in the direction perpendicular to the effective "reflecting" planes. For unpolarized neutron beams, $\mathbf{q}\cdot\boldsymbol{\lambda} = 0$ and the effective scattered intensity structure factor for a unit cell is

$$F^2 = F^2_{\text{nucl}} + q^2 F^2_{\text{mag}} \qquad (156)$$

where

$$F^2_{\genfrac{\{}{\}}{0pt}{}{\text{nucl}}{\text{mag}}} = \left| \sum_{x,y,z} \begin{Bmatrix} b \\ p \end{Bmatrix} \exp 2\pi i(hx/a_0 + ky/b_0 + lz/c_0) \right|^2 \exp(-2W)$$

Here h, k, l are the Miller indices appropriate to $\boldsymbol{\epsilon}$; a_0, b_0, c_0 are the dimensions of the crystallographic unit cell; and x, y, z are the Cartesian coordinates of the scattering center. W is the Debye-Waller factor and $p \propto Sf$, where S is the net atomic spin and f is an amplitude form factor. Thus given a knowledge of the crystalline structure and of the variation of f with $(\sin\theta)/\lambda$, where $\lambda \backsim 1$ A is the wavelength of monochromatized incident neutrons, it is possible to obtain the magnitude of the atomic moments, the spin configuration, and (at least in single-crystal specimens) the direction of the spin configuration relative to the crystallographic axes (32). It should be realized that the spin-configuration determination is rarely unique since it is derived by trial and error. However, it is usually possible to find a single satisfactory solution from among the more obvious possibilities. The spin configurations that have been directly obtained by neutron diffraction are listed in Tables VIII and XI.

IV. Neutron Diffraction Data

CHAPTER III

Atomic Moments and Their Interactions

I. Insulators and Semiconductors

A. DESCRIPTION OF OUTER ELECTRONS

As was pointed out in Chapter I, outer s and p electrons are best described by a MO approach. In the case of insulators and semiconductors, the s–p bands are split by discrete energy gaps, and stoichiometric samples have their Fermi level within such a gap. Bands below E_F are completely filled; bands above E_F are completely empty at $T = 0°K$. In the simpler structures, such as the diamond structure of Ge-type compounds or ionic structures like rock salt, corundum, zinc blende, or wurtzite, the compound contains two sublattices that are distinguishable by symmetry and/or atom occupation. This means that there are two atoms per unit cell, so that the s and p bands are split in two. If the splitting is larger than the separation between s and p levels, there is an effective energy gap E_g^{eff} between the bottom of the upper s band and the top of the lower p band. In some of the heavier compounds, like PbSe, there is little mixing of s and p states, and the energy gap of interest is between the bottom of the upper p band and the top of a lower p band that is overlapped to a greater or lesser extent by the upper s band (see Fig. 39).

From equation 46 it is possible to derive a necessary condition for semiconductor or insulator properties: *The Fermi level may lie within an energy gap if the number of electrons per atom (only atoms whose orbitals participate in band formation are counted) is* $n \sum_l 2(2l + 1)/\nu$, *where l is the angular momentum of the atomic orbitals participating in partially filled bands, ν is the number of atoms per primitive unit cell, and n is an integer.* (Perturbation mixtures from higher states do not change the number of states in the band.) Thus if s and p states are admixed (d and f electrons neglected), a compound may be a semiconductor or insulator if the number of electrons per atom is

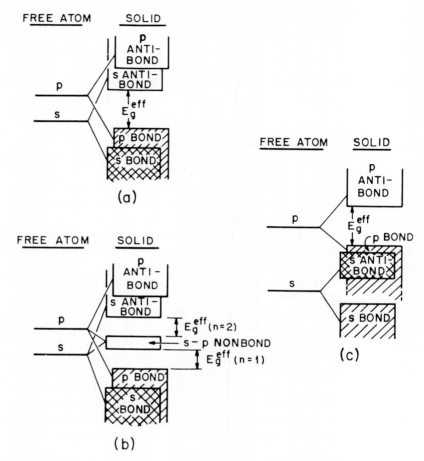

Fig. 39.   Energy-band splittings for some typical semiconductors.   (a) Zinc-blende, s and p states mixed.   (b) Fluorite (Mg_2Sn has $n = 1$, CaF_2 has $n = 2$). (c) Rock salt for case where s and p states do not mix appreciably.

$n8/\nu$.   For zinc blende with $\nu = 2$, the compound may be a semi-conductor if $n = 1$ and there are four s–p electrons per atom; for fluorite with $\nu = 3$, the compound may be a semiconductor if $n = 1$ or 2 and there are 8/3 or 16/3 electrons per atom.   (Some cations may have s–p states that are unstable relative to the bonding s–p bands so that their orbitals do not participate in band formation although they donate electrons to the bonding s–p bands. This situation is believed to be illustrated by Li_3Bi where one-third of the Li^+ cations occupy octahedral Bi interstices of a fluorite Li_2Bi matrix. The octahedral Li atoms are farther from the anions than the tetrahedral Li and therefore polarize the anion sublattice considerably less. Formally the compound might better be designated $Li^+[Li_2Bi]^-$; and with 8/3 electrons per atom of the fluorite sublattice, the compound is a semiconductor.) In some heavier compounds like PbSe, there is little mixing of s–p states, so that only p states ($l = 1$) can be considered in the rule: i.e. the rock salt structure ($\nu = 2$) is a semiconductor if the number of p electrons per atom is 3. [Although compounds with the $C33$ structure, such as Bi_2Te_3, are apparent exceptions to this rule, the semiconducting properties are probably due to a trapping of the "extra" p electrons into three-electron Te–Te bonds along the cleavage planes.] The splitting of the bands is larger the greater the difference in the electron potentials of the two sublattices. A large electronegativity difference between the two sublattices and a small cation/anion size ratio contributes to large splitting. Insulators have a large E_g^{eff}. With a large electronegativity difference between sublattices, the outer s and p electrons are primarily associated with the anion sublattice whereas the unoccupied s–p states are primarily associated with the cation sublattice. If the cation/anion size ratio is small, the hole mobility is high; but if the ratio is large, the hole mobility is smaller as the anion-anion interactions are weaker.

If the cations of such a semiconducting or insulating material also possess outer d or f electrons, these electrons may be described by a MO, a "polaron," or a HL approach depending upon the cation--cation separation $R < R_c$, $R \approx R_c$, or $R > R_c$. The Fermi surface E_F falls in the s-p energy gap between occupied and unoccupied d or f levels (see Fig. 40).

It was pointed out in Chapter I that the f electrons are always best described by a HL approach, but that the d electrons may be described by either a collective or a localized model, depending upon the situation. If a collective description is appropriate for some of the d orbitals and the corresponding d states are only partially occupied, the compound is metallic (or has a small activation energy for electron transport if $R \approx R_c$ and there is an integral number of d electrons per atom) unless the cations themselves form a two-

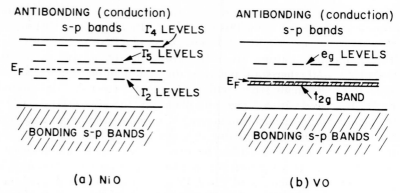

(a) NiO   **(b)** VO

Fig. 40.   Schematic energy-level diagrams for two types of ionic compound.
(a) An insulator.   (b) A metal.

sublattice structure such that the d bands are split in two and the number of d electrons just fills a subband.   In primarily ionic compounds with $R \approx R_c$, ligand-field splittings may exceed the width of the collective d subbands.   Metallic conductivity may also be quenched by electron ordering into homopolar cation--cation bonds (see Chapter III, Section II).   This section is concerned with insulating or semiconducting transition metal compounds for which a HL description of the d electrons is appropriate.

1. *Evidence from Electrical Properties*

Evidence from electrical properties in support of the HL d electrons among transition metal oxides (TiO, Ti_2O_3, VO, V_2O_3, and VO_2 excepted) has been summarized by Jonker and Van Houten (309). They point out that the stoichiometric oxides, excluding the noted exceptions, are all insulators.   Further, there is a linear variation of $\ln \sigma$ vs. $\ln x$, where $\sigma = ne\mu$ is the electrical conductivity and x is a measure of the impurity content or lack of stoichiometry.   These plots, together with Seebeck voltage data, indicate that the donor or acceptor levels associated with impurity-neighbor cations have ionization energies $\lesssim 0.04$ eV, so that the number of mobile extra or missing d electrons n is directly calculable from the oxygen and/or impurity content.   Since σ appears to vary as $\sigma = \sigma_0 \exp(-q/kT)$, this means that the mobility varies as $\mu = \mu_0 \exp(-q/kT)$ and that

μ_0 and q can be obtained from measurements of σ vs. T. The experimental q is the same for polycrystalline and single-crystal samples. Therefore q represents an activation energy for a localized electron to jump from a low-valence cation to a high-valence cation; it does not represent a grain-boundary effect or an energy gap between a donor (or acceptor) level and a conduction band. The activation energy $q = 0.1$ to 0.5 eV is relatively high near stoichiometry, but rapidly drops off to a nearly constant value with increasing impurity concentration. This drop-off is due to a change from intrinsic to extrinsic conduction. Near stoichiometry, where there is an integral number of electrons per cation, q contains two terms: the energy required to create a separated hole-electron pair (Mott's localization mechanism) and the energy associated with relaxation of the crystal about a cation of abnormal valence (Landau trapping (384,455)). In the extrinsic region, where the electron/cation ratio is nonintegral, it is not necessary to create separated hole-electron pairs for conduction, and q contains only the Landau-trapping energy. (Yamashita and Kurosawa (701) discuss the HL treatment for the conducting electrons given Landau trapping the principal reason for d-electron localization.) Heikes and Johnston (263) have shown that with localization due to Landau trapping, the mobility is given by

$$\mu = \frac{a^2 e v_0}{kT} e^{-q/kT} \tag{157}$$

where q is related to the "trapping," a is the closest cation--cation separation, and v_0 is the jump frequency. This expression fits the data as well as the empirically derived relation $\mu = \mu_0 \exp(-q/kT)$. It is found that $\mu = 10^{-3}$ to 10^{-5} cm^2/V-sec for cation-anion-cation hopping (transfer of e_g electrons between octahedral-site cations) and $\mu = 0.1$ to 10 cm^2/V-sec for cation-cation hopping (transfer of t_{2g} electrons between octahedral-site cations). Materials of the first type are called *low-mobility semiconductors*. Material of the second type are *intermediate-mobility semiconductors* if $R > R_c$, are metallic if $R < R_c$. The jump frequency v_0 is sensitive to q and varies between 10^{11} to 10^{14} sec^{-1} for different materials. In mixed systems, only one v_0 is found for electrons, one for holes. Since lattice vibrations have $v \sim 10^{13}$ sec^{-1}, the electron jumps appear to be induced by vibrations that bring the neighboring cations closer together. Finally, the Seebeck voltage is given by

$$\alpha = (\alpha_n \sigma_n + \alpha_p \sigma_p)/(\sigma_n + \sigma_p) \tag{158}$$

$$\sigma_n = ne\mu_n, \quad \sigma_p = pe\mu_p$$

$$\alpha_n = -\frac{k}{e}\{A_n - E_F/kT\}, \quad \alpha_p = \frac{k}{e}\{A_p + (E_g + E_F)/kT\}$$

where n and p are the electron and hole densities, μ_n and μ_p are the electron and hole mobilities, E_F and E_g are referred to the energy of the high-valence-state cation (or bottom of the conduction band) and E_g is the energy required to create a separated hole-electron pair (or is the energy gap between conduction and valence bands). A_n and A_p are transport parameters of order unity. For an extrinsic semiconductor ($p \approx 0$ and n equals the number of high-valence cations),

$$E_F/kT = \ln Q$$

$$Q = \begin{cases} (N - n)/n & \text{for HL electrons} \\ 2(2\pi m^* kT/h^2)^{3/2} & \text{for MO electrons} \end{cases} \tag{159}$$

N is the number of transition metal atoms per cm^3. For high-mobility semiconductors like PbS, in which outer s–p (MO) electrons are the charge carriers, $m^* = 0.1$ to 1.0 and the effective value of N is $N \approx 10^{19}$ cm^{-3}. For oxides, $m^* \approx 100$ if the MO description is used, and $N \approx 10^{22}$ cm^{-3}, which is the number of transition metal ions per cm^3, indicating a band width $\lesssim kT$. These facts, together with the magnetic data, support a HL description for the outer d electrons in most insulating and semiconducting transition metal compounds. (The fact that q does not contribute to the Seebeck effect renders the low-mobility semiconductors impractical for thermoelectric applications. For a partially filled band due to $R < R_c$, the Seebeck coefficient varies linearly with the temperature (455a): $\alpha_n = -(\pi^2 k^2/3e)T[d \ln\sigma(E)/dE]_{E_F})$.

2. Evidence from Magnetic Properties

The principal magnetic property in support of the HL description of the d electrons in these materials is the magnitude of the individual atomic moments. The magnitudes of μ_{eff} and μ that are predicted from equations 84 and 85 require only a small ϵ in the factor $g = 2 + \epsilon$, and this can be attributed to the influence of incompletely quenched orbital angular momenta. However, it must be remembered that spin quenching by large ligand fields can occur as illustrated in Table VII.

3. Site-Preference Energies

Finally, a HL description is supported by the fact that site-preference stabilizations can be estimated qualitatively with a localized-electron model. There are five energies that must be considered in a calculation of electronic energy levels: ionization potentials or electron affinities of the constituent ions, Madelung energies, polarization energies, ligand-field stabilizations, and elastic energies. The first two energies are the largest, being of the order of 10 to 50 eV. Ionization potentials are listed by Finkelnburg and Humbach (177), and Madelung energies for different crystal structures are given in a review by Waddington (643). It is difficult, however, to obtain a satisfactory estimate of the polarization and elastic energies.

In a comparison of the energies for octahedral versus tetrahedral occupancy, the ionization potentials cancel out and differences in Madelung energy are small, so that polarization and ligand-field stabilizations are important. In the case of spinels, the Madelung energy (144,638) is a function of the structural u parameter for the spinel lattice.* (In a cubic spinel, the occupied tetrahedral sublattice forms a diamond structure whose cubic cell edge a equals that for the spinel. The spinel u parameter is defined by setting ua equal to the distance from an (001) cation plane of the diamond sublattice to the next-near-neighbor (001) anion plane.) The critical u parameter above which Madelung energies stabilize a normal 2–3 spinel, below which an inverse 2–3 spinel, is $u_c = 0.379$. For ideal close packing of the anion sublattice, $u = 3/8$. However, in most spinels $u > 3/8$, a random distribution of cations giving $u = 0.382$. The Madelung energy contribution to the B-site-preference energy in spinels turns out to be $\sim 30(Z_1 - Z_2)$ kcal/mole, where Z_1 and Z_2 are the charges on the two cations under comparison. It is difficult to obtain a quantitative value for the difference in polarization energy between octahedral and tetrahedral sites. Two contributions can be distinguished: one due to coordinate covalence via empty cation d states, the other via empty cation s–p states. The first contribution adds to the ligand-field splittings and removes the conservation of energy of the degenerate level in the splitting because the e_g and t_{2g} states do not participate equally in the polarization effects. Although the nonconservation of energy introduces large uncertainties

---

* Interaction of anion polarization with the Madelung potential is also important (591), but is neglected.

into any quantitative estimate of ligand-field effects, a reasonable *qualitative* estimate of the ligand-field stabilizations is obtained with a point-charge model and the measured splittings obtained from spectroscopic data (156,421). For trivalent and divalent cations in an oxygen lattice, $Dq_{oct} \approx 1800$ cm^{-1} and 1200 cm^{-1}, respectively, if there are no e_g electrons, $Dq_{oct} \approx 1400$ cm^{-1} and 750 cm$^{-1} < Dq_{oct} < 1000$ cm^{-1}, respectively, if there are two e_g electrons. Jahn-Teller stabilizations give $\Delta Dq_{oct} \sim 300$ cm^{-1} if an odd e_g electron is present. A point-charge model gives $Dq_{oct} = 4Dq_{oct}/9$ for the relative ligand-field splittings at tetrahedral and octahedral sites. The ligand-field stabilizations follow immediately from Figures 10 and 11. This contribution amounts to ~ 45 kcal/gaw for Cr^{3+}, which is the reason that Cr^{3+} is almost never found in a tetrahedral interstice.

The significance of this contribution to site-preference energies was first pointed out by Goodenough and Loeb (222), who showed that from such qualitative considerations it is possible to account for most of the observed cation distributions over tetrahedral (A) and octahedral (B) sublattices of the spinels. They also emphasized that the remaining portion of the polarization energy, which depends upon the relative stability of (sp^3) versus p^3 coordinate covalence, is important; for cations with full, or half-filled, outer shells, it is dominant. Since (sp^3) hybrids, which have tetrahedral symmetry, provide greater opportunity for polarization, the s-p polarization energy favors tetrahedral sites. This site-preference contribution is greater for cations of smaller atomic number, where the hybridization energy is smaller. This effect is also greater the smaller the electronegativity difference between cation and anion and the larger the cation-anion size ratio. Van Houten (626) has suggested an ionic-model method for calculating this contribution. Miller (439) has suggested an empirical method, which is based on a Born-repulsion formalism, that is meant to give an estimate of the combined polarization and elastic effects. Neither suggestion is too satisfactory. Spin-dependent terms, which are responsible for coupling the magnetic moments of neighboring ions or for magnetostriction and anisotropy effects, are neglected since they are only of the order of 0.01 eV.

With these energies, it is possible to calculate not only the preferred cation distribution over two types of available anion interstice, as in the spinel lattice, but also the valency distribution given two atoms on the same site, each with multiple-valence alternatives. This point has been illustrated by Jonker and Van Houten (309). However, their numbers cannot be taken too seriously because of the inadequacy of their treatment of anion polarization.

B. THEORY OF MAGNETIC COUPLING

It was pointed out in Chapter II that the Heisenberg exchange Hamiltonian of equation 90, which can be directly related to the Weiss field parameters at $T = 0°K$ by equation 94, is an excellent formal expression for the interactions between atomic spins (or moments) of neighboring atoms. There remains the problem of establishing the various spin-dependent mechanisms that contribute to the J_{ij}. In general, there are two types of interaction: cation- -cation and cation-anion-cation (or even cation-anion-anion-cation) interactions.

1. Cation- -Cation Interactions

The significance of cation- -cation interactions in ionic and semiconducting transition metal compounds has been argued on semiempirical grounds (216,670). It was pointed out in Chapter II, Section I-A that the HL direct-exchange integrals appear to contribute a relatively small term to the cation- -cation interactions. In the Nesbet (478) formalism of equation 164 this term is C and is always positive because he starts with an orthogonal set of wave functions. (This corresponds to the orthogonal HL formalism or Wannier functions, in which the configuration interactions corresponding to the so-called polar terms are extremely important. In fact without those polar terms, the triplet state appears to be lowest in the H_2 molecule and there is no binding.) Although there may be cases in which this term determines the sign of the interaction, in general it is not dominant. Therefore it is neglected in the present qualitative discussions where the mechanisms responsible for D and/or E of equation 164 are assumed to dominate the sign of the interaction. In order to educate the intuition, it is necessary to consider the sign of the couplings to be associated with these mechanisms.

With $R > R_c$, the Coulomb repulsion of the electrons when they are on the same ion is the dominant electron-interaction term, so that the lowest states correspond to an exact number of electrons on each ion rather than to running waves. Although the mutual repulsion of electrons on the same ion prevents the permanent occupation of "ionized" (within cation sublattice) states, the system can gain a certain amount of energy by the admixture of "polar" terms, as was seen in Chapter I. This means that the Coulomb term is the principal term in the Hamiltonian, that the usual band-energy terms are treated as a perturbation. In the case of insulators, there is only a "virtual" occupation of the "ionized" states: The transferred electrons are not free to become separated from the hole they leave behind, either because of the exciton binding proposed by Mott or because of Landau trapping due to polarization of the lattice.

(a) *Half-filled, overlapping orbitals.* In the simplest model, all the degenerate states in the ground-state manifold have exactly one electron per ion, and all the excited states with one transferred electron have energy U. Between any pair of ions at a distance $\mathbf{R} - \mathbf{R}'$, there is only one transfer integral $b_{\mathbf{R}-\mathbf{R}'}$, which is proportional to the orbital overlap; this must act twice to return the state to one of the ground manifold. This leads to a second-order perturbation of the energy

$$\Delta E = - \sum_{\mathbf{R},\mathbf{R}'\sigma,\sigma'} (b_{\mathbf{R}-\mathbf{R}'}^2/U)s^*(\mathbf{R}, \sigma)s(\mathbf{R}', \sigma)s^*(\mathbf{R}', \sigma')s(\mathbf{R}, \sigma') \qquad (160)$$

Where $s^*(\mathbf{R}, \sigma)$ and $s(\mathbf{R}', \sigma)$ are fermion creation and annihilation operators for an electron spin σ at position $\mathbf{R}$ or $\mathbf{R}'$. The transfer integral is a matrix element connecting one-electron functions:

$$b_{\mathbf{R}-\mathbf{R}'} = \int \phi_{\mathbf{R}',\sigma}(p^2/2m + V(r))\phi_{\mathbf{R},\sigma} \, d\tau$$

Anderson (20) has shown that equation 160 reduces to

$$\Delta E = \text{const.} + \sum_{\mathbf{R},\mathbf{R}'} \frac{2|b_{\mathbf{R}-\mathbf{R}'}|^2}{U} \mathbf{S_R} \cdot \mathbf{S_{R'}}$$

or that the exchange parameter for the cation- -cation contribution in this case is given by

$$J_{ij}^{c-c}(\text{two half filled orbitals}) = -2b_{ij}^2 U^{-1} \qquad (161')$$

which is *negative*. In a substance with n unpaired d electrons per cation, the exchange integral for the total cation spin $S = n/2$ is

$$J_{ij}^{c-c}(\text{half filled, half filled}) = -2b_{ij}^2/4S^2U \qquad (161)$$

Physically, the antiferromagnetic character of this *superexchange* effect follows from the fact that the transfer integrals b_{ij} carry an electron without change of spin. Since the overlapping orbitals are half filled and the Pauli exclusion principle limits a given orbital to one electron of each spin, this means that the interacting electrons must be antiparallel if transfer is to take place.

It should be noted that the electrostatic energy U can be estimated directly (as discussed for site-preference energies) or obtained from the observed activation energy for d-electron conduction, to which is added the ionic polarization energy. The parameter b_{ij} is more difficult to estimate. It is proportional to the orbital overlap and so must increase exponentially with decreasing cation-cation separation.

(b) *Overlap of a half filled and an empty orbital.* Suppose that orbital n on the ion at R is half filled, orbital n' at R' is completely empty. A simple electron transfer is spin-independent in this case unless there is a non-overlapping (or orthogonal), partially occupied orbital n'' at R'. Given a partially occupied n'' at R', the transfer integral is much greater if the spin of the transferred electron is *parallel* to the spin of n'', because of exchange coupling *within* the ion at R' that is proportional to the intraatomic exchange constant $J_{n'n''} = J^{\text{intra}}$. This gives rise to a third-order perturbation of the energy, and an effective *ferromagnetic* exchange parameter given by

$$J_{ij}^{c\text{-}c}(\text{half filled, empty}) = +2b_{ij}^2 J^{\text{intra}}/4S^2U^2 \qquad (162)$$

This superexchange coupling is weaker than the first by the factor J^{intra}/U. It may therefore be only slightly larger than the direct exchange coupling. However, both effects are ferromagnetic and add.

(c) *Overlap of a half-filled and a full orbital.* If orbital n at $\mathbf{R}$ is half full and orbital n' at $\mathbf{R}'$ is full, the only electron transfer possible is from $\mathbf{R}'$ to $\mathbf{R}$ and back. The spin of the transferred electron must be antiparallel to the spin at $\mathbf{R}$. If n'' at $\mathbf{R}'$ is partially filled, exchange coupling *within* the ion at $\mathbf{R}'$ favors transfer of the electron of n' that is antiparallel to n''. Thus the transferred electron is antiparallel to the net spin at both $\mathbf{R}$ and $\mathbf{R}'$, and the atomic moments are coupled *ferromagnetically*. Again this effect contributes a third-order perturbation to the energy, so that the effective ferromagnetic exchange parameter is

$$J_{ij}^{c\text{-}c}(\text{half filled, full}) = +2b_{ij}^2 J^{\text{intra}}/4S^2U^2 \qquad (163)$$

There is one other effect that should be mentioned. This is the exchange interaction between one spin and the spin polarization of its neighbor.   It is the complete analog of the proposed (81,537,546) mechanism of indirect-exchange coupling between nuclear spins. This mechanism is smaller than direct exchange, and therefore only the dominating superexchange terms of equations 161, 162, 163 are retained for discussion.   However, this indirect-exchange mechanism falls off as the third power of the orbital overlap, so that it may be important for coupling between distant ions that are coupled by cation-anion-cation interactions where the b_{ij}^2 vary as the fourth power of the orbital overlap (20).

2. *180° Cation-Anion-Cation Interactions*

These interactions couple two cations on opposite sides of an anion. Clearly there is little direct overlap of the orbitals on the two cations, and the anion must be playing the role of an intermediary.   Such a mechanism was originally proposed by Kramers (373).   The first quantitative estimate by Anderson (16) substantiated the order of magnitude of the effect and pointed out the dependence of cation-anion-cation interactions on the subtended angle.   However, failure to account for the anisotropic character of the $3d$ orbitals led to incorrect predictions.   Goodenough and Loeb (222) pointed out that symmetrical conditions must be considered for each side of the anion simultaneously.   This plus explicit account of the splitting of the anisotropic $3d$ orbitals by crystalline fields provided a physical basis for the formulation (213,214) of coupling rules that have been substantiated by subsequent empirical investigations.   Slater (583) suggested an antiferromagnetic interaction arising from polarization of the anion electron cloud.   Keffer and Oguchi (343) have considered this problem with a formalism based on nonorthogonal orbitals. Yamashita and Kondo (360,700) have also considered various contributions to the cation-anion-cation interactions with a formalism based on nonorthogonal orbitals.   Nesbet (477,478) has provided an analytic formalism for the correlation effect (originally called semicovalent exchange) proposed by Goodenough and Loeb (222) and compared it to Anderson's (20) more recent delocalization effect formulation, which is the cation- -cation superexchange with transfer integrals enhanced by the anion intermediary, and to the Keffer-Oguchi and Yamashita-Kondo considerations.   Kanamori (321) has given a qualitative discussion of the various mechanisms and has also considered the 90° correlation superexchange.   Goodenough (216) has emphasized the importance of 90° cation- -cation superexchange. The conclusion from this work is that there are several mechanisms contributing to the exchange coupling that are of comparable magnitude, and that these contributions usually add, so that *qualitative* criteria for the sign and relative strengths of the exchange parameters can be given.

To illustrate the various physical mechanisms, consider two transition metal cations in octahedral interstices that share a common corner, such as would be found in an ideal, cubic perovskite (see Figure 56(a) for structure). In Figure 41(a) is shown the symmetry

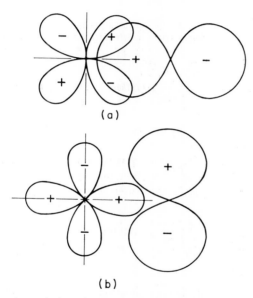

(a)

(b)

Fig. 41. Symmetry relations between (a) t_{2g} and $p\sigma$ orbitals, (b) e_g and $p\pi$ orbitals.

relation between the cation t_{2g} and the anion $p\sigma$ orbitals, and in Figure 41(b) between the cation e_g and the anion $p\pi$ orbitals. It is at once obvious that the $p\sigma$ orbital is orthogonal to the t_{2g} orbitals, but not the e_g orbital of principal overlap, and that the $p\pi$ orbitals are orthogonal to the e_g orbitals, but not the t_{2g} orbital of principal overlap. Therefore electron transfer, or partial covalence, can only take place between a $p\sigma$ orbital and the e_g orbital of principal overlap, or between a $p\pi$ orbital and the t_{2g} orbital of principal overlap. The first mechanism will be referred to as σ transfer, the second as π transfer. Since the orbital overlap involved in σ transfer is greater than that in π transfer, processes involving σ transfer are the stronger. (It should be noted that the e_g-s bond has the same symmetry properties as the $p\sigma$-e_g. Since there is no means of distinguishing between the two, only the $p\sigma$-e_g bond is discussed. This in no way alters the qualitative arguments.)

There are three situations to be distinguished. These are illustrated in Figure 42. Case 1 represents coupling between cations

CASE	OUTER-ELECTRON CONFIGURATION	CORRELATION SUPEREXCHANGE		DELOCALIZATION SUPEREXCHANGE		SUM	STRENGTH °K (OXIDES)
		$p\sigma$	$p\pi$	$p\sigma$	$p\pi$		
#1	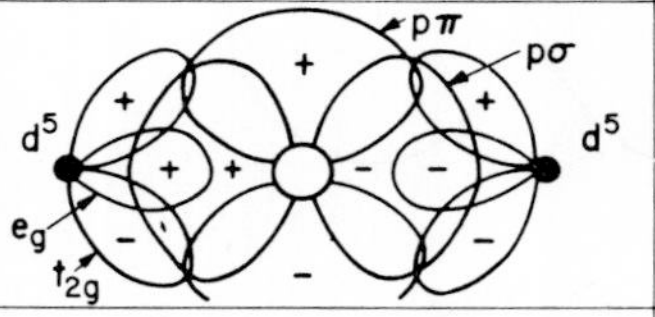 d^5 ... d^5	STRONG ↑↓	WEAK ↑↓	STRONG ↑↓	WEAK ↑↓	↑↓	~750
#2	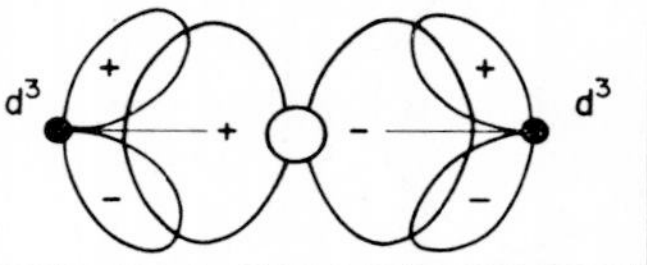 d^3 ... d^3	WEAK TO MODERATE ↑↓	WEAK ↑↓	—	WEAK ↑↓	↑↓	≲300
#3	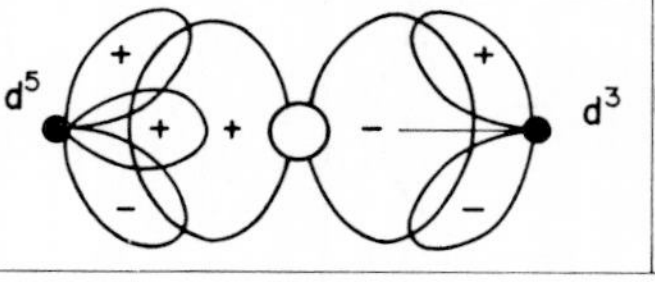 d^5 ... d^3	MODERATE ↑↓	WEAK ↑↓	MODERATE ↑↓	WEAK ↑↓	↑↓	~400

Fig. 42. Three possible 180° cation-anion-cation interactions between octahedral-site cations. (The $p\pi$ orbitals are not indicated in the diagrams for cases 2 and 3.)

that have a half-filled e_g orbital directed towards the anion intermediary, Case 2 represents half filled t_{2g} orbitals and empty e_g orbitals directed towards the anion, Case 3 represents a cation with a half filled e_g orbital overlapping $p\sigma$ on one side and an empty e_g orbital overlapping $p\sigma$ on the other. Case 1 could represent the magnetic coupling in the perovskite $LaFeO_3$, Case 2 that in $LaCrO_3$, and Case 3 that in the hypothetical ordered perovskite $La(Cr_{0.5}Fe_{0.5})O_3$. (Ordering does not occur in this latter compound, presumably because the cations are all trivalent and of comparable size.) The predominant contribution to the superexchange comes from the covalency of the σ bonds. Therefore *the more ionic the bonds, the smaller the 180° cation-anion-cation interaction.*

There are three principal contributions to the superexchange: a correlation effect, a delocalization effect, and a polarization effect. If orthogonal orbitals are used, the last of these appears to be definitely the smallest (478).

(*a*) *Correlation effect.* The correlation mechanism takes into account the simultaneous partial bond formation on each side of the anion. The cation spins are so coupled that the two $p\sigma$ electrons, one of each spin, can *simultaneously* form partial-covalent bonds on opposite sides of the anion. For Case 1, only $p\sigma$ spins that are antiparallel to the cation spins can participate in bond formation (be transferred to the half filled e_g orbitals), and the spins are coupled antiparallel. Similarly, the weaker π transfer gives antiparallel coupling. For Case 2, the $p\sigma$ spins that are parallel to the cation spins are stabilized in the covalent bond by intracation exchange. With similar coupling on each side of the anion, this mechanism gives antiferromagnetic coupling. This coupling is weaker than that of Case 1 as it involves third-order, rather than second-order, perturbation theory, in analogy with equation 162. The π transfer process is similar to that of Case 1, and so also contributes to the antiferromagnetic coupling. In Case 3, the transferred $p\sigma$ orbitals are antiparallel to the cation spin on one side, parallel on the other. This gives ferromagnetic coupling of intermediate strength. The π bonding favors antiferromagnetic coupling, but is weaker, so that the net interaction is ferromagnetic.

(*b*) *Delocalization.* In this mechanism an electron is assumed to drift from one cation to the other, the transfer integral b_{ij} depending sensitively on the amount of partial covalent bonding since covalency causes the cation d orbitals to spread out over the anion. In fact the lack of direct overlap of cation orbitals means that b_{ij} varies as the square of the overlap of cation and anion orbitals, or that b_{ij}^2 varies as the fourth power of the overlap. Case 1 represents superexchange between half filled e_g orbitals, which, by equation 161, is antiferromagnetic and relatively strong. There is also some antiferromagnetic superexchange via the half filled t_{2g} orbitals (π bonding). In Case 2 only the π bond interaction is present, and weak antiferromagnetism results. Case 3 corresponds to superexchange between an empty and a half filled e_g orbital, which gives moderate to weak ferromagnetic coupling by equation 162. Weak antiferromagnetic π bonding is simultaneously present.

(c) *Polarization.* The anion-polarization effects may be nonlinear in $S(S + 1)$, and hence not properly included in the Heisenberg formalism. However, the contributions that have a different form than that for correlation superexchange are sufficiently small relative to the correlation and delocalization effects that they may be legitimately omitted from the discussion (478).

Cation-anion-cation superexchange interactions involving orbitals that are more than half filled are considerably weaker. However, antiferromagnetic correlation exchange is possible for that fraction of the time that the anion orbitals overlap half filled orbitals on each cation. Since a knowledge of the orbital occupations follows from the crystal-field considerations of Chapter I, it is possible to use arguments similar to those for Cases 1–3 to obtain the qualitative coupling rules given in Table XII.

Nesbet's (478) analytical formulation for the problem results in the following expression:

$$J_{ij}^{c-a-c} = \frac{1}{4S^2} \{C - D - E\} \tag{164}$$

where

$$C = \sum_{k,l} [a_{ki}a_{lj}|a_{lj}a_{ki}]$$

is the sum of ordinary electrostatic exchange integrals between two similar paramagnetic ions with singly occupied, orthonormal spatial orbitals $a_{1i} \ldots a_{ni}$ and $a_{1j} \ldots a_{nj}$. [In the Mulliken notation,

$$[a_n a_m | a_k a_l] = \int d\tau_1 \int d\tau_2\, a_n^*(1)a_m(1)(e^2/r_{12})a_k^*(2)a_l(2).]$$

Since the two-electron exchange integrals between orthonormal orbitals are positive definite, C is necessarily positive and represents ferromagnetic coupling. In ionic insulators or semiconductors, the cations are sufficiently far apart that this term is very small even for nearest-neighbor interactions. E is the contribution from delocalization superexchange, and D is the correlation superexchange contribution that arises from the interaction of configurations that differ by two occupied orbitals. D and E may be either positive or negative, according to the schedule of Table XII. Since the more usual coupling is antiferromagnetic, they are accompanied by a negative sign in equation 164.

For the contribution D, the three cases of Figure 42 are given by:

$$D_\text{I} = \sum_{m=e_g,t_{2g}} \frac{[ba_{mi}|ba_{mj}]^2}{U_{AA}}$$

$$D_\text{II} = \frac{n^2}{(n+1)^2} \sum_{l=e_g} \frac{[ba_{li}|ba_{lj}]^2}{U_{BB}} + \sum_{k=t_{2g}} \frac{[ba_{ki}|ba_{kj}]^2}{U_{AA}} \qquad (165)$$

$$D_\text{III} = -\sum_{k=t_{2g}} \sum_{l=e_g} \frac{[ba_{kj}|ba_{li}]^2}{U_{AB}^2} \sum_{m=t_{2g},e_g} [a_{mi}a_{li}|a_{lk}a_{mi}]$$

where $n = 3$ for Case 2 (three t_{2g} electrons), b^2 is the anion $p\sigma$ orbital and U_{AA}, U_{BB}, U_{AB} represent energy differences between the ground state and two electrons simultaneously transferred from the anion to the neighboring cations. The ferromagnetic term D_III is a third-order perturbation term similar to those of equations 162, 163. The polarization superexchange that is linear in $S(S + 1)$ is of the same form as D and adds a small contribution to it. Since estimates of U_{AA}, U_{BB}, and U_{AB} are difficult, little quantitative improvement is to be gained by adding the polarization terms.

In a calculation of the term E, it is reasonable to neglect all matrix elements between localized cation orbitals (given 180° cation-anion-cation interactions) because of the large cation separation. In this approximation the matrix elements arise from exchange-potential contributions to the doubly occupied orbitals of the intermediary anion. With an appropriate choice of basis, it is possible to pick out a single intervening orbital b for which the delocalization superexchange is greatest. Then the transfer integrals of equations 161, 162 can be expressed as $[ba_{ki}|ba_{kj}]$ so that

$$E_\text{I} \approx \sum_{k=e_g,t_{2g}} \frac{2[ba_{ki}|ba_{kj}]^2}{U}$$

$$E_\text{II} \approx \sum_{k=t_{2g}} \frac{2[ba_{ki}|ba_{kj}]^2}{U} \qquad (166)$$

$$E_\text{III} \approx -\frac{2[ba_{egi}|ba_{egj}]^2}{U^2} J^\text{intra} + \sum_{k=t_{2g}} \frac{2[ba_{ki}|ba_{kj}]^2}{U}$$

Anderson (20) has attempted to estimate the transfer integrals by relating them to the covalent contribution of the crystalline-field

TABLE XII

Sign of Interaction and Relative Strengths of Transfer Integrals for 180° Cation-Anion-Cation Superexchange between Octahedral-Site Cations

Number of d electrons	d^1: $t_{2g}^1 e_g^0$	d^2: $t_{2g}^2 e_g^0$	d^3: $t_{2g}^3 e_g^0$	d^4: $t_{2g}^3 e_g^1$	d^4: $t_{2g}^4 e_g^0$	d^5: $t_{2g}^3 e_g^2$	d^5: $t_{2g}^5 e_g^0$
Illustrative cations	Ti^{3+}, V^{4+} Nb^{4+} Re^{6+}	Ti^{2+}, V^{3+}, Cr^{4+} Ru^{6+} Os^{6+}	V^{2+}, Cr^{3+}, Mn^{4+} Mo^{3+} W^{3+}, Re^{4+}, Ir^{5+}	Cr^{2+}, Mn^{3+}, Fe^{4+}	Mn^{III}, Fe^{IV} Ru^{IV} Os^{IV}	Mn^{2+}, Fe^{3+}	Co^{IV} Ru^{III}, Rh^{IV} Ir^{IV}
d^1: $t_{2g}^1 e_g^0$ Ti^{3+}, V^{4+} Nb^{4+} Re^{6+}	Negligible	↑↓ (Weak)	↑↓ (Weak)	Quasistatic ↑↑ ↑↓ / Static ↑↑ and ↑↓	↑↓ (Weak)	↑↑ (Moderate)	Negligible
d^2: $t_{2g}^2 e_g^0$ Ti^{2+}, V^{3+}, Cr^{4+} Ru^{6+} Os^{6+}		↑↓ (Weak)	↑↓ (Weak)	Quasistatic ↑↑ ↑↓ / Static ↑↑ and ↑↓	↑↓ (Weak)	↑↑ (Moderate)	↑↓ (Weak)
d^3: $t_{2g}^3 e_g^0$ V^{2+}, Cr^{3+}, Mn^{4+} Mo^{3+} W^{3+}, Re^{4+}, Ir^{5+}			↑↓ (Weak)	Quasistatic ↑↑ ↑↓ / Static ↑↑ and ↑↓	↑↓ (Weak)	↑↑ (Moderate)	↑↓ (Weak)
d^4: $t_{2g}^3 e_g^1$ Cr^{2+}, Mn^{3+}, Fe^{4+}				Quasistatic (mod.) Static ↑↑ and ↑↑	Quasistatic Static ↑↑ and ↑↑	Quasistatic Static ↑↑ and ↑↑	Quasistatic Static ↑↑ and ↑↑

d^4: Mn^{III}, Fe^{IV} $t_{2g}^4 e_g^0$: Ru^{IV} Os^{IV}	↑↓ (Weak)		↑↑ (Moderate)	↑↓ (Weak)
d^5: Mn^{2+}, Fe^{3+} $t_{2g}^3 e_g^2$			↑↑ (Strong)	↑↑ (Moderate)
d^5: Co^{IV} $t_{2g}^5 e_g^0$: Ru^{III}, Rh^{IV} Ir^{IV}				Negligible
d^6: Fe^{2+}, Co^{3+} $t_{2g}^4 e_g^2$				
d^6: Co^{III} $t_{2g}^6 e_g^0$: Rh^{III}, Pd^{IV} Ir^{III}, Pt^{IV}				
d^7: Co^{2+}, Ni^{3+} $t_{2g}^5 e_g^2$				
d^7: Ni^{III} $t_{2g}^6 e_g^1$				
c^8: Ni^{2+a} $t_{2g}^6 e_g^2$: Pd^{2+a} Pt^{2+a}, Au^{3+a}				
d^9: Cu^{2+} $t_{2g}^6 e_g^3$				

(continued)

TABLE XII (continued)

Number of d electrons	Illustrative cations	$d^6:t_{2g}^4 e_g^2$	$d^6:t_{2g}^6 e_g^0$	$d^7:t_{2g}^5 e_g^2$	$d^7:t_{2g}^6 e_g^1$	$d^8:t_{2g}^6 e_g^2$	$d^9:t_{2g}^6 e_g^3$
	Illustrative cations	Fe²⁺, Co³⁺	Co^{III}, Rh^{III}, Pd^{IV}, Ir^{III}, Pt^{IV}	Co²⁺, Ni³⁺	Ni^{III}	Ni^{2+}[a], Pd^{2+}[a], Pt^{2+}[a], Au^{3+}[a]	Cu²⁺
d^1: $t_{2g}^1 e_g^0$	Ti³⁺, V⁴⁺, Nb⁴⁺, Re⁶⁺	(Moderate) ↑↑	None	(Moderate) ↑↑	Negligible	(Moderate) ↑↑	Negligible
d^2: $t_{2g}^2 e_g^0$	Ti²⁺, V³⁺, Cr⁴⁺, Ru⁶⁺, Os⁶⁺	(Moderate) ↑↑	None	(Moderate) ↑↑	Quasistatic ↑↑ / Static ↑↑ and ↑↓	(Moderate) ↑↑	Quasistatic (weak) ↑↑ / Static ↑↑ and none
d^3: $t_{2g}^3 e_g^0$	V²⁺, Cr³⁺, Mn⁴⁺, Mo³⁺, W³⁺, Re⁴⁺, Ir⁶⁺	(Moderate) ↑↑	None	(Moderate) ↑↑	Quasistatic ↑↑ / Static ↑↑ and ↑↓	(Moderate) ↑↑	Quasistatic (weak) ↑↑ / Static ↑↑ and none
d^4: $t_{2g}^3 e_g^1$	Cr²⁺, Mn³⁺, Fe⁴⁺	Quasistatic ↑↓ / Static ↑↑ and ↑↓	None	Quasistatic ↑↓ / Static ↑↑ and ↑↓	Quasistatic ↑↓ / Static ↑↓, ↑↑ or ↑↓, ↑↑	Quasistatic ↑↓ / Static ↑↑ and ↑↓	Quasistatic (weak) ↑↓ / Static ↑↑, ↑↓ and/or none

Configuration / Ions				Quasistatic / Static		Quasistatic (weak) / Static
d^4: $t_{2g}^4 e_g^0$ — Mn^{III}, Fe^{IV}, Ru^{IV}, Os^{IV}	↑↑ (Moderate)	None	↑↑ (Moderate)	Quasistatic ↑↓ ↑↑ / Static ↑↓ and ↑↑	↑↑ (Moderate)	Quasistatic (weak) ↑↑ ↑↑ / Static ↑↑ and none
d^5: $t_{2g}^3 e_g^2$ — Mn^{2+}, Fe^{3+}	↑→ (Strong)	None	↑→ (Strong)	Quasistatic ↑→ / Static ↑↑ and ↑→	↑→ (Strong)	Quasistatic (weak) / Static ↑↑ and none
d^5: $t_{2g}^5 e_g^0$ — Co^{IV}, Ru^{III}, Rh^{IV}, Ir^{IV}	↑↑ (Weak)	None	↑↑ (Moderate)	Negligible	↑↑ (Moderate)	Quasistatic (weak) / Static ↑↑ and none
d^6: $t_{2g}^4 e_g^2$ — Fe^{2+}, Co^{3+}	↑→ (Strong)	None	↑↓ (Strong)	Quasistatic ↑→ / Static ↑↓ and ↑↑	↑↓ (Strong)	Quasistatic (weak) / Static ↑↑ and none
d^6: $t_{2g}^6 e_g^0$ — Co^{III}, Rh^{III}, Pd^{IV}, Ir^{III}, Pt^{IV}		None	None	None	None	None
d^7: $t_{2g}^5 e_g^2$ — Co^{2+}, Ni^{3+}			↑↓ (Strong)	Quasistatic ↑→ / Static ↑↓ and ↑↑	↑↓ (Strong)	Quasistatic (weak) / Static ↑↑ and none

(continued)

TABLE XII (continued)

Number of d electrons	$d^6:t_{2g}^4e_g^2$	$d^6:t_{2g}^6e_g^0$	$d^7:t_{2g}^5e$	$d^7:t_{2g}^6e_g^1$	$d^8:t_{2g}^6e_g^2$	$d^9:t_{2g}^6e_g^3$
Illustrative cations	Fe^{2+}, Co^{3+}	Co^{III}, Rh^{III}, Pd^{IV}, Ir^{III}, Pt^{IV}	Co^{2+}, Ni^{3+}	Ni^{III}	Ni^{2+a}, Pd^{2+a}, Pt^{2+a}, Au^{3+a}	Cu^{2+}
d^7: $t_{2g}^6e_g^1$ Ni^{III}				Negligible	Quasistatic ↑↓/↑↓ Static ↑↓ and ↑↑	Quasistatic Negl. Static ↑↑, ↑↑, and/or none
d^8: $t_{2g}^6e_g^2$ Ni^{2+a}, Pd^{2+a}, Pt^{2+a}, Au^{3+a}					↑↓ (Strong)	Quasistatic (weak) ↑↓/↑↓ Static ↑↓ and none
d^9: $t_{2g}^6e_g^3$ Cu^{2+}						Quasistatic (weak) ↑↓/↑↓ Static ↑↑ and none

[a] Low-spin-state ion is diamagnetic and distorts octahedron to tetragonal ($c/a < 1$) symmetry.

parameter $10Dq$. With this procedure he was able to establish a correct order of magnitude for the effect. Nesbet (478) has used equation 166 as it can be compared directly with equation 165, the relative magnitude of the two contributions becoming $E_I/D_I = 2U_{AA}/U$.

The internal consistency of this treatment has been demonstrated (478) by a consideration of the series of antiferromagnetic compounds MnO, FeO, CoO, NiO. Each of these compounds has a rock salt structure and exhibits f.c. magnetic ordering of the second kind (see Table VIII and Fig. 18). The Néel temperatures for this series increase regularly from 116 to 523°K. It was shown in Chapter II that although nearest-neighbor interactions contribute to the paramagnetic Curie temperature Θ_a, they do not influence T_N for this type of order. T_N is related to J_{ij} via equation 94 in the molecular field approximation. (The relationships given in Table XIII represent

TABLE XIII

Néel Temperatures of Some Antiferromagnetic Oxides

	Substance			
	MnO	FeO	CoO	NiO
Spin	$\frac{5}{2}$	2	$\frac{3}{2}$	1
U_{AA}^{-1}, (eV)$^{-1}$	0.1287	0.2020	0.3096	0.5917
$2U^{-1}$, (eV)$^{-1}$	0.1198	0.1768	0.1546	0.1492
Total, (eV)$^{-1}$	0.2485	0.3788	0 4642	0.7409
$kT_N/4S^2J$[a]	1.128	1.202	1.323	1.552
T_N (calc.), °K	(116)	188	254	476
T_N (obs.)[b], °K	116	186	292	523

[a] From results for the antiferromagnetic s.c. lattice by ref. (337).
[b] See ref. (180).

those obtained from a statistical treatment.) Therefore a consistent prediction for the series of Néel temperatures would be significant. Meaningful prediction is possible because the common integral $[ba_i|ba_j]$ varies only as the inverse cube of the cation separations and can therefore be assumed constant for the entire series, the lattice parameters for the series being of comparable magnitude. The value of this integral that is required to fit the transition temperature of

MnO is approximately 0.1 eV. The results of Nesbet's calculations are given in Table XIII. Although the agreement between observed and calculated Néel temperatures is quite good, it is important to realize that U_{AA} has been estimated only for a three-atom cluster, and considerable modification of this term can be anticipated for a solid where the clusters are located in the electrostatic Madelung field of the crystal.

3. 90° Cation-Anion-Cation Interactions

If the octahedral interstices of two neighboring cations share a common edge, then there is a direct overlap of the d_{xy} (or d_{yz} or d_{zx}) orbitals of the two cations (see Fig. 43(a)). In this case the anion plays a less obvious role in the delocalization-superexchange process: The transfer integral for t_{2g} electrons varies as the overlap of the t_{2g} orbitals of the two cations rather than as the product of their respec-

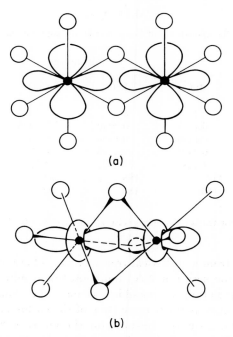

(a)

(b)

Fig. 43. Symmetry relations for overlapping orbitals of cations in octahedral sites that share (a) a common edge and (b) a common face.

CASE	OUTER-ELECTRON CONFIGURATION	DELOCALIZATION SUPEREX.			CORRELATION SUPEREX.			SUM	
		t_{2g}–t_{2g}	e_g–t_{2g}	e_g–e_g	via s	via $p\sigma, p\pi$	via $p\sigma, p\sigma'$	OXIDES	CHLORIDES
#1	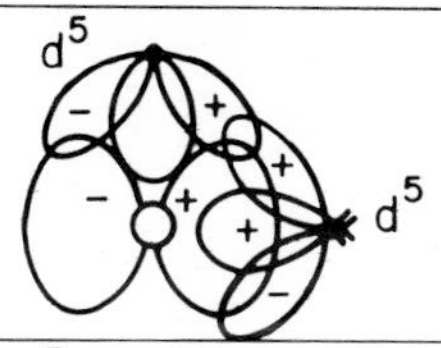 d^5 / d^5	⇄	⇄	⇄	⇄	⇄	[⇄]	⇄ ~200°K	⇄ ~50°K
#2	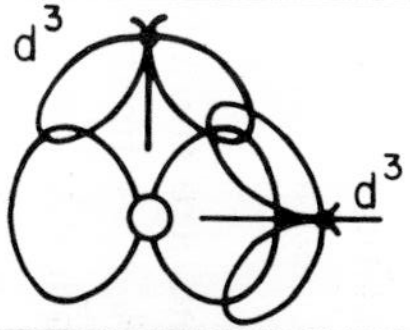 d^3 / d^3	⇄	[⇄]	—	⇄	[⇄]	[⇄]	⇄ ~300°K	⇄ ~50°K
#3	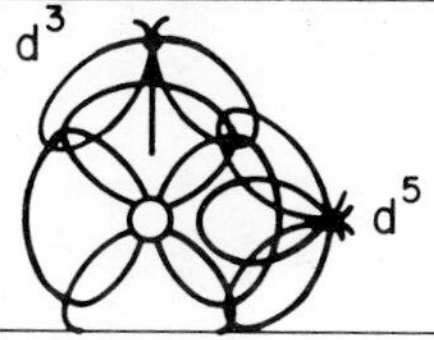 d^3 / d^5	⇄	(⇄)	[⇄]	⇄	(⇄)	[⇄]	⇄ ~100°K	?
#4	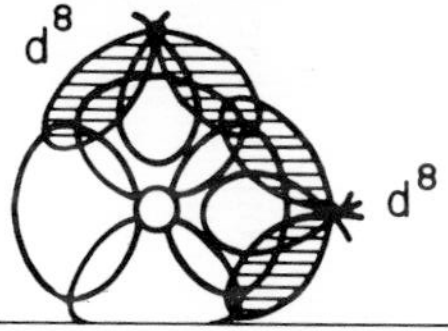 d^8 / d^8	—	[⇄]	⇄	⇄	—	[⇄]	⇄ AND ⇄	⇄ ~50°K

Fig. 43 (*continued*). (c) Four illustrative, 90° superexchange interactions.

tive overlap of a given anion orbital. It is for this reason that they have been referred to as cation- -cation interactions (216). Although the magnitude of the transfer integral is therefore very sensitive to cation- -cation separation and difficult to estimate, the signs of the interactions follow from equations 161–163.

Delocalization superexchange between an e_g orbital and a 90° cation can only occur via an intermediary anion orbital. Although considerably smaller, the magnitude of the transfer integral increases with the degree of covalence, as in the 180° case, and the signs of the interactions follow from equations 161–163. The 90° e_g-e_g contribution is enhanced if strong 180° cation-anion-cation interactions are simultaneously present.

The correlation superexchange also contributes to the 90° cation-anion-cation interaction. There are three possible situations: either two anion s orbitals, or two p electrons from the same p orbital ($p\sigma$ for one cation and $p\pi$ for the other), or two p electrons from different p orbitals ($p\sigma$ for each cation) are excited. In the first two cases, the sign of the interaction is the same as for 180° superexchange, the s orbitals coupling the e_g orbitals of the two cations and the p orbitals coupling t_{2g} electrons of one cation with e_g electrons of the other. Because of the smaller radial extension of the s orbital, this contribution is the smaller. The third alternative is weaker than the second unless the t_{2g} orbitals are more than half filled since it requires third-order perturbation theory to correlate, via J^{intra}, the net spin on the oxygen atoms. In this case, electrons of *like* spin are simultaneously excited from the oxygen ion to the e_g orbitals of the coupled cations, and the sign of this superexchange term is just the *opposite* of 180° superexchange. (From correlation of these rules with empirical data, it appears that this contribution may be strongly influenced by strong 180° interactions via the same anion or by hybrid-orbital formation on the anion.)

Four illustrative 90° interactions are shown in Figure 43(c). The final interaction sums are empirical estimates. The cation- -cation distance is shorter for the oxides than the chlorides; and the cation- -cation interactions tend to dominate the 90° superexchange in oxides if the t_{2g} orbitals are half filled. In the case of d^8-d^8 interactions, the empirical data are contradictory for the oxides: NiO has a $\Theta_a/T_N = -3.1$ indicative of antiferromagnetic 90° interactions whereas $NiTiO_3$ has a $\Theta_a \approx 0$, which is indicative of ferromagnetic 90° interactions. This would seem to imply that the simultaneous existence of strong 180° superexchange (NiO case) enhances the e_g-e_g contribution at the expense of the dominant ferromagnetic contribution, which there is probably the $p\sigma$, $p\sigma'$ correlation superexchange.

If two octahedral-site cations share a common face, as in the corundum or NiAs structures, the cation--cation interactions may be particularly important since the cation separations are relatively small and the t_{2g} orbital stabilized by the resulting trigonal field is directed through the common face (ψ_0' of equation 68), as shown in Figure 43(b).

Shulman and Knox (573) have obtained the difference in occupancy of the fluorine p_σ and p_π orbitals in $KMnF_3$, $KNiF_3$, and K_2NiCrF_6 by measuring the nuclear magnetic resonance of fluorine in single-crystal specimens. In octahedral-site symmetry, the $Mn^{2+}(3d^5)$ ion participates in both $p\sigma$ and $p\pi$ bonding, the $Ni^{2+}(t_{2g}^6 e_g^2)$ in only $p\sigma$, and the $Cr^{3+}(t_{2g}^3 e_g^0)$ in only $p\pi$. For the three cases, they found the fraction of unpaired $2p\sigma$-$2p\pi$ spins in fluoride orbitals to be f_σ-$f_\pi = (0.18 \pm 0.1)\%$, $(4.95 \pm 0.6)\%$, and $-(4.90 \pm 0.8)\%$, respectively. These results indicate that in $KMnF_3$ the π interactions are nearly as strong as the σ interactions, which implies that 90° superexchange interactions may be of the same order of magnitude as 180° superexchange interactions.

4. Intermediate-Angle Cation-Anion-Cation Interactions

Frequently intermediate cation-anion-cation angles are encountered. In spinels, for example, the predominant A-B interactions are via an angle of $\sim 125°$. In wurtzite structures, the angle is $\sim 109°$. In these cases the simple orthogonality relations diagramed in Figure 41 are no longer valid, and the number of interacting orbitals that must be considered becomes more complicated in practice, though not in principle. From considerations similar to those given above, it is possible to obtain the sign of the interactions. For some cation-anion-cation angle $\alpha_c < 180°$, d^3-d^5 type of coupling must change from ferromagnetic for $\alpha > \alpha_c$ to antiferromagnetic for $\alpha < \alpha_c$. It is reasonable to expect $135° < \alpha_c < 150°$. (From the ferromagnetic coupling in (001) pseudotetragonal planes of MnF_3 with $\alpha = 150°$, and antiferromagnetic A-B coupling in the spinel

$MnCr_2O_4$, $125° < \alpha_c < 150°$ indicated.) Similarly d^3-d^3 cation-anion-cation coupling probably changes from antiferromagnetic to ferromagnetic in the range $125° < \alpha_c < 150°$.

5. *Cation-Anion-Anion-Cation Interactions*

If a pair of cations is separated by two anions, delocalization superexchange is still possible, though very much weakened, since the cation d orbitals spread out over the entire anion with which they form a partial covalent bond. Correlation superexchange is also weakened by the anion-anion correlation factor. Polarization superexchange may be competitive in this case, but it is cooperative. It follows that *the rules for the sign of 180° cation-anion-anion-cation interactions are the same as those for 180° cation-anion-cation interactions, but the magnitude is reduced, probably by an order of magnitude.*

6. *Anisotropic Superexchange*

Moriya (451) has extended the Anderson formalism for superexchange to include spin-orbit coupling in the perturbation Hamiltonian that appears in the transfer integral b_{ij} of equation 160. To first order, this leads to a second-order perturbation in the energy of the form

$$\Delta E = J_{ij}\mathbf{S}_i \cdot \mathbf{S}_j + \mathbf{D}_{ij} \cdot [\mathbf{S}_i \times \mathbf{S}_j] + \mathbf{S}_i \cdot \mathbf{\Gamma}_{ij} \cdot \mathbf{S}_j \qquad (167)$$

where the scalar J_{ij} is the isotropic superexchange of equations 161, 162, 163 and the magnitudes of the vector and tensor quantities are

$$D_{ij} \sim J_{ij}(\Delta g/g) \qquad \Gamma_{ij} \sim J_{ij}(\Delta g/g)^2 \qquad (168)$$

Here g is the gyromagnetic ratio and Δg is its deviation from the free-electron value $g = 2$. The last term represents a symmetric, pseudo-dipolar interaction. The term in $\mathbf{D}_{ij}$ is seen to favor canted-spin configurations over collinear, antiferromagnetic configurations. Therefore this term is just the antisymmetric spin-coupling term first suggested by Dzialoshinski (161,162) from symmetry arguments. As was pointed out in Chapter II, such a canting is essential for a parasitic ferromagnetism that is an intrinsic property of the crystal. The vector $\mathbf{D}_{ij}$, which is a constant independent of any symmetry operation R, must be in such a direction that a crystal with canted spins $(\mathbf{S}_i \times \mathbf{S}_j \neq 0)$ has an energy that is invariant under the symmetry operations of the collinear antiferromagnetic unit cell $(E(R\mathbf{S}_1, R\mathbf{S}_2, \ldots) = E(\mathbf{S}_1, \mathbf{S}_2, \ldots) = \sum \mathbf{D}_{ij} \cdot \mathbf{S}_i \times \mathbf{S}_j)$. This means that crystal symmetry is of particular importance for the anisotropic coupling. For example, if the line AB, with midpoint C, joins two atoms i and j, then the following rules apply:

1. $\mathbf{D} = 0$ if a center of inversion is located at C.
2. $\mathbf{D} \perp AB$ if a mirror plane perpendicular to AB passes through C.
3. $\mathbf{D} \perp$ mirror plane if the mirror plane includes AB.
4. $\mathbf{D} \perp$ two-fold axis if the two-fold rotation axis is perpendicular to AB at C.
5. $\mathbf{D} \parallel AB$ if AB is an n-fold rotation axis ($n \geq 2$).

C. CRYSTALLOGRAPHIC CONSIDERATIONS

The magnetic interactions cannot be discussed without reference to the crystallographic structure. The crystallographic phase at the melting point is usually determined by the relative ion sizes and the outer s–p electrons. However, below the melting point there are often significant crystallographic changes that reflect ordering of atoms or outer electrons. In transition metal compounds, martensitic phase changes generally reflect an ordering of the outer d electrons. There are eight (and possibly nine) types of electronic ordering that can be distinguished. (Superconducting $\rightleftharpoons$ normal-conducting transitions among collective electrons reflect a tenth type of electronic order.)

1. Ordering of Two Valence States Among Ions of the Same Atom on the Same Sublattice

Such ordering optimizes the Madelung energy. The classic illustration of this effect is found in the spinel $Fe^{3+}[Fe^{2+}Fe^{3+}]O_4$. Ordering of the B-site Fe^{2+} and Fe^{3+} ions into alternate (001) B-site layers below 119°K distorts the crystal to orthorhombic symmetry (248,637,639).

Although Fe_3O_4 is cited as the classical example of this effect, it should be noted that the transition temperature is about four times smaller than is predicted from electrostatic considerations. Also the room-temperature Hall mobilities of the charge carriers are $\sim$0.5 cm^2/V-sec (719), which might be thought to represent narrow-band conductivity. (In Fe_3O_4 there are 3.5 t_{2g} electrons per B-site cation, so that if $R < R_c$, and upper B-site t_{2g} band, which is split from a lower t_{2g} band by intraatomic exchange via the localized e_g electrons, would be one-sixth filled.) However, intermediate mobilities are characteristic of t_{2g}-electron conductivity, and the fact that Fe_3O_4 is a semiconductor, not a metal, indicates that the electrons are localized at high temperatures. Because electron-lattice interactions are strong, there must be a large entropy associated with Landau trapping, and this entropy would reduce the ordering temperature calculated from purely electrostatic considerations. In addition, Van Santen (626a) has argued for short-range ordering above T_t that reduces the long-range-ordering temperature on purely electrostatic grounds. Anderson (19) has shown that all but 5 percent of the long-range Coulomb energy can be achieved by short-range order. In the distorted, low-temperature phase, the Landau trapping is cooperative, and therefore especially large. Since below T_t the activation energy for electron mobility must include both the cooperative Landau trapping energy and the electrostatic ordering energy, there is an abrupt increase in the activation energy for conduction as the temperature is lowered through T_t.

2. *Cooperative Jahn-Teller Ordering*

The physical origins of this effect were discussed in Chapter I. The significance of this phenomenon was first pointed out in studies of spinels (222) and perovskites (213) containing Mn^{3+} ions. (In the original discussion emphasis was placed on ordering of empty $(d_{x^2-y^2}sp^2)$ orbitals for enhanced coordinate-covalent bonding. In the more general ligand-field language, the symmetry of the problem orders the $d_{x^2-y^2}$ orbitals without reference to the various mechanisms that contribute to the ligand field. The sign of the splitting is that given by either a point-charge model or a covalent model.) In spinels, cooperative Jahn-Teller ordering at the Mn^{3+} ($3d^4$) ions causes a distortion to tetragonal $(c/a > 1)$ symmetry, the classic example being $Mn^{2+}[Mn_2^{3+}]O_4$ with $c/a = 1.16$. Many spinels have been investigated for this effect. These are listed in Table XV. In perovskites this effect gives rise to a change from orthorhombic symmetry having $a < c/\sqrt{2} < b$, hereafter called O-orthorhombic, to orthorhombic symmetry having $c/\sqrt{2} < a \leq b$, hereafter called O'-orthorhombic (219).

3. *Spin-Orbit Coupling*

If spin-orbit coupling is present, there must be an ordering of the electron orbits associated with any collinear ordering of the spins. Therefore spin-orbit distortions are usually associated with a magnetic-ordering temperature T_c or T_N. However, they may occur at a $T_t < T_N$ (or T_c) if there is a collinear $\rightleftharpoons$ noncollinear spin-configuration transformation at T_t. This effect manifests itself as a magnetostrictive distortion. Other effects, such as exchange striction and dipole-dipole interactions, may also contribute to the magnetostriction: However, if appreciable spin-orbit effects are present, the magnetostriction is abnormally large and the cooperative distortion gives rise to a small thermal hysteresis of the magnetic-ordering temperature. The classic example of this effect is CoO, which distorts to tetragonal ($c/a < 1$) symmetry below $T_N = 292°K$. This effect has been discussed by Kanamori (319) (see Chapter III, Section I-D).

4. Cation- -Cation Homopolar Bonding

If the cation- -cation separation is $R < R_c$, so that the transition metal compound is metallic at high temperatures, there may be an ordering of the d electrons into homopolar cation- -cation bonds. Such ordering may be cooperative (if it introduces a change in lattice symmetry) or noncooperative. If all the d electrons are tied up in homopolar bonds, the compound becomes semiconducting. Goodenough (216) has pointed out that this phenomenon may be associated with the semiconducting $\rightleftharpoons$ metallic transformations found in VO, V_2O_3, VO_2, Ti_2O_3 (see Chapter III, Section II).

5. Bonding-Band Formation

Because bonding bands in a two-sublattice structure contain greater band-formation energy than metallic bands in a close-packed structure, elements tend to crystallize in structures that permit the formation of half filled bonding bands. (The most stable bonding bands contain two electrons per bond, and this gives rise to the $(8 - N)$ rule for elements of Groups IV, V, VI, and VII.) For transition elements, the critical temperature at which bonding-band formation of the d electrons takes place may be below the melting point. Goodenough (217) suggested that the f.c.tet. $\rightleftharpoons$ f.c.c. transition in γ-Mn and the b.c.c. $\rightleftharpoons$ f.c.c. transition in iron are due to this effect (see Chapter III, Section III).

6. Covalent-Bond Ordering

Rundle (548) has pointed out that resonating, hybrid sp orbitals are probably active in bonding in interstitial carbides and nitrides.

If so, there may be an ordering of the covalent portion of the bond, that is of the s-p hybrid, to give covalent bonding along one axis and either ionic or bonding-band bonding in the perpendicular plane. This type of order seems to occur in CrN (see Chapter III, Section II-B-2). It is, of course, closely related to the ordering cited in Sections I-C-4 and I-C-5.

7. *Three-Membered-Ring Formation*

The formation of an odd-membered ring by like ions, as is found in triangular O_3, is relatively unstable since it does not permit the stabilizing antiparallel-spin correlations that are possible if the atoms form a two-sublattice array such that the near-neighbors of an atom of one sublattice all belong to the other sublattice. The two-sublattice criterion is satisfied in diatomic molecules or in even-membered rings like benzene. However, if the atoms are constrained to form a close-packed plane, as may be the case for cations in a primarily ionic compound, then the elastic energies may stabilize triangular-cluster formation against homopolar pairing, or six-membered-ring formation with one-third of the cations nonbonded. But even then, triangular-cluster formation can only be expected if the intercation distance is $R \approx R_c$. For $R \approx R_0$, metallic bonding with all near neighbors is more stable than triangular-cluster formation since elastic energy favors close packing and no bonding energy is achieved by clustering. Cluster formation that reduces the intercation separation R within a cluster, increasing R between clusters, gives a change in cation-cation binding energy $\Delta E_{\text{binding}}$ that is linear in ΔR and proportional to the curvature of the cation-cation potential-energy curve seen by the binding electrons. At $R = R_0$, this curvature is positive. However, if $R \approx R_c \approx 2R_0$, this curvature is negative. Since $\Delta E_{\text{elastic}}$ is quadratic in ΔR, a finite ΔR can occur to give measurable cluster formation. It has been suggested (220) that this phenomenon accounts for the room-temperature structure (420) of $Mn_2Mo_3O_8$ and the low-temperature phase found in nearly stoichiometric FeS (see Chapter III, Section II-C-4).

8. *Small Cation in a Large Interstice*

Usually an ionic compound crystallizes into a structure that permits optimum packing of the ions. With close packing, the distance between negative and positive ions is as short as possible, and this optimizes the Madelung energy. This effect is sufficiently important that small cations will occupy tetrahedral rather than octahedral interstices, even though this means a reduction in anion coordination from six to four. (This size effect must be distinguished from covalent effects. Covalent bonding favors open structures compatible with electron-pair bonding, ionic bonding favors close-packed structures that optimize the Madelung energy.) However, there are situations where stable tetrahedral sites are not available. In the perovskite structures, for example, the large cations together with the anion sublattice make up a cubic-close-packed array (see Fig. 56(a)): The small cations cannot go to the tetrahedral interstices of this array since they would then have a large-cation near neighbor. Therefore this structure may stabilize a small cation in a relatively large, octahedral interstice. In order to improve the packing, there may be a spontaneous movement of the small cation from the center of symmetry of the interstice toward a face or an edge. This situation can be distinguished from homopolar-bond formation since cations move to increase the Madelung energy, and therefore never move toward one another. These motions give rise to large polarizations, and hence to ferroelectricity or antiferroelectricity. The classical material of this type is the ferroelectric $BaTiO_3$.

9. Low-Spin-State $\rightleftharpoons$ High-Spin-State Transitions

A ninth possible electron-ordering transition could occur at a cation for which $\Delta_{ex} \approx \Delta_c$. Since Δ_c is more sensitive to variations in lattice parameter, it is possible that temperature variations in lattice parameter could induce a low-spin-state $\rightleftharpoons$ high-spin-state transition. Trivalent cobalt in the perovskite $LaCoO_{3-\lambda}$ appears to be such an ion, and it has been suggested (214) that an anomaly in the χ_m vs. T curve of $LaCoO_{3.01}$ at 500°C may be due to such a transition. Such transitions might occur in an opposite sense for Jahn-Teller ions. For example, trivalent manganese might be in a low-spin-state at high temperatures, but become stabilized as Mn^{3+} by a Jahn-Teller distortion of its interstice at low temperatures. The peculiar antiferromagnetic $\rightleftharpoons$ ferromagnetic transition found in $Li_{0.1}Mn_{0.9}Se$ (264,523) may reflect such a transition.

D. ROCK SALT STRUCTURES

1. *Magnetic Properties*

All of the insulator rock salt structures of Table VIII exhibit face-centered ordering of the second kind, which means that the 180° cation-anion-cation interactions are stronger than the 90° interactions. Comparison of the calculated and observed Néel temperatures for the oxides was given in Table XIII. That T_N for α-MnS is greater than that for MnO follows qualitatively from the fact that the S^{2-} ion has a greater tendency for covalent bonding than O^{2-}.

In Chapter II the ratio $|\Theta_a|/T_N$ was found to give a measure of the relative strengths of the 90° interactions. From Table XIV and

TABLE XIV

Sign of the 90° Superexchange Interactions between High-Spin-State Cations in Octahedral Interstices That Share Either a Common Edge or a Common Face

(Interactions involving d^9 and/or low-spin-state cations are small and usually of uncertain sign.)

Electron config.	d^1, d^2, d^3	d^{4a}, d^5	d^6, d^7, d^8
d^1, d^2, d^3	Deloc[b]: ↑ ↓ ; Corr: ↑ ↑	↑ ↓	↑ ↑ [c]
d^{4a}, d^5		↑ ↓	↑ ↑ [c]
d^6, d^7, d^8			↑ ↑ [d]

[a] Quasistatic case.

[b] Decreases more rapidly with increasing cation separation.

[c] An antiferromagnetic 90° correlation superexchange may predominate at larger cation-cation separations.

[d] Strong 180° interactions simultaneously present may reverse the sign of the 90° interactions.

Figure 43(c) the strongest 90° interactions should be between Mn^{2+} ions, and that the delocalization contribution is sensitive to cation separation, being stronger the shorter the cation--cation distance. This is consistent with a maximum $|\Theta_a|/T_N$ for MnO and a regular decrease in $|\Theta_a|/T_N$ on going from MnO to MnS to MnSe. In MnO, $\epsilon = 1$, which means that the 90° near-neighbor interactions are as strong as the 180° next-near-neighbor interactions. In the case of FeO and CoO, the t_{2g} orbitals are more than half filled. This means that cation--cation interactions, though favoring ferromagnetism, are relatively small. They must vanish in NiO, which has full t_{2g} orbitals. The 90° cation-anion-cation interactions correspond to Case 4 of Figure 43(c). With strong 180° interactions simultaneously present, the dominant term is probably the antiferromagnetic e_g-e_g delocalization superexchange term. However, a $|\Theta_a|/T_N \lesssim 1.0$ for FeO and CoO suggests that $\epsilon \leq 0$, or that whatever near-neighbor interaction exists is ferromagnetic. Kanamori (318) has shown that this discrepancy of the simple theory is the result of strong spin-orbit coupling. (Note that spin-orbit coupling quenches out any Jahn-Teller effect for octahedral site $3d^6$ or $3d^7$ ions.) It was pointed out in Chapter I that the Curie law for free atoms, and hence the Curie-Weiss law for solids, depends upon a multiplet separation $\Delta \gg kT$ or $\Delta \ll kT$. In first-order theory, with the interaction of the ^4P level neglected, the ground-state Γ_4 level of Co^{2+} ($3d^7$) is split into three levels corresponding to $J = 1/2, 3/2, 5/2$ (see Fig. 14). The spin-orbit parameter for Co^{2+} is $\lambda \approx -180$ cm^{-1}. With this value, $E_{3/2} - E_{1/2} = 405$ cm^{-1} and $E_{5/2} - E_{1/2} = 1080$ cm^{-1}. Since $kT_N = 204$ cm^{-1} for CoO, this means that $\Delta \approx kT$, so that χ_m is a complicated function of temperature. Kanamori has gone through with the calculation and shown that although the temperature dependence of χ_m is complicated just above T_N, it approximates a Curie-Weiss law for $T > 500°$K. However, the effect of the unquenched angular momentum manifests itself in two ways: The magnetic moment associated with the angular momentum changes the apparent g value, and spin-orbit coupling raises the paramagnetic Curie temperature Θ_a. The influence of spin-orbit coupling on T_N is small, so that lowering the magnitude of Θ_a reduces the ratio $|\Theta_a|/T_N$. Thus the low value of $|\Theta_a|/T_N$ in CoO can be quantitatively accounted for even in the presence of considerable antiferromagnetic coupling between nearest neighbors. (In the case of FeO, quantitative comparison is not possible because the experimental data is rendered unreliable by the instability of FeO.) That these interactions are not negligible is apparent from $|\Theta_a|/T_N \sim 5$ for NiO, in which the spin-orbit interactions are largely quenched by the crystalline fields. Kanamori's calculated atomic moments are $\mu(\text{Co}^{2+}) = 3.83\mu_B$ [to be compared with the experimental $\mu(\text{Co}^{2+}) \approx 3.7\mu_B$ (570)] and $\mu(\text{Fe}^{2+}) = 4.44\mu_B$.

2. *Crystallographic Properties*

The crystallographic features of these compounds are also of interest. The small, trigonal ($\alpha > 60°$) distortions in MnO and NiO below T_N are presumably magnetostrictive effects due to dipole-dipole interactions (spins lie in (111) planes) and spontaneous development of a multidomain structure (344,398,544). In FeO and CoO, on the other hand, strong spin-orbit coupling results in a spin-orbit distortion below the Néel temperature. If the spins are oriented along the [001], or z, axis, maximum spin-orbit coupling results if the t_{2g} hole of a Co^{2+} ion, or the "extra" t_{2g} electron of an Fe^{2+} ion, occupies the orbital ($d_{yz} \pm id_{zx}$). Then spin-orbit distortions would be to tetragonal ($c/a < 1$) symmetry for CoO, but $c/a > 1$ for FeO. If the spins are directed along the [111], maximum spin-orbit coupling results if the Γ_{T3} level of equation 68 is partially occupied. As shown in Figure 44, such an electron ordering would stabilize a trigonal

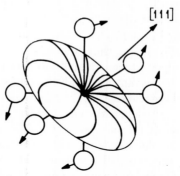

Fig. 44.   Octahedral-site distortion resulting from spin-orbit ordering of a single t_{2g} electron into Γ_{T3} orbitals. Ordering of a single t_{2g} hole into Γ_{T3} orbitals would cause a distortion of opposite sign.

($\alpha < 60°$) distortion for FeO, $\alpha > 60°$ for CoO. Below T_N, CoO has tetragonal ($c/a < 1$) symmetry, and the atomic moments are nearly parallel to the [001]. There is a small deflection from this direction that is presumably due to second-order anisotropy terms. In FeO the spins are directed along the [111] axis, and there is a trigonal ($\alpha < 60°$) deformation below T_N. Dipole-dipole interactions increase the distortion. (In the above discussion, FeO stands for $Fe_{1-\delta}O$ since stoichiometric FeO has not been prepared. Neutron-diffraction work (543a) has shown that the oxygen deficiency is not random through the structure, but is associated with small inclusions of an Fe_3O_4 microphase. Although these inclusions may be responsible for orthorhombic vs. tetragonal symmetry below T_N, they probably do not alter the general considerations presented here.)

E. SPINEL STRUCTURES

Some features of the ferrospinels were discussed in Chapter II. In Figure 45 is shown the orientation of the d orbitals at the two types

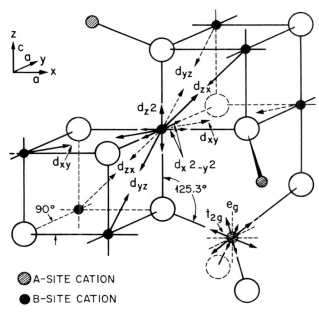

Fig. 45. Orientation of cation d orbitals with respect to the spinel structure. (After Wickham and Goodenough (670).)

of cation, octahedral(B) and tetrahedral(A). It is also apparent from this figure that each B-site ion is subject to a trigonal field, the unique axis varying among all four $\langle 111 \rangle$ axes within a unit cell. This trigonal field stabilizes Γ_{T1} of equation 68 and is sufficiently strong to partially quench the spin-orbit coupling associated with Fe^{2+}. How-

TABLE XV

Room-Temperature Lattice Parameters for Several Spinels Containing Mn^{3+} and/or Cu^{2+} Cations

Compound	Probable formula	Lattice parameters			Ref.
		a	c	c/a	
$CdMn_2O_4$	$Cd^{2+}[Mn_2^{3+}]O_4$	8.22	9.87	1.20	577
$ZnMn_2O_4$	$Zn^{2+}[Mn_2^{3+}]O_4$	8.10	9.24	1.14	577
		8.087	9.228	1.141	82
		8.092	9.244	1.142	414
		8.087	9.254	1.144	668
	at 800°C	8.10	9.35	1.15	291a
$Zn_{0.8}Mg_{0.2}Mn_2O_4$	$Zn_{0.8}Mg_{0.2}[Mn_2^{3+}]O_4$	8.091	9.248	1.143	82
$Zn_{0.5}Mg_{0.5}Mn_2O_4$	$Zn_{0.5}Mg_{0.5}[Mn_2^{3+}]O_4$	8.095	9.278	1.146	82
$MgMn_2O_4$	$Mg_{0.85}Mn_{0.15}^{3+}[Mg_{0.15}^{2+}Mn_{1.85}^{3+}]O_4$	8.07	9.28	1.15	577,(459)
		(8.07)	(9.31)	(1.15)	82
	$Mg_{(1-x)}^{2+}Mn_x^{3+}[Mg_x^{2+}Mn_{2-x}^{3+}]O_4$	8.128	9.201	1.13	38
	at 800°C	8.09	9.32	1.15	291a
$LiMn_2O_4$	$Li^+[Mn^{3+}Mn^{4+}]O_4$	8.246			668
$Li_{0.5}Mn_{2.5}O_4^a$	$Li_{0.5}^+Mn_{0.5}^{3+}[Mn_2^{3+}]O_4^a$	8.132	9.340	1.15	38
$CuMn_2O_4$	$Cu_x^{2+}Mn_{1-x}^{2+}[Cu_{1-x}^{2+}Mn_{1-x}^{4+}Mn_{2x}^{3+}]O_4$, $0 < x < 0.33$	8.33			577,558a
		(8.30)			82
		8.28			378

Compound	Formula				Ref
$NiMn_2O_4$	$Mn^{2+}[Ni^{III}Mn^{3+}]O_4$	8.37			577
		8.38			82
		8.39			38
$CoMn_2O_4$	$Co^{2+}[Mn_2^{3+}]O_4$	8.10	9.31	1.15	82
	$Co_{1-x}^{2+}Mn_x^{2+}[Co_x^{III}Mn_{2-x}^{3+}]O_4$	8.04	9.04	1.12	577
	at 800°C	8.10	9.25	1.14	291a
$FeMn_2O_4$	$Mn_{1-x}^{2+}Fe_x^{2+}[Fe_x^{2+}Fe_{1-2x}^{3+}Mn_{1+x}^{3+}]O_4$	8.31	8.85	1.05	577
	$(0 \leq x \leq 0.33)$	8.49			176
Mn_3O_4	$Mn^{2+}[Mn_2^{3+}]O_4$	8.15	9.44	1.16	577
		8.151	9.450	1.159	82
		8.157	9.454	1.159	414
	at 800°C	8.15	9.54	1.17	291a
γMn_2O_3	$\square_{1/3}Mn_{2/3}^{3+}[Mn_2^{3+}]O_4$	8.1	9.4	1.16	636
$CrMn_2O_4$	$Mn^{2+}[Cr^{3+}Mn^{3+}]O_4$	8.33	8.75	1.05	82
$Zn_{0.5}Ge_{0.5}Mn_2O_4$	$Zn_{0.5}^{2+}Ge_{0.5-x}^{4+}Mn_x^{2+}[Ge_x^{4+}Mn_{1-x}^{2+}Mn^{3+}]O_4$	8.37			440
$ZnCrMnO_4$	$Zn^{2+}[Cr^{3+}Mn^{3+}]O_4$	8.25	8.62	1.04	82
$ZnGaMnO_4$	$Zn^{2+}[Ga^{3+}Mn^{3+}]O_4$	8.23	8.64	1.05	493
$ZnFeMnO_4$	$Zn^{2+}[Fe^{3+}Mn^{3+}]O_4$	8.494			440
$ZnCoMnO_4$	$Zn^{2+}[Co^{2+}Mn^{4+}]O_4$	8.25			82
$ZnNiMnO_4$	$Zn^{2+}[Ni^{2+}Mn^{4+}]O_4$	8.31			82
$GaNiMnO_4$	$Ga^{3+}[Ni^{2+}Mn^{3+}]O_4$	8.38			82
$GaMgMnO_4$	$Mg_x^{2+}Ga_{1-x}^{3+}[Mg_{1-x}^{2+}Ga_x^{3+}Mn^{3+}]O_4$	8.35			82
$Mn_{1.5}FeTi_{0.5}O_4$	$Mn^{2+}[Ti_{0.5}^{4+}Fe_{0.5}^{2+}Fe_{0.5}^{3+}Mn_{0.5}^{3+}]O_4$	8.6025			229

(continued)

TABLE XV (continued)

Compound	Probable formula	Lattice parameters			Ref.
		a	c	c/a	
$ZnMg_{0.5}Ti_{0.5}MnO_4$	$Zn^{2+}[Mg_{0.5}^{2+}Ti_{0.5}^{4+}Mn^{3+}]O_4$	8.397			493
Cr_2CuO_4	$Cu^{2+}[Cr_2^{3+}]O_4$	8.532	7.788	0.913	57,665
Mn_2CuO_4	$Cu_{2/3}^{2+}Mn_{1/3}^{3+}[Cu_{1/3}^{2+}Mn_{5/3}^{3+}]O_4$ (?)	8.31			150
Fe_2CuO_4	$Fe_{0.88}^{3+}Cu_{0.12}^{2+}[Cu_{0.88}^{2+}Fe_{1.12}^{3+}]O_4$	8.22	8.70	1.06	52
Co_2CuO_4	Does not exist				150
Al_2CuO_4	$Cu_{0.56}^{2+}Al_{0.44}^{3+}[Cu_{0.44}^{2+}Al_{1.56}^{3+}]O_4$	8.086			150
Ga_2CuO_4	$Cu_{1-x}^{2+}Ga_x^{3+}[Cu_x^{2+}Ga_{2-x}^{3+}]O_4$	8.39			150
Rh_2CuO_4	$Cu^{2+}[Rh_2^{3+}]O_4$	8.70	7.91	0.91	62

System	a Å at $x = x_t$	c/a for $x > x_t$	x_t	Ref.
$Zn_{2x-1}^{2+}Li_{2-2x}^{+}[Mn_{2x}^{3+}Mn_{2-2x}^{4+}]O_4$		>1	0.60	291
$Zn_x^{2+}Ge_{1-x}^{4+}[Mn_{2-2x}^{2+}Mn_{2x}^{3+}]O_4$	8.50	>1	0.60	668
$Zn_x^{2+}Ge_{1-x}^{4+}[Fe_{2-2x}^{2+}Mn_{2x}^{3+}]O_4$	8.37	>1	0.60, 0.73	440,493
$Zn_x^{2+}Ge_{1-x}^{4+}[Co_{2-2x}^{2+}Mn_{2x}^{3+}]O_4$	8.395	>1	0.65	668
$Co^{2+}[Co_{2-2x}^{III}Mn_{2x}^{3+}]O_4$	8.32	>1	0.60	668
$Mn_y^{2+}Fe_{1-y}^{3+}[Fe_{1-y}^{2+}Fe_{1+y-2x}^{3+}Mn_{2x}^{3+}]O_4, 1 \geq y \geq x$	8.49	>1	0.40–0.60	414,176
$Mn_x^{2+}Fe_{1-x}^{3+}[Co_{1-x}^{2+}Fe_{1-x}^{3+}Mn_{2x}^{3+}]O_4$	8.47	>1	0.55	176
$Mn_x^{2+}Fe_{1-x}^{3+}[Ni_{1-x}^{2+}Fe_{1-x}^{3+}Mn_{2x}^{3+}]O_4$	8.46	>1	0.625	176
$Mg^{2+}[Mn_{2x}^{3+}Al_{2-2x}^{3+}]O_4$	8.34	>1	0.59	291
$Mg_{1-x}^{2+}Mn_x^{2+}[Mn_{2x}^{3+}Al_{2-2x}^{3+}]O_4$	8.32	>1	0.58	291

System		c/a for $x > x_t$	x_t	Ref.
$Cu_x^{2+}M_{1-x}^{2+}[Cr_2^{3+}]O_4$	M = Co, Mg, Zn, Cd	< 1	0.5	150
$Cu_x^{2+}Ni_{1-x}^{2+}[Cr_2^{3+}]O_4^b$		< 1	0.1	150
$Cu^{2+}Cr_{2x}^{3+}M_{2-2x}^{3+}O_4$	M = Fe, Ga	< 1	0.7–0.75	488
	M = Mn	< 1	0.8	150
	M = Al	< 1	0.2	150
$Fe_{1-\delta}^{3+}Cu_\delta^{2+}[Cu_{1-\delta}^{2+}Fe_{x+\delta}^{3+}M_{1-x}^{3+}]O_4$	M = Al	> 1	0.75	150
	M = Cr	> 1	0.65	150
$Fe_{1-\delta}^{3+}Cu_\delta^{2+}[Cu_{x-\delta}^{2+}M_{1-x}^{2+}Fe_{1+\delta}^{3+}]O_4$	M = Ni	> 1	0.65	150
	M = Mg, Co	> 1	0.75	150
$M_{1-x}^{2+}Fe_{x-\delta}^{3+}Cu_\delta^{2+}[Cu_{x-\delta}^{2+}Fe_{2+\delta}^{3+}]O_4$	M = Zn, Cd, Ca	> 1	0.9–0.95	150
$Fe_{1-\delta}^{3+}Cu_\delta^{2+}[Fe_{1.5-x+\delta}^{3+}Cu_{2x-\delta}^{2+}Li_{0.5-x}^{+}]O_4$		> 1	0.3	150
$Cu^{2+}Fe_{2x}^{3+}M_{2-2x}O_4$ has $c/a > 1$ for $x < 0.45$				150
$(CuFe_2O_4)_{1-x}(Mn_3O_4)_x$ has $c/a > 1$ for $x < 0.015$				150

[a] Existence of compound uncertain as preparation has not been reproduced.

[b] Ni[Cr$_2$]O$_4$ is tetragonal ($c/a > 1$), and for $0.125 < x < 0.175$ the system is orthorhombic at room temperature (Ref. 692a). In the system Ni$_x$Fe$_{1-x}$[Cr$_2$]O$_4$, the low-temperature symmetry is tetragonal with $c/a < 1$ for $x \leq 0.20$ and $c/a > 1$ for $x \geq 0.30$, is orthorhombic for $0.23 \leq x \leq 0.26$ (Ref. 692a).

ever, it stabilizes spin-orbit coupling on Co^{2+} since it stabilizes the t_{2g} hole in Γ_{T3}. Therefore the Co^{2+} contribution to the crystalline anisotropy and magnetostriction is abnormally large and increases with decreasing temperature, whereas the Fe^{2+} contribution, though large, is abnormal only in its temperature sensitivity, decreasing with temperature as the Γ_{T3} population decreases. These effects have been discussed quantitatively by Slonczewski (587) and Wolf (693). (With large, bivalent A-site cations, such as Mn^{2+}, the sign of the trigonal field may be reversed to stabilize Γ_{T3}. In this case the anions are both moved and polarized towards the trigonal axes to shield and overcompensate the cation contribution (591). Such a reversal makes the anisotropy associated with an Fe^{2+} ion abnormally large.) More pertinent for this discussion are the magnetic couplings and the Jahn-Teller distortions.

1. *Magnetic Coupling*

From Figure 45 and the schedules of Table XIV, it is anticipated that antiferromagnetic A-B interactions predominate to cause Néel ordering if the B-site cations have half filled e_g orbitals and the A-site cations have half filled t_{2g} orbitals. This is particularly true if the A-site cation is Fe^{3+}, since the energies U_{AA} and U that appear in equations 165, 166 are relatively small for this ion. This conclusion has been widely supported by studies of the ferrospinels (see Chapter II). Nevertheless the 90° B-B interactions are antiferromagnetic and of comparable strength if the B-site t_{2g} orbitals are half filled, or contain one or two electrons. (The trigonal fields stabilize the electron of a d^1 cation in Γ_{T1}, which points along a $\langle 111 \rangle$. Nevertheless antiferromagnetic cation--cation superexchange is still possible.) Therefore there is the possibility that $J_{BB}S_B/J_{AB}S_A > 2/3$, or that there is some noncollinear character to the spins, if some ion other than Fe^{3+}, for example Mn^{2+}, is in the A sites and the B-site ions have half filled t_{2g} orbitals. Evidence of canted spins has been found in the system $Mn^{2+}[Mg_xMn_{1-x}Sn]O_4$ (671).

The A-B interactions are especially weak if the B-site e_g orbitals are empty, and noncollinear spin configurations are anticipated if the B-site $3d^n$ ions have $n \leq 3$. The common occurrence of noncollinear configurations is evident from Table XVI, where the saturation magnetizations of several spinels containing V^{4+} and Cr^{3+} are found to be incompatible with Néel ordering. That the ratio $J_{BB}S_{BB}/J_{AB}S_A$

is critical in the determination of the stable spin configuration is
illustrated experimentally by the systems $NiCr_tFe_{2-t}O_4$, $NiV_tFe_{2-t}O_4$,
$CoCr_tFe_{2-t}O_4$, and $MnCr_tFe_{2-t}O_4$. In the first three systems Néel
ordering is maintained for $t < 1$, whereas it is not present in the latter
system for all $t > 0$ (see Fig. 46). In $MnCr_tFe_{2-t}O_4$, the A-B

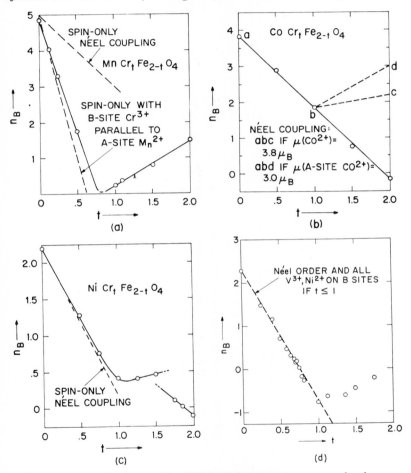

Fig. 46. Magnetization at $T = 0°K$ in Bohr magnetons per molecule n_B vs.
composition parameter t for the four systems $MCr_tFe_{2-t}O_4$ (M = Mn, Co, and Ni)
and $NiV_tFe_{2-t}O_4$. Negative n_B signifies A-site moments predominate. Sign of
n_B for $MnCr_tFe_{2-t}O_4$ with $t > 0.8$ is uncertain. (Experimental points after
Gorter (229) McGuire and Greenwald (426) and Blasse and Gorter (78).)

TABLE XVI

Ferrimagnetic and Crystallographic Data for Several Spinels

Compound[a]	n_B (Néel)	n_B (4°K)[b]	T_c (°K)	Structure (25°C)	a_0	c_0	Ref.
$Co^{2+}[Co_{0.9}^{III}Mn_{1.1}^{3+}]O_4$	1.4	1.1	190	Cubic	8.295		668
$Co^{2+}[Mn_2^{3+}]O_4$	5.0	0.1	85	Tet.	8.157	9.454	668
$Cu_{0.04}^{2+}Fe_{0.96}^{3+}[Cu_{0.96}^{2+}Fe_{1.04}^{3+}]O_4$	1.3	1.3	728	Tet.	8.24	8.68	229
$Mn^{2+}[Cr_2^{3+}]O_4$	1.0	1.20	55	Cubic	8.437		229,664
$Mn^{2+}[Fe_{1.5}^{3+}Cr_{0.5}^{3+}]O_4$	4.0	1.73	483	Cubic	8.498		229
$Mn^{2+}[Fe^{3+}Cr^{3+}]O_4$	3.0	0.25	370	Cubic	8.481		229
$Fe^{2+}[Cr_2^{3+}]O_4$	2.0	0.84	90	Cubic[c]	8.377		402,664
$Co^{2+}[Cr_2^{3+}]O_4$	3.0	0.18	100	Cubic	8.332		426,664
$Ni^{2+}[Cr_2^{3+}]O_4$	4.0	0.33	70	Tet.	8.248	8.454	402,426,664
$Cu^{2+}[Cr_2^{3+}]O_4$	5.0	0.72		Tet.	8.532	7.788	664
$Fe^{3+}[Fe^{2+}Cr^{3+}]O_4$	2.3	2.4	473	Cubic	8.396		151,189
$Fe^{3+}[Co^{2+}Cr^{3+}]O_4$	1.7	1.0		Cubic	8.35		443

$Fe^{3+}[Ni^{2+}Cr^{3+}]O_4$	0.2	0.4	690	Cubic	8.301		402,443
$Mn^{2+}[Mn^{2+}V^{4+}]O_4$	1.0	0.7–0.8		Cubic	8.579		673
$Mn^{2+}[V_2^{3+}]O_4$	2.2	2.05	~56	Cubic	8.520		673
$Fe^{2+}[V_2^{3+}]O_4$	1.2	1.06	110	Cubic[d]	8.454		542
$Fe^{2+}[Fe^{2+}V^{4+}]O_4$	1.3	0.76	448	Cubic	8.421		542
$Co^{2+}[V_2^{3+}]O_4$	0.2	1.20		Cubic	8.411		542
$Co^{2+}[Co^{2+}V^{4+}]O_4$	1.7	0.21	158	Cubic	8.379		542
$Mn^{2+}[Mn_2^{3+}]O_4$	3.0	1.85	43	Tet.	8.15	9.44	157

[a] Probable chemical formula.

[b] n_B is the measured magnetization at 4°K in Bohr magnetons per molecule. Calculated magnetizations for Néel ordering n_B (Néel) follow from spin-only atomic moments except for B-site $Ni^{2+}(2.2\ \mu_B)$, $Co^{2+}(3.7\ \mu_B)$, $Fe^{2+}(4.3\ \mu_B)$, $V^{3+}(1.4\ \mu_B)$.

[c] Tetragonal $(c/a < 1)$ below $-138 \pm 3°C$.

[d] Tetragonal $(c/a < 1)$ below ~111°K.

interactions are weaker (lower T_N) because the A-site cation is Mn^{2+}. More important, perhaps, is the fact that the initial Cr^{3+} ions of this system see only strong B-B interactions as all B-site ions have half filled t_{2g} orbitals. In the first three systems Cr^{3+}– –Ni^{2+}, V^{3+}– –Ni^{2+}, and Cr^{3+}– –Co^{2+} B-B interactions are ferromagnetic, and it is only for $t > 1$, where the Cr^{3+} (with strong B-site, ligand-field stabilization) are forcing Ni^{2+} and Co^{2+} into the A sites, that the number of Cr^{3+}– –Cr^{3+} interactions becomes sufficiently great to destroy the Néel order. [It is to be noted that delocalization must be assumed to dominate the 90° interactions in oxides. This is supported not only by the magnetic order of Cr_2O_3, but also by evidence for noncollinear spins in Cr-containing ferrogarnets (63).]

Several spinels in which only B-B interactions are present have been studied magnetically. The cubic spinels $Zn[Cr_2]O_4$ ($a_0 = 8.31$ a) and $Zn[Fe_2]O_4$ ($a_0 = 8.42$ A) have, respectively, $T_N = 15°K$ and $9°K$ (124), the larger Néel temperature being associated with the shorter cation- -cation separation. That T_N is low is consistent with the fact that long-range antiferromagnetic order among the B sites of a cubic spinel cannot be achieved with nearest-neighbor interactions alone (19). More significant, therefore, is the fact that $\Theta_a \approx -300°K$ for $Zn[Cr_2]O_4$, but is only $\Theta_a \approx -50°K$ in $Zn[Fe_2]O_4$. Tetragonal $Zn[Mn_2]O_4$ ($c/a > 1$) has a $T_N \sim 200°K$ (82), a fact that is compatible with cooperative antiferromagnetic coupling within (001) planes where the cation- -cation interactions are enhanced by the distortion. (Reduced, but still competitive, B-B interactions out of this plane probably induce a complex magnetic order.) Cubic $Zn[Cr_2]S_4$ ($a_0 = 9.983$ A), on the other hand, is paramagnetic (402). These data indicate that the cation- -cation superexchange is quite sensitive to cation separation. This, of course, follows from equation 161, since the effect falls off as the square of the orbital overlap. If the dominant mechanism were via an anion intermediary, the effect would be much less sensitive to cation separation, especially as S^{2-} is a more covalent anion than O^{2-}.

2. B-Site Jahn-Teller Effects

(a) It was pointed out in Chapter I that $Cu^{2+}(3d^9)$ and $Mn^{3+}(3d^4)$ are Jahn-Teller ions. In an octahedral interstice, Cu^{2+} has an e_g hole, Mn^{3+} an e_g hole in the half-shell stabilized by intraatomic exchange (Hund's rule), and the orbital angular momentum is quenched by the cubic fields. Therefore the ground state may be stabilized by a splitting of the doubly degenerate Γ_3 level. It was pointed out that ligand-field considerations alone are unable to distinguish whether stabilization of the d_{z^2} or the $d_{x^2-y^2}$ orbital is greatest. To answer this question, Kanamori (322) considered interactions between the electron order and the normal modes of vibration about an octahedral interstice. Van Vleck (629) has shown that the normal vibration modes that split the Γ_3 level are those illustrated in Figure 47. Positive Q_3 stabilizes d_{z^2}, negative Q_3 stabilizes $d_{x^2-y^2}$. Q_2 stabilizes a mixture of the two. If polar coordinates ρ and Θ in the space of the coordinates Q_3, Q_2 are defined ($Q_3 = \rho \cos \Theta$, $Q_2 = \rho \sin \Theta$), then to first order in the coupling between modes Q_2, Q_3 and orbitals $d_{z^2}, d_{x^2-y^2}$, the ground-state energy for an isolated MX_6 complex is independent of Θ. (M is a $3d^4$ or $3d^9$ cation and X is an anion.) This means that the ground state is not uniquely determined, but corresponds to any point on the circle with radius $\rho = \delta$, where δ is proportional to the coupling constant g and the inverse root of the stiffness constant C associated with the vibrations. A consequence of this is that the degeneracy may be removed by resonance between the stable configurations. The degeneracy may also be removed by the addition of anharmonic terms in the potential energy and higher order coupling terms, which makes the total energy at $T = 0°K$

$$E = -\delta^2\{C/2 + (A_3\delta - B_3) \cos 3\Theta\} \qquad (169)$$

where A_3 is generally positive (484). With a point-charge model, B_3 is calculated to be positive (394), and the sign of the $\cos 3\Theta$ term is uncertain. However, if covalency favors square-bond formation at Cu^{2+} or Mn^{3+}, as is probable, B_3 is negative. In this case the stable state unambiguously favors $\cos 3\Theta = 1$, or $\Theta = 0, \pm2\pi/3$. This corresponds to Q_3 ($c/a > 1$) with c axis oriented along the z, x, and y axes, respectively. Therefore the Jahn-Teller effect should unambiguously stabilize a static distortion of the octahedral molecule to tetragonal ($c/a > 1$) symmetry, provided the temperature is low enough that the entropy contribution to the free energy does not stabilize the dynamic Jahn-Teller effect. (The magnitude of the critical temperature depends upon the magnitude of the anharmonic contributions.) One exception to this rule appears to occur in the crystal K_2CuF_4 (352) where the octahedral interstices of the Cu^{2+} ions are distorted to tetragonal ($c/a < 1$) symmetry corresponding

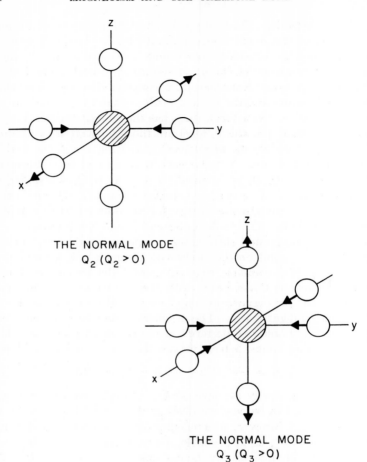

(a)

Fig. 47.   Normal vibrational modes Q_2 and Q_3 compatible with Jahn-Teller splitting of the degenerate ground state of an octahedral-site $3d^4$ and $3d^9$ cation. (a) Definition of modes for a free ion complex.   (See following pages for Figs. 47(b) and 47(c).)

to a $Q_3 < 0$ mode. However, the interstices of the Ni_2^+ ions in isomorphous K_2NiF_4 are similarly distorted, though to a lesser extent. Since octahedral-site Ni^{2+} is not a Jahn-Teller ion, it appears that in this structure the Cu^{2+} ion is subject to tetragonal ligand fields even in the absence of the Jahn-Teller effect. These fields determine the sign of Q_3.

(b) The spinel structure favors a cooperative distortion in which all octahedral interstices of the same sublattice deform parallel to one another. In this case the elastic energy, to the same approximation as equation 169, becomes

$$E = -N\delta^2 \{C'/2 + (K_1\delta + K_2) \cos 3\theta\} \qquad (170)$$

where $C' \equiv (c_{11} - c_{12})\Omega/N$, c_{11} and c_{12} are elastic constants, and Ω/N

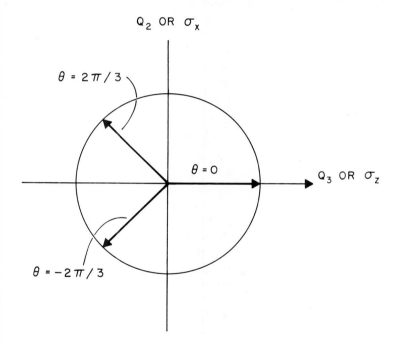

(b)

Fig. 47 (continued). (b) The Q_2-Q_3 plane for a spinel.

is the volume per unit cell. Thus if $(K_1\delta + K_2) > 0$, the crystal distortion is to tetragonal $(c/a > 1)$ symmetry.

The fact that Mn^{3+} or Cu^{2+} ions occupying more than a critical fraction of the spinel B sites produce distortions from cubic to tetragonal $(c/a > 1)$ symmetry has been well established, as can be seen from Table XV. In fact Satomi (552) has measured the oxygen parameters in Mn_3O_4 to demonstrate directly that it is the octahedral sites that are distorted; that the tetrahedral sites resist the distortion.

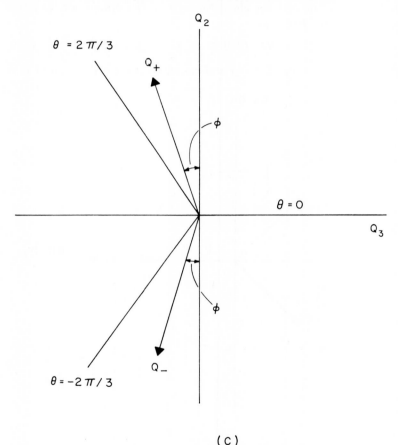

(c)

Fig. 47 *(continued)*.   (c) The Q_2-Q_3 plane for a perovskite. (After Kanamori (322).)

Wickham and Croft (668) found that in several oxide spinels the critical fraction of B sites that must be occupied by Mn^{3+} ions is $0.6 < f_c < 0.65$. Investigation of a wider range of materials (see Table XV) indicates that in general $f_c > 0.5$ but that $f_c < 0.5$ may occur. In Figure 48 the temperature T_t for the tet. $\rightleftharpoons$ cubic transition is plotted against composition for the system

$$Zn_xGe_{1-x}[Co^{2+}_{2-2x}Mn^{3+}_{2x}]O_4.$$

Simple extension of the Kanamori formalism leads to a linear varia-

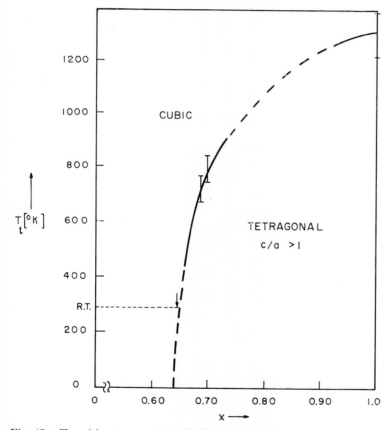

Fig. 48. Transition temperature T_t for martensitic tetragonal $(c/a > 1) \rightleftharpoons$ cubic transitions in the system $Zn_xGe_{1-x}[Co^{2+}_{2-2x}Mn^{3+}_{2x}]O_4$. (After Wickham and Croft (668).)

tion of T_t with concentration of the Jahn-Teller ions.   The transition with composition from cubic to tetragonal symmetry is seen to be quite abrupt.   (A similar plot for Cu^{2+} is shown in Figure 55(b).) This fact, together with site-preference energies, can serve as a useful aid in the determination of the valencies in these systems.   However, care must be exercised.   For example, B-site Fe^{2+} and Co^{2+} ions, which have partially filled, but not half full, t_{2g} orbitals may alter f_c, but the sign of the alteration is not obvious since the relative magnitudes of spin-orbit coupling and trigonal and tetragonal ligand-field splittings must be considered.   Cation size also plays a small, but observable role.   Also, the simultaneous presence of A-site Jahn-Teller ions must strongly influence f_c.   [It has been suggested in the literature that, if the A-site ions are stabilized by $c/a < 1$, they tend to quench static Jahn-Teller effects.   The fact that $CuMn_2O_4$ is cubic has been claimed to represent such quenching.   However, the compound is not a normal spinel, as originally reported, and its probable ionic distribution is (558a) $[Cu_x^{2+}Mn_{1-x}^{2+}][Cu_{1-x}^{2+}Mn_{1-x}^{4+}Mn_{2x}^{3+}]O_4$, where $0 < x < 0.33$.]

For Cu^{2+} in $CuFe_2O_4$ the apparent critical fraction is $0.2 < f_c < 0.3$ (52,222,489).   This fraction is determined by quenching the specimen from different annealing temperatures so as to vary the proportion of Cu^{2+} ions on A and B sites.   However, substitution of a relatively small amount of a nonmagnetic A-site cation for Cu^{2+} destroys the tetragonal distortions at room temperature.   For $M_yCu_{1-y}Fe_2O_4$, where $M = Zn, Cd, Ca$, tetragonal $(c/a > 1)$ symmetry is only observed for $y < 0.1$ (see Table XV).   Because these ions are relatively large, they increase the spinel u parameter to make Madelung energies favor a greater fraction of the Cu^{2+} ions on the A sites (see Chapter III, Section I-A-3).   These results suggest that the low apparent f_c of $CuFe_2O_4$ may be largely due to cooperative distortions about A-site Cu^{2+} that have the sign of spin-orbit effects (see Chapter III, I-E-4).

(c) The temperature dependence of the cooperative distortions is analogous to that of the spontaneous magnetization.   The distortion should be determined by the thermal averages over the d_{z^2} and $d_{x^2-y^2}$ states.   If σ_z is an ordering parameter for the Q_3 mode, and u_z is the normalized sum of the strains associated with the $Q_3 > 0$ mode, then the distortion is given by

$$u_z(T) = u_{z0}\langle\sigma_z\rangle_T \tag{171}$$

where u_{z0} is the distortion at $T = 0°K$ and $\langle \sigma_z \rangle_T$ is a thermal average. Kanamori (322) has calculated $\langle \sigma_z \rangle_T$ to derive the temperature dependencies shown in Figure 49, where the constants k_1 and k_2 are propor-

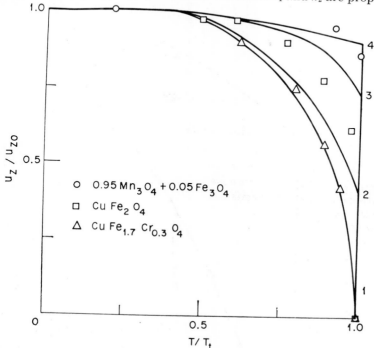

Fig. 49.   Curves of u_z/u_{z0} vs. T/T_t and experimental data for several spinels. Curve 1: $k_1 = k_2 = 0$; Curve 2: $k_1 = 0.25$, $k_2 = 0$; Curve 3: $k_1 = 0$, $k_2 = 0.175$; Curve 4: $k_1 = 0$, $k_2 = 0.263$.   The constants k_1, k_2 are defined by $k_1 = 3K_1\delta/C$ and $k_2 = K_2/C$, where K_1, K_2 are defined by equation 170, $C = \Omega(c_{11} - c_{12})/N$ is a stiffness constant per octahedral-site cation, g_0 is a coupling constant, and $\delta = g_0/C^{1/2}$.   (After Kanamori (322).)

tional to the $K_1\delta$ and K_2 appearing in equation 170.   If $k_1 = k_2 = 0$, the transition is of the second kind, like the magnetic transition of a ferromagnet.   In the presence of vibrational and/or coupling anisotropies, the transition is of the first kind.   Lattice-parameter variations give definite evidence of a two-phase region near the critical composition for tetragonal distortions, as can be seen from Figure 50. This indicates a transition of the first kind.   A more definite indication that the transitions are first order and that the k_1, k_2 are large

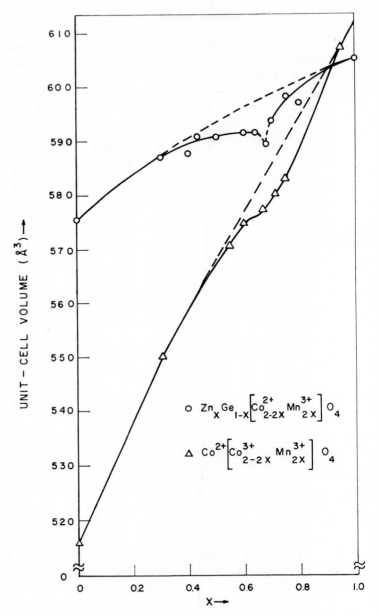

Fig. 50.   Unit cell as a function of composition for the systems
$Zn_xGe_{1-x}[Co^{2+}_{2-2x}Mn^{3+}_{2x}]O_4$.   (After Wickham and Croft (668).)

is found in the fact that the c/a ratios of several end-member manganites are nearly temperature independent up to the transition temperature (291a).

Kanamori's theory does not consider static, local distortions around each Jahn-Teller ion at high temperatures without anisotropy. Without anisotropy, a local distortion corresponds to a point on a circle in the Q_3-Q_2 plane (Fig. 47). Similarly a degenerate electronic state corresponds to a point on a circle in $d_{z^2}d_{x^2-y^2}$ space. The dynamic Jahn-Teller effect corresponds to a coupling between vibrational and electronic states that is represented by a circling in phase of the points in the two spaces. Therefore the possible alternative distortions are not properly described as orientations of the tetragonal axis among the three principal, crystallographic axes. Static, local distortions of this latter description correspond to the case of *strong local anisotropy*, in which the anisotropy energy is much larger than kT_t, where T_t is the transition temperature. It was used by Finch, Sinha, and Sinha (176), and in a more correct manner by Wojtowicz (689), to obtain a temperature dependence similar to that shown in Figure 49. However, it seems unlikely that the extreme anisotropy case is the correct description in most solids (see Chapter III, Section I-F). The abnormally large $\overline{u^2}$ found (117) in $MnFe_2O_4$, which has some B-site Mn^{3+} ions, may be attributed to dynamic as well as to static Jahn-Teller effects.

3. The System $Co_{3-x}Mn_xO_4$

In Figure 51 are shown magnetic and crystallographic data for the system $Co_{3-x}Mn_xO_4$. These data contain four points of interest. First, Co_3O_4 is nonmagnetic because the B-site ligand-field splitting is $\Delta_c > \Delta_{ex}$, so that the spins of the B-site, trivalent cobalt atoms are quenched (132). That is $Co^{3+}(t_{2g}^4e_g^2) \rightarrow Co^{III}(t_{2g}^6e_g^0)$ so that Co^{III} is diamagnetic. (Arabic valencies refer to high-spin state, Roman valencies to low-spin state.) Since the A-A interactions are negligible, $Co^{2+}[Co_2^{III}]O_4$ remains paramagnetic to 4.2°K. Site preferences give as the ideal formula for the system

$$Co^{2+}[Co_{2-x}^{III}Mn_x^{3+}]O_4 \qquad \text{for } 0 \leq x \leq 2$$

$$Mn_{x-2}^{2+}Co_{3-x}^{2+}[Mn_2^{3+}]O_4 \qquad \text{for } x > 2$$

Second, the crystallographic data of Figure 51 show a typical variation with Mn³⁺ content of the room temperature lattice parameters.

Third, addition of paramagnetic Mn³⁺ ions into the B sites initiates A-B coupling of sufficient magnitude that Néel ordering occurs in the

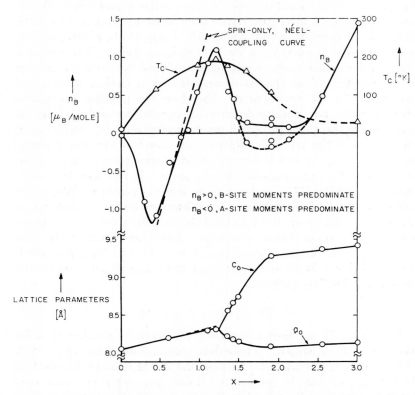

Fig. 51. Saturation magnetization, n_B, expressed as the number of Bohr magnetons per molecule, Curie Temperature T_c, and lattice parameter for the system $Co_{3-x}Mn_xO_4$. (After Goodenough (215), data from Wickham and Croft (668).)

cubic phase for $x > 0.5$. Since the number of paramagnetic A-site ions is initially greater than the number of B-site ions, the A-site moment predominates for $x < 0.75$. However, the large Mn³⁺ moment causes the magnetization to decrease through a compensation composition, and then increase as more Mn³⁺ are added.   In the cubic phase there is no static ordering of the single e_g electrons at a Mn^{3+} ion, and relatively strong A-B coupling results.

Fourth, the magnetization cannot be accounted for by Néel ordering in any of the tetragonal spinels. Electron ordering at the Mn^{3+} ions in the tetragonal phase introduces the possibility of anisotropic, but all antiferromagnetic A-B interactions. The distortion increases the cation--cation contribution to the 90° Mn^{3+}--Mn^{3+} interactions in (001) planes, but decreases it along the [011] axes, so that large anisotropies are expected in the B-B interactions. This gives rise to complex spin configurations, as discussed in Chapter II. (Tetragonal distortions in $CuFe_2O_4$ do not destroy Néel order since Cu^{2+}, with full t_{2g} orbitals, couples ferromagnetically with 90° Fe^{3+}.) Some of the interesting magnetic properties that may accompany these complex distortion-induced spin configurations have been presented by Dwight and Menyuk (157) in a magnetic study of a natural crystal of Mn_3O_4. Similar effects have also been found in $(M_xMn_{1-x})Mn_2O_4$, where M = Zn, Mg (296).

Cossee and Van Arkel (133) have pointed out that tetrahedral-site Co^{2+} does not obey a Curie-Weiss law in the paramagnetic region because the triplet Γ_5 and Γ_4 levels, which are at distances of only $\sim$4000 cm^{-1} and $\sim$7000 cm^{-1} from the singlet ground state Γ_2 (see Fig. 12), introduce a measurable high-frequency, temperature-independent component into χ_m that is given by equation 17.

4. A-Site Jahn-Teller Effects versus Spin-Orbit Coupling

It was emphasized in Chapter I that if the orbital angular momentum is not quenched by the ligand fields of the undistorted crystal (t_{2g} orbitals in cubic fields partially filled, but not half full), the spin-orbit energy $\lambda\mathbf{L}\cdot\mathbf{S}$ may be comparable to, or greater than, any Jahn-Teller deformation stabilization. Jahn-Teller deformations stabilize nondegenerate orbitals. Therefore they order the electrons into a state that has zero contribution to the angular momentum from the cubic Γ_5 states, so that spin-orbit coupling is largely quenched. Spin-orbit coupling, on the other hand, stabilizes a degenerate level. [Then $\phi(r)$ is complex. Only the imaginary part of $\phi(r)$ contributes to $\mathbf{L}\cdot\mathbf{S}$, L_z being imaginary.] This gives a deformation of opposite sign, and a stabilization energy δ_t due to cooperative deformations from cubic symmetry that may accompany collinear spins and spin-orbit coupling is only half as great as the Jahn-Teller

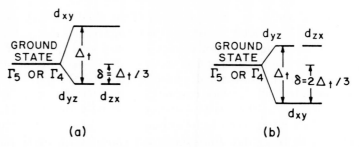

Fig. 52.   Deformation stabilization of a tetragonal interstice.   (a) Spin-orbit ordering given one t_{2g} electron or Jahn-Teller ordering given two t_{2g} electrons. (b) Jahn-Teller ordering given one t_{2g} electron or spin-orbit ordering given two t_{2g} electrons.

stabilizations, because the three t_{2g} levels that are split by trigonal or tetragonal distortions conserve their total energy (see Fig. 52). Therefore if the spins are collinear and $(\delta_t + \lambda \mathbf{L} \cdot \mathbf{S}) > 2\delta_t$, or $\lambda \mathbf{L} \cdot \mathbf{S} > \delta_t$, any deformation should have the sign of the spin-orbit effect.   This was found to be the case for FeO and CoO.   On the other hand, distortions of the Jahn-Teller type are associated with A-site Ni^{2+} and Cu^{2+} in the spinels $Ni[Cr_2]O_4$ $(c/a = 1.04)$ (149), $Ni[Rh_2]O_4$ $(c/a = 1.038)$ (62), $Cu[Rh_2]O_4$ $(c/a = 0.91)$ (62), and $Cu[Cr_2]O_4$ $(c/a = 0.91)$ (57,442).   Neutron diffraction studies by Prince (531,533) have confirmed the fact that the distortions are due to deformations of the tetrahedral interstices in these compounds; in fact, the octahedral coordination around a Cr^{3+} ion is more nearly perfect than in most cubic spinels.   This means that the spins are not collinear, or $\lambda \mathbf{L} \cdot \mathbf{S} < \delta_t$ in these spinels.   Dunitz and Orgel (156) first pointed out that Jahn-Teller ordering of the partially filled t_{2g} orbitals could account for the sign of the observed distortions (see Fig. 53), but they failed to discuss the spin-orbit couplings that are simultaneously present.   Actually it is only because the two effects give distortions of opposite sign that it is possible to distinguish the dominant perturbation to be associated with a given deformation (221).   The fact that $Ni[Cr_2]O_4$ carries the sign of the Jahn-Teller effect whereas FeO, which is analogous, the sign of the spin-orbit coupling suggests that for a free-ion complex the stabilization is about equal for different signs of the deformation.   This speculation has been confirmed for the case of tetrahedral-site Ni^{2+} by detailed calculations (37).   This means that the cooperative terms in the Hamil-

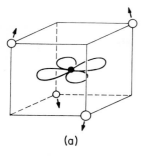 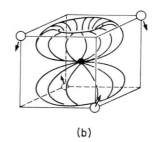

(a)   (b)

Fig. 53. Tetrahedral-site distortions due to ordering of a single electron. (Ordering of a single hole gives distortions of opposite sign.) (a) Jahn-Teller ordering into a d_{xy} orbital. (b) Spin-orbit ordering into the $(d_{yz} \pm id_{zx})$ orbitals.

tonian, $V_\lambda + \sum_{ij} J_{ij} \mathbf{S}_i \cdot \mathbf{S}_j$, may determine the sign of the distortion in any particular case. V_λ governs δ_t, the deformation stabilization per Jahn-Teller ion. This term decreases sensitively with the fraction of cations that are Jahn-Teller ions. The exchange term governs $\lambda \mathbf{L} \cdot \mathbf{S}$ in that the spin-orbit effects are optimum for magnetic ordering that aligns the spins on the Jahn-Teller ions parallel to the axis of the angular momentum vector. Whereas the spins are ordered collinear below T_N in FeO and CoO, in $Ni[Cr_2]O_4$ competing exchange forces give a noncollinear spin configuration below T_c. In $Ni[Rh_2]O_4$ and $Cu[Rh_2]O_4$ the Rh^{III} ions are diamagnetic, so that there is no magnetic ordering to very low temperatures. Thus $\lambda \mathbf{L} \cdot \mathbf{S}$ is relatively small in these spinels, which is compatible with $\lambda \mathbf{L} \cdot \mathbf{S} < \delta_t$. However, if the fraction of A cations that are Jahn-Teller ions is reduced, thus reducing δ_t, and the magnetic coupling is simultaneously altered so as to give collinear A-site spins, then a change in the sign of the A-site distortion may occur.

The temperature dependence of A-site Jahn-Teller distortions has also been discussed by Kanamori (322). The phase transition in this case is of the first kind. Comparison of theory and experiment for $CuCr_2O_4$ is shown in Figure 54.

5. The Systems $NiCr_tFe_{2-t}O_4$ and $Fe_{3-x}Cr_xO_4$

In the system $NiCr_tFe_{2-t}O_4$, with ideal chemical formulae

$$Fe^{3+}[Ni^{2+}Fe^{3+}_{1-t}Cr^{3+}_t]O_4 \qquad \text{for } 0 \leq t \leq 1$$

$$Fe^{3+}_{2-t}Ni^{2+}_{t-1}[Ni^{2+}_{2-t}Cr^{3+}_t]O_4 \qquad \text{for } 1 \leq t \leq 2$$

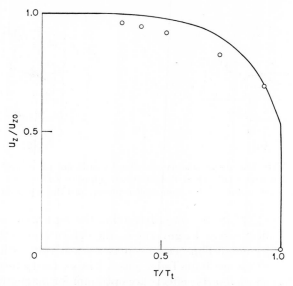

Fig. 54.   Temperature dependence of cooperative, tetragonal ($c/a < 1$) distortions in $CuCr_2O_4$.   (After Kanamori (322).)

the deformation stabilization per A-site Ni^{2+} decreases with increasing
Fe^{3+} content.   Further, Pickart and Nathans (518), who made a
neutron diffraction study of compositions with $t = 1.0, 1.5$ at $4.2°K$,
have reported collinear A-site spins at these temperatures, even
though the magnetization of the B sites was lower than can be
accounted for by a parallel alignment of spins.   (With disordered
ionic constituents on the B sites, the apparent B-site collinear array
is probably due either to disordered Yafet-Kittel angles or to a spin
reversal of some Cr^{3+} ions (670).)   This suggests that at some $T_t \leq T_N$
crystalline anisotropy and magnetostrictive effects associated with
spin-orbit coupling have stabilized collinear A-site spins.   If this is
so, then there must be a crystallographic distortion for $T < T_t$ that
has the sign of the spin-orbit effect and there must be a critical composition t_c such that for $1 < t < t_c$ (where $1.5 < t_c < 2.0$) the spinel
is tetragonal ($c/a < 1$) and for $t > t_c$ it is tetragonal ($c/a > 1$).
Long-range order is established by the magnetic coupling if spin-orbit
effects predominate, so that only a small fraction of A cations need be
Ni^{2+} for a cooperative spin-orbit distortion to occur.   McGuire and

Greenwald (426) have indeed found tetragonal ($c/a < 1$) distortions for $1 < t \le 1.85$. In the range $1.75 \le t < 2.0$ they found tetragonal ($c/a > 1$) symmetry, which is characteristic of Jahn-Teller distortions. In the compositional range $1.75 \le t \le 1.85$, both distortions appear to be present simultaneously. The low-temperature phase appears to be orthorhombic, which is compatible with two tetragonal distortions of opposite sign having mutually perpendicular axes. The various transition temperatures for this system are summarized in Figure 55.

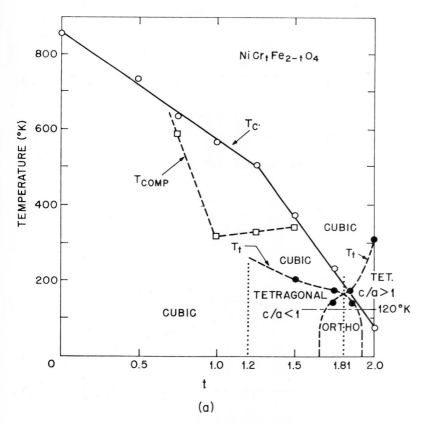

(a)

Fig. 55. (a), (b), and (c) Crystallographic and magnetic data for the system $NiCr_tFe_{2-t}O_4$. (After McGuire and Greenwald (426).) (See following pages for Figs. 55(b)–55(d).)

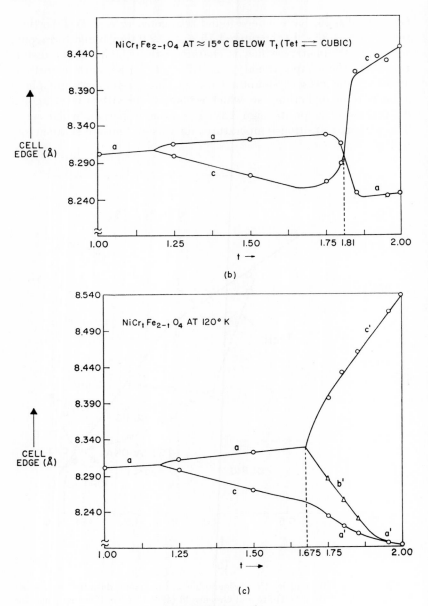

Fig. 55 *(continued)*.

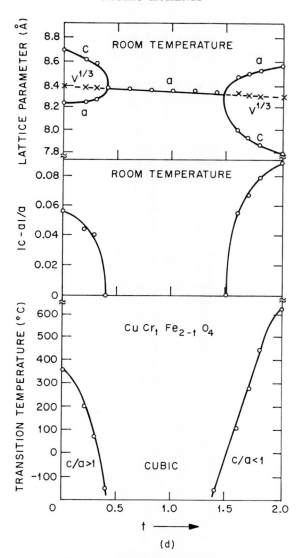

Fig. 55 (*continued*). (d) Crystallographic and magnetic data for the system
CuCr$_t$Fe$_{2-t}$O$_4$ (after Ohnishi and Teranishi (488).)

There are two objections to this explanation for the crystallographic data: (1) The same ion cannot be simultaneously stabilized by both types of distortions. (2) The crystallographic transitions are independent of the Curie temperature. Since the materials of this study undoubtedly possessed very poor chemical homogeneity, it is reasonable to anticipate a compositional range in which two types of Ni^{2+} are simultaneously present. The second objection is less easily answered. Although it is anticipated that noncollinear A-site spins will be present at low temperatures in the cubic phase (ferrimagnetic spirals), nevertheless from molecular field theory (as applied to a system with all A and B cations similar) a Néel configuration is anticipated in the temperature interval just below T_c (see Chapter II, Section III-C-1). Therefore it does not appear legitimate to argue that the A-site spins are only ordered collinear below T_t. However, the nature of the magnetic order in the interval $T_t < T < T_c$ has not been investigated experimentally, and the theory may not apply to a heterogeneous system. Magnetic evidence to support a spin-orbit distortion below T_t is an anomalous increase in g_{eff} as the temperature is lowered through T_t (426); the electron ordering associated with a spin-orbit distortion optimizes the orbital momentum contribution to the moment.

Other evidence that A-site Ni^{2+} may distort the spinel structure to $c/a < 1$ (spin-orbit coupling) comes from the system $Cu_x^{2+}Ni_{1-x}^{2+}[Cr_2]O_4$, where the room-temperature phase is tetragonal ($c/a < 1$) for $x > 0.1$. Other systems $Cu_x^{2+}M_{1-x}^{2+}[Cr_2]O_4$ are tetragonal ($c/a < 1$) only for $x > 0.5$ (see Table XV).

A-site $Fe^{2+}(e_g^3 t_{2g}^3)$ is a Jahn-Teller ion with quenched angular momentum, but the sign of the Jahn-Teller distortion is uncertain without a knowledge of second-order effects. If the four anions of an A site are labeled 1, 2, 3, 4, then a clockwise twist of 1 and 2, an equal counterclockwise twist of 3 and 4, gives orthorhombic symmetry whereas a simultaneous reduction or increase in the angles 1-Fe^{2+}-2 and 3-Fe^{2+}-4 gives tetragonal ($c/a > 1$ or $c/a < 1$, respectively) symmetry. Since these normal vibrational modes are degenerate and belong to the same irreducible representation as the degenerate e_g ground state of the Fe^{2+} electron, the tetragonal and orthorhombic distortions are degenerate, to first order. (Compare with Section III-E-2.) Therefore whether a dynamic Jahn-Teller stabilization or a static distortion to $c/a > 1$, orthorhombic, or $c/a < 1$ symmetry occurs at A-site Fe^{2+} depends upon relatively small (anion-Fe^{2+} distances unchanged) second-order effects. Francomb (189) has reported $c/a > 1$, orthorhombic, and $c/a < 1$ symmetries in the system $Fe_{3-x}Cr_xO_4$. The distortions in this system are probably entirely due to Jahn-Teller effects at A-site Fe^{2+} rather than to competitive spin-orbit vs. Jahn-Teller effects.

Although there is a change from tetragonal ($c/a > 1$) to tetragonal ($c/a < 1$) symmetry in the system $CuCr_tFe_{2-t}O_4$ (see Fig. 55(b)), the changes reported by Ohnishi and Teranishi (488) are due, at least partially, to the fact that B-site Cu^{2+} is also a Jahn-Teller ion.

F. PEROVSKITE (ABX₃) STRUCTURES

The perovskite structure is particularly suited to an experimental study of 180° cation-anion-cation interactions as there are no 90° interactions present provided the large cation is nonmagnetic (see Fig. 56). Although the ideal perovskite structure is cubic, cubic symmetry is rarely encountered. (Interstitial alloys of the Fe_4N or $AlCMn_3$ class are cubic and have a perovskite structure, but in these perovskites the magnetic and nonmagnetic atoms are the inverse of the ionic perovskites. Further, the interstitial N or C atom is not ionic, so that the cation-anion-cation exchange interactions of this section do not apply. These perovskites are discussed in Chapter III, Section III-B-6.) The usual perovskite symmetry is either orthorhombic or rhombohedral, depending upon the relative ionic size (203). Typical of the orthorhombic structures is $GdFeO_3$, which is illustrated in Figure 56(b). The anion octahedra are cooperatively buckled so as to improve the packing about the larger (A) cation. The smaller this cation relative to the anion, the greater the distortion to O-orthorhombic symmetry $(a < c/\sqrt{2} < b)$. The largest packing-induced distortions occur in the MF_3 structures, where the A cation is missing. As in the case of spinels, spin-orbit and Jahn-Teller effects may also occur. The spin-orbit effects are similar to those encountered in the rock salt structures. Octahedral Fe^{2+} and Co^{2+} cause large magnetostrictive distortions below T_N to rhombohedral ($\alpha < 60°$) and tetragonal ($c/a < 1$) symmetry, respectively, in $KFeF_3$ and $KCoF_3$. The Jahn-Teller effects play a decisive role in the magnetic-exchange interactions.

1. *Jahn-Teller Effects: Static and Quasistatic*

Perovskites in which all the B sites are Mn^{3+}, Cr^{2+} $(t_{2g}^3 e_g^1)$ or Cu^{2+} $(t_{2g}^6 e_g^3)$ have tetragonal $(c/a < 1)$ or O'-orthorhombic symmetry $(c/\sqrt{2} < a \le b)$ at low temperatures (219).   Examples are $LaMnO_3$,

● B CATION ◉ A CATION ○ ANION

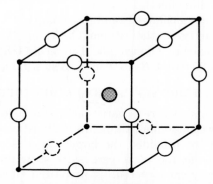

(i) CELL SHOWING CATION-ANION-CATION LINKAGES

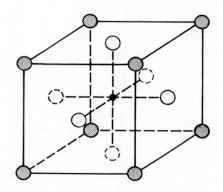

(ii) CELL SHOWING F.C.C. AX_3 SUBLATTICE

(a)

Fig. 56.   The perovskite structure ABO_3 or ABF_3.   (a) Ideal, cubic. (See following pages for Figs. 56(b)–56(d).)

KCrF$_3$, and KCuF$_3$.   A detailed study (268) of the structure of MnF$_3$ (A cation missing) reveals three different Mn–F distances.   Those along the [001] axis (m) are equal, but those in the (001) plane are alternately l and s, as shown in Figure 56(c).   Since $s < m < l$ and $m < (l + s)/2$, the bulk symmetry has $c/\sqrt{2} < a \leq b$, or is pseudo-tetragonal ($c/a < 1$).   This feature was predicted (213) earlier for this class of compound, the d_{z^2} orbitals of the Jahn-Teller ions ordering as shown in Figure 56(d).   The strain energy of this type of ordering is smaller than that resulting from a parallel orientation of the c axes

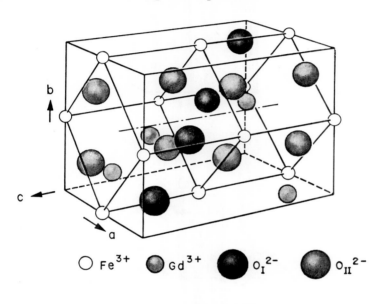

Ion	Position	Coordinates		
		x	y	z
Gd^{3+}	4 (c)	-0.018	0.060	1/4
Fe^{3+}	4 (b)	1/2	0	0
O$_I^{2-}$	4 (c)	0.05	0.470	1/4
O$_{II}^{2-}$	8 (d)	-0.29	0.275	0.05

(b)

Fig. 56 (*continued*).   (b) Unit cell of GdFeO$_3$, showing the perovskite pseudocell, which is typical of the orthorhombic structures (after Geller (203).)

• Mn³⁺   ◯ F⁻

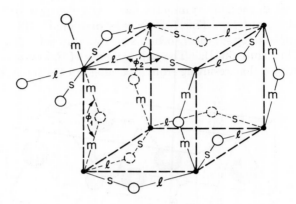

l = 2.1 Å, m = 1.9 Å, s = 1.8 Å, ϕ_1 = 144°, ϕ_2 = 148°

(c)

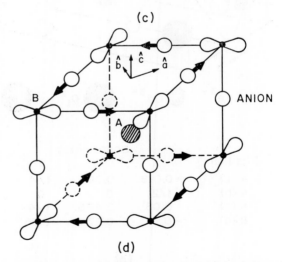

(d)

Fig. 56 (*continued*). (c) Pseudotetragonal cell of MnF₃ (adapted from Hep-worth and Jack (268)). (d) Ordering of occupied d_{z^2} orbital on B-cation sub-lattice that produces O'-orthorhombic symmetry, given extreme anisotropy.

of the distorted octahedra. Subsequently Kanamori (322) showed that a pure d_{z^2} state at the Jahn-Teller ions represents extreme anisotropy due to vibrational anhormonicities, and that the actual ground state is a mixture of $d_{x^2-y^2}$ and d_{z^2}. The normal modes that interact with d_{z^2} and $d_{x^2-y^2}$ are, as before, the Q_2 and Q_3 modes of Figure 47. With no anharmonicity, the lowest mode in this structure turns out to be "antiferromagnetic" Q_2, the short and long axes alternating along the [100] and [010] axes of the pseudotetragonal cell. In the Q_2-Q_3 plane, the stable configuration is represented by two vectors, $\mathbf{Q}_2^+$ and $\mathbf{Q}_2^-$, representing the two sublattices. Addition of the anharmonic terms corresponding to $(K_1\delta + K_2)$ of equation 170 bends the two vectors towards $\Theta = \pm 2\pi/3$, as shown in Figure 47(b). Therefore the distortion at each interstice has either a positive or negative Q_2-type contribution and a small, negative Q_3-type contribution. The angle ϕ and the interstice parameters l, m, s are related by

$$\tan \phi = (Q_3/Q_2) = \frac{(2/\sqrt{6})(2m - l - s)}{\pm(2/\sqrt{2})(l - s)} \tag{172}$$

Ordering into d_{z^2} states as indicated in Figure 56(d) would call for $m = s$ and $\phi = 30°$. Substitution of the experimental values for l, m, s found in MnF_3 gives

$$\phi(MnF_3) = 6°35'$$

which indicates only a modest anisotropy. Kanamori has shown that the Jahn-Teller ordering in this case gives rise to a transition of the second kind.

The essential point for magnetic couplings is that the electron ordering producing this Jahn-Teller effect gives (for $3d^4$ ions) completely empty e_g orbitals directed along the s bonds, half filled orbitals directed along the l bonds, and less than half filled orbitals along the m bonds. This fact, coupled with the rules of Figure 42, permits interpretation of the various types of *antiferromagnetic* order that are encountered in the perovskites.

In order to understand the *ferromagnetic* order that is sometimes found in perovskites containing $3d^4$ ions, it is necessary to investigate the effect of Jahn-Teller stabilizations when there is no *static*, cooperative distortion of the entire lattice. Lack of a *static* Jahn-Teller stabilization may indicate either (*1*) noncooperative, static distortions or (*2*) removal of the ground-state degeneracy by resonance between stable configurations.   It will be shown that the magnetic data for perovskites containing Mn^{3+} ions supports the latter alternative.

The dynamic problem, which represents a doubly degenerate electronic state Γ_3 whose degeneracy is removed in first order by a doubly degenerate vibration, has been studied by several workers (401,444, 445).   These studies, which were restricted to an isolated complex, indicate not only that the ground-state degeneracy is removed by coupling between the nuclear vibrations and the electron configuration, but also that for strong coupling the electronic configuration "follows" the nuclear vibrations.   (Born and Oppenheimer (84) have shown that the large ratio of electron to nuclear mass insures that electron processes are fast relative to the nuclear motions.)   Thus for sufficiently large coupling, the electronic configuration corresponds to the symmetry of the nuclei, the nuclear motions being slow relative to the electronic ordering.   In this strong-coupling limit, the electronic configuration at any moment of time can be approximated by the "quasistatic" ground-state configuration associated with the nuclear positions at that moment.   This limit is therefore referred to as the *quasistatic limit* (225).   In order to have the quasistatic limit apply, it is necessary that $\nu_n \ll \Delta_t/h$, where ν_n is the relevant nuclear vibration frequency, and Δ_t/h is the frequency for electron ordering as a result of the ligand-field splitting Δ' of the Γ_3 level.   Although the relevant vibrational mode represents the vibration of neighboring anions against one another along a $\langle 100 \rangle$ axis, as indicated in Figure 57, its frequency may be estimated from the *Restrahl* frequency.   Restrahl wavelengths are $\approx 10^{-2}$ cm (545), corresponding to $h\nu_n \approx 100$ cm^{-1}.   In the perovskite $LaMnO_3$, an O'-orthorhombic $\rightleftharpoons$ rhombohedral transition occurs at about 900°K (690), and in the spinel Mn_3O_4 a tetragonal $\rightleftharpoons$ cubic transition occurs at about 1443°K (428).   The fact that the cooperative transition temperature varies with the number of Mn^{3+} ions that are present indicates that the Jahn-Teller stabilization per Mn^{3+} ion Δ_t can be estimated properly from the transition temperature only if all the cations present are octahedral-site Mn^{3+}.   However, the transitions cited provide a lower bound, so that $\Delta_t > 750$ cm^{-1}.   This means that the strong-coupling condition is fulfilled, or that the quasistatic limit gives a reasonable approximation.   From Figure 57, it is apparent that in this limit the outer-electron configurations at neighboring cations are so correlated by the lattice vibrations that the 180°

cation-anion-cation superexchange interactions correspond to Case 3 of Figure 42, or to *ferromagnetic* coupling.

Observation of ferromagnetic, 180° $3d^4$-anion-$3d^4$ interactions uniquely distinguishes the quasistatic model from the two alternate models that can be proposed: (*1*) There are static, local Jahn-Teller distortions, but these distortions are random having no cooperative, long-range order. (*2*) There are no static, local distortions; and weak coupling to the nuclear vibrations, although it removes the degeneracy of the "vibronic" ground state, leaves the spin configurations

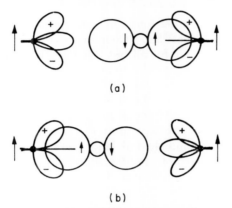

(a)

(b)

Fig. 57. Quasistatic, ferromagnetic 180° cation-anion-cation superexchange between $3d^4$ cations in octahedral sites. (a) and (b) represent electron configurations for two extreme amplitudes of the lattice vibrations.

of neighboring Jahn-Teller ions uncorrelated. It has already been pointed out that statistical treatments of the order ⇌ disorder transition and of the temperature variation of the c/a ratio for tetragonal spinels cannot distinguish between a static and a dynamic model, let alone between the two dynamic alternatives. However, the three models predict quite different electron configurations for cubic, rhombohedral, or O-orthorhombic perovskites, and therefore different magnetic coupling. Whereas the quasistatic limit calls for ferromagnetic $3d^4$-anion-$3d^4$ coupling, alternative (*2*) above calls for antiferromagnetic coupling via Case 1 of Figure 42 (an arithmetic average for electron occupancy of d_{z^2} and $d_{x^2-y^2}$ states are used) and alternative (*1*) calls for some antiferromagnetic, some ferromagnetic interactions and no long-range magnetic order.

Finally, it should be noted that whereas electron-vibration correlations must be considered whenever a $3d^4$ cation interacts with another Jahn-Teller ion having only one outer e_g electron, in all other cases the e_g configuration at the other cation remains fixed, and an arithmetic average for the occupancy of d_{z^2} and $d_{x^2-y^2}$ orbitals at the $3d^4$ ion should be used. With an arithmetic average, the e_g orbitals at a $3d^4$ cation are each 1/4 filled and therefore contribute to the exchange interactions as though they were half filled.

2. Illustrative Examples

(a) The magnetic order found in various antiferromagnetic perovskites is given in Table VIII. Coupling between like atoms is found to be antiferromagnetic for all but the Jahn-Teller ions Mn^{3+}, Cr^{2+}, and Cu^{2+}. This conforms with Figure 42, and it gives the G structure (Figure 18). Indicative of Jahn-Teller ordering at low temperatures, $LaMnO_3$ and $KCrF_3$ have the O'-orthorhombic structure, $KCuF_3$ is tetragonal ($c/a < 1$). Although low-spin-state Ni^{III} appears (from a one-electron model) to have only one e_g electron ($t_{2g}^6 e_g^1$), the compound $LaNiO_3$ is rhombohedral, and there is apparently no static Jahn-Teller distortion of the structure. Since Ni^{III} represents a three-hole problem, extrapolation from a one-electron model is dangerous, as these experimental results indicate. In the O' structure, the alternating l and s cation-anion distances within a (001) plane introduce ferromagnetic coupling via Case 3 of Figure 42. Along the [001] axis the m distances indicate less than half filled anion-directed orbitals and antiferromagnetic coupling via a weakened Case 1. (For the extreme anisotropy case, $m = s$ and the coupling is antiferromagnetic via Case 2.) Such interactions give the A structure that is observed. It should be appreciated how significant a test of the theory this example is, for this structure can only occur if there simultaneously exist both ferromagnetic and antiferromagnetic interactions between identical ions. In tetragonal ($c/a < 1$) $KCuF_3$, there can be no coupling within the (001) planes because a full orbital is directed along the l linkage. Antiferromagnetic coupling may exist along the [001] only if there is extreme anisotropy. This conclusion is confirmed by the lack of any observable magnetic order down to 4°K. Rhombohedral $LaNiO_3$ also shows no observable magnetic order down to 4°K. Ni^{III} has only one unpaired outer electron, and it is not unreasonable to anticipate a breakdown of superexchange coupling between cations with total spin $S = 1/2$. This follows from the assumption within each of the principal superexchange mechanisms that in the excited states that are admixed to the ground state to give the magnetic coupling, the excited-electron spins remain correlated with the net spins on the two cations. For the case $S = 1/2$, there is no net cation spin with which the "excited" electron can remain correlated, since the excited states are singlets with zero net spin at each cation. That the lack of magnetic order in $LaNiO_3$ is due to a breakdown of the superexchange mechanism between cations with spin $S = 1/2$ is supported by the observation that RuF_3 and PdF_3, like $LaNiO_3$, exhibit no magnetic order above $4°K$. The structure of these fluorides is like perovskite with the A cations missing, and Ru^{III}, Pd^{III} are both spin-quenched by the ligand fields so that $S = 1/2$.

(b) The system $(La,Ca)MnO_{3+\delta}$ is particularly informative as it

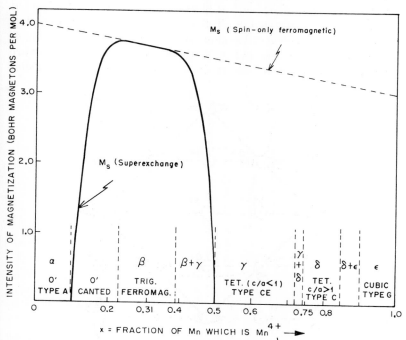

Fig. 58. Semiempirical phase diagram for the system $(La, Ca)MnO_3$. (After Goodenough (213).)

supports two types of electronic ordering, Jahn-Teller ordering and ordering of Mn^{3+} and Mn^{4+} ions. This fact gives rise to five different perovskite phases, each characterized by a different crystallographic symmetry and magnetic order (see Fig. 58). The O'-symmetry, A-type order of $LaMnO_3$ and the cubic symmetry, G-type order of $CaMnO_3$ have already been discussed. The β-phase region is rhombohedral and ferromagnetic. There is no static Jahn-Teller ordering in this phase, so that from quasistatic considerations the Mn^{3+}–O^{2-}–Mn^{3+} and the Mn^{3+}–O^{2-}–Mn^{4+} interactions are both ferromagnetic. Since electrostatic energies minimize the number of Mn^{4+}–O^{2-}–Mn^{4+} interactions (ionic order is here accomplished by electron ordering), the system is ferromagnetic. (By contrast the compound $La(Mn_{.75}Cr_{.25})O_3$ is only ferrimagnetic (51,308) since the number of antiferromagnetic Cr^{3+}–Cr^{3+} interactions is not minimized by electrostatic forces.) At 50% Mn^{4+}, the two types of manganese ion order on the simple-cubic B sublattice like the two kinds of ion in rock salt. There is also a Jahn-Teller ordering at the Mn^{3+} ions that produces tetragonal ($c/a < 1$) symmetry. Along the c axis all cation-anion distances are m, and in the basal plane the l and s distances are predicted (213) to be as shown in Figure 59. Such Jahn-Teller

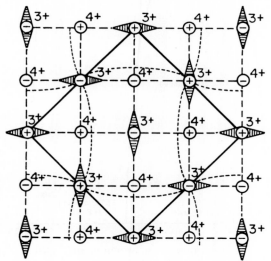

Fig. 59.   Ordering of half filled d_{z^2} orbitals in (001) planes of the CE structure. (After Goodenough (213).)

ordering would give the $c/a < 1$ symmetry and the CE magnetic order that is observed. At 75% Mn^{4+}, electrostatic forces would order the Mn^{3+} ions into every other (001) plane, and they would be next-near neighbors within the planes they occupied. The sequence along a given [001] axis would be 3+, 4+, 4+, 4+, 3+. Jahn-Teller stabilization of the d_{z^2} state along the c axis would give the observed tetragonal ($c/a > 1$) symmetry and C-type order. Although the Mn^{4+} ions of the Mn^{3+}-occupied planes have only four out of six correct magnetic linkages, the order is stable.

In the compositional range between the α (A-type order) and β (ferromagnetic) phases, neutron-diffraction data is unable to distinguish between two magnetic phases and an A structure with canted spins. The cant angle Θ_0 measures the angle between the moments of successive ferromagnetic layers of the A structure. However, high-field magnetization curves (297a) reveal a marked high-field susceptibility characteristic of complex spin configurations (see Fig. 34). In order to have a Θ_0 that varies smoothly with x from π to 0 radians between the α and β phase, it is necessary to have some additional exchange mechanism that is ferromagnetic and has a different Θ_0 dependence than the $\cos \Theta_0$ dependence of interlayer superexchange. De Gennes (145a) has pointed out that Zener's double exchange (716), which would be applicable to this case, is ferromagnetic and proportional to a transfer integral varying as $b \cos (\Theta_0/2)$. Minimization of the total exchange energy gives a cant angle defined by

$$\cos (\Theta_0/2) = bx/4|J|S^2$$

where x is the number of mobile carriers and J is the superexchange integral. [The Zener mechanism requires the presence of mobile carriers (ions of the same atom on equivalent lattice sites, but with different valence), a strong intraatomic exchange, and conservation of the sign of the mobile-carrier spin during a hop from one lattice site to the next. Then the mobile carriers can contribute to the binding energy provided the spins on neighboring sites are parallel. This mechanism undoubtedly contributes also to the ferromagnetic coupling found in the β phase.]

(c) Further evidence for ferromagnetic $Mn^{3+}-O^{2-}-Mn^{3+}$ interactions in systems having no static Jahn-Teller ordering is obtained from studies of $La(Mn,Ni)O_{3+\delta}$, (692), $La(Mn,Co)O_{3+\delta}$ (225),

La(Mn,Ga)O$_3$ (225), and (La,Ba)(Mn,Ti)O$_3$ (308). With less than 50% cobalt, trivalent cobalt is diamagnetic Co^{III}($t_{2g}^6 e_g^0$). Ga^{3+} and Ti^{4+} are also diamagnetic. The electronic configuration of Ni^{III} may also be correlated with the lattice vibrations (quasistatic model).

In Figure 60 are shown the ratios $c/\sqrt{2}a$ for the lanthanum sys-

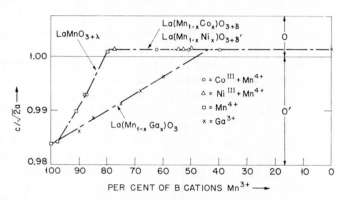

Fig. 60. Lattice-parameter ratio $c/\sqrt{2}a$ for orthorhombic perovskites in the systems La(Mn$_{1-x}^{3+}$M$_x$)O$_{3+y}$, where M = Co^{III} + Mn^{4+}, Ni^{III} + Mn^{4+}, and Ga^{3+}. (After Goodenough, Wold, Arnott, and Menyuk (225).)

tems, a ratio $c/\sqrt{2}a < 1$ indicating Jahn-Teller ordering at the Jahn-Teller ions. (La,Ba)(Mn,Ti)O$_3$ becomes rhombohedral with more than 10% BaTiO$_3$. The systems La(Mn,Ni)O$_{3+\delta}'$ and La(Mn,Co)O$_{3+\delta}$ become ferromagnetic in the O-orthorhombic phase. (Ni^{III} contributes $1\mu_B$. Thus the expected ferromagnetic coupling of quasistatically correlated ions is realized. The complications responsible for no magnetic order in LaNiO$_3$ do not appear so long as Ni^{III} couples to another Jahn-Teller ion having more than one unpaired electron.) (La,Ba)(Mn,Ti)O$_3$ approaches ferromagnetism in the O-orthorhombic phase; probably chemical inhomogeneities introduce some ferrimagnetism. La(Mn$_{1-x}$Ga$_x$)O$_3$ is unique in that the O' phase remains stable to $x = 0.5$. In the range $0 \leq x \leq 0.4$, the moment is compatible with ferrimagnetism due to ordering of the Ga^{3+} into alternate (001) planes and the retention of A-type order (see Fig. 61). Although the origin of an ordering energy is not obvious, the change in T_c with composition supports this interpretation. If the Ga ordering begins to disappear as x approaches 0.5, this would be reflected in the anomalous increase of T_c that is observed and in the magnetization. For $x > 0.5$, the magnetization is as nearly ferromagnetic as can be expected given considerable dilution of the matrix by diamagnetic Ga^{3+}. Consistent with these findings is an increase in Θ_a for $LaMnO_3$ from about $30°K$ to nearly $200°K$ as the tempera-

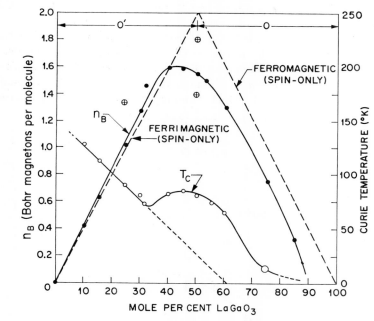

Fig. 61. Saturation magnetization and Curie temperature for the system $La(Mn_{1-x}Ga_x)O_3$. The points $\oplus$ are Curie temperatures for $La(Mn_{0.75}Co_{0.25})O_{3+\delta}$ and $La(Mn_{0.5}Co_{0.5})O_{3+\delta}$. The double Curie temperature of the latter sample reflects two magnetic phases. (After Goodenough, Wold, Arnott, and Menyuk (225).)

ture is increased through the $O' \rightleftharpoons$ rhombohedral transition at approximately $615°C$ (308,690).

Watanabe (649) has observed antiferromagnetic $Mn^{3+}-Mn^{3+}$ interactions in cubic phases of the system $La_{1-y}Sr_yMnO_x$, which would appear to support Jonker's (308) suggestion that the sign of the $Mn^{3+}-Mn^{3+}$ interaction changes as the lattice parameter gets smaller than a critical value of $a \sim 3.87$ A. However, it is to be noted that the Watanabe compounds that were Mn^{3+} rich, antiferromagnetic, and cubic were all anion-defect structures, the greatest number of vacancies occurring at $SrMnO_{2.5}$. Since occupied d_{z^2} orbitals would be stabilized by static orientation towards an anion vacancy, it is reasonable to expect that the dynamic Jahn-Teller effect is quenched by static electron ordering if there are vacancies present. Thus the Watanabe results are not inconsistent with the quasistatic hypothesis.

(d) The system $La_{1-x}Sr_xCoO_{3-\lambda}$ is complicated by the fact that the quadrivalent cobalt is low-spin-state $Co^{IV}(t_{2g}^5 e_g^0)$. Also trivalent cobalt, though high-spin-state $Co^{3+}(t_{2g}^4 e_g^2)$ for pure $LaCoO_3$, appears to be partially converted to diamagnetic $Co^{III}(t_{2g}^6 e_g^0)$ in the presence of Co^{IV}. Magnetic (311,354,647) and crystallographic (28) measure-

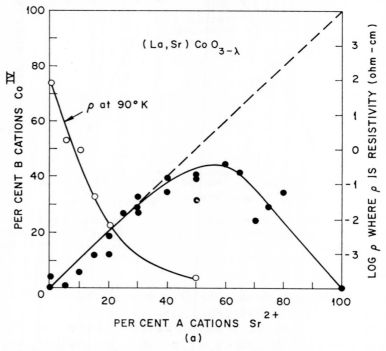

Fig. 62. Some compositional, electric, and magnetic properties of the system $La_{1-x}^{3+}Sr_x^{2+}(Co_{z'}^{3+}Co_y^{IV}Co_{0.5-y-z'}^{III})(Co_{z''}^{3+}Co_{\xi-y}^{IV}Co_{0.5-\xi+y-z''}^{III})O_{3-\lambda}$. (a) Per cent of B cations that are Co^{IV} and electrical resistivity at 90°K as a function of Sr content. (After Jonker and Van Santen (311).) (See following page for Fig. 62(b).)

ments give the following results: (*i*) The system has rhombohedral symmetry and it is difficult to obtain more than about 50% Co^{IV}, strontium cobaltite tending toward the formula $Sr_2Co_2O_5$. (*ii*) The paramagnetic Curie temperature is $\Theta_a < -200°K$ for stoichiometric $LaCoO_3$, but increases to a positive value if more than 10% of the cobalt concentration is Co^{IV}, to above room temperature for over 40% Co^{IV}. (*iii*) The effective paramagnetic moment $n_{eff} = \mu_{eff}/\mu_B$ and the spontaneous magnetization $n_B = \mu/\mu_B$ per cobalt atom are anomalously low, as shown in Figure 62. (*iv*) A neutron diffraction study

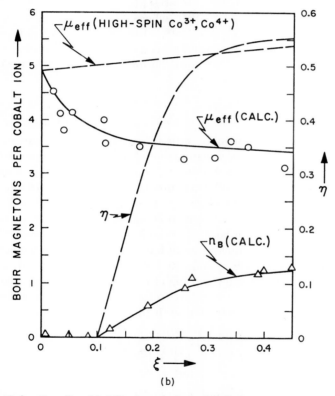

(b)

Fig. 62 (*continued*). (b) Effective number of Bohr magnetons $n_{eff} = \mu_{eff}/\mu_B$, ordering parameter η, and saturation magnetization n_B in Bohr magnetons per molecule at 4°K as a fraction of the percentage of cobalt ions that are Co^{IV}. (After Goodenough (214); experimental points after Jonker and Van Santen (311).)

of $LaCoO_{3.05}$ found no magnetic ordering down to 4.2°K. These peculiar properties have been interpreted (214) with the aid of the following rather special assumption: *Introduction of a Co^{IV} ion into ideal $LaCoO_3$ stabilizes Co^{3+} near neighbors, but introduces Co^{III} next-near and next-next-near neighbors.* This assumption has three consequences: (*1*) There is a tendency for ordering of low-spin-state and high-spin-state ions on alternate (111) planes; (*2*) initial clusters of one Co^{IV} with six Co^{3+} near neighbors become magnetically isolated by a layer of diamagnetic Co^{III}; and (3) given perfect order, the fraction of total cobalt ions that are present as Co^{3+} in the low-spin-state (111) planes is $2z \sim \exp(-18\xi)$, where $\xi = (x - 2\lambda)$ is the fraction of total cobalt ions that are Co^{IV}. Ideally the cobalt sublattice is split into two sublattices, each representing a set of alternate (111) planes. Therefore the chemical formula for the system is more appropriately written as:

$$La_{1-x}^{3+}Sr_x^{2+}[Co_{z'}^{3+}(\uparrow)Co_y^{IV}(\downarrow)Co_{0.5-y-z'}^{III}]_A$$

$$[Co_{z'}^{3+}(\downarrow)Co_{\xi-y}^{IV}(\uparrow)Co_{0.5-\xi+y-z''}^{III}]_B O_{3-\lambda}$$

Since the dominant magnetic interactions are between sublattices A and B, the various spin assignments follow from the rules of Figure 42 and Table XII. The fraction y, where $0 \le y \le 0.5\xi$, is a measure of the ordering of the Co^{IV} ions onto a given sublattice, and an ordering parameter η is defined as $\eta = 1 - (2y/\xi)$ such that $0 \le \eta \le 1$. For low values of ξ there can be no long-range order ($\eta = 0$) as there are not sufficient numbers of low spin-state cations available. At higher ξ values, the long-range order is never complete even though only electron transfers among the cobalt ions are involved, because there will always be regions of high Sr^{2+} density that force some Co^{IV} into sublattice A. In the estimate for z' and z'', it is assumed that the Co^{3+} are always correlated with the Co^{IV} so that

$$2z' \sim \exp(-18y) + 12(\xi - y)[1 - 2(y + z')]$$

$$2z'' \sim \exp[-18(\xi - y)] + 12y[1 - 2(\xi - y + z'')]$$

The spin-only values for n_{eff} and n_B follow immediately:

$$n_{eff} = [24(z' + z'') + 3\xi]^{1/2}$$

$$n_B = 4(z' - z'') + \xi\eta$$

The theoretical curves are compared with the experimental points in Figure 62, where the parameter η chosen for the best fit to n_B is also shown. The lack of long-range magnetic order for $LaCoO_{3.05}$ ($\xi = 0.1$) is therefore attributed to the presence of isolated, ferromagnetic Co^{IV}–Co^{3+} clusters. (Also an anomaly in χ_m at 500°K is suggestive of a $Co^{III} \rightleftharpoons Co^{3+}$ transition for at least some trivalent cobalt at this temperature.) The negative Θ_a for stoichiometric $LaCoO_3$ confirms antiferromagnetic Co^{3+}–O^{2-}–Co^{3+} interactions, and the positive Θ_a for $\xi > 0.1$ confirms ferromagnetic Co^{3+}–O^{2-}–Co^{IV} interactions.

(e) Several rare earth orthoferrites $MFeO_3$, where M is a rare earth, have been studied (7,96,98,100,244,245,355,507,508,560,648). These compounds tend to exhibit parasitic ferromagnetism. There are four possible contributions to this magnetism: (i) preferential ordering of impurities or defects into alternate (111) planes of the antiferromagnetic Fe sublattice, (ii) interstitial Fe ions in inhomogeneity-induced regions of high Fe concentration, (iii) Fe^{3+} spins canted in a common direction either by the cooperative buckling of the O^{2-} octahedra associated with O-orthorhombic symmetry or by anisotropic superexchange [if the single-atom crystalline anisotropy differs in different sites, a small canting will lower the anisotropy energy in first order while raising the exchange energy only in the second order, so that canting will occur where it is consistent with symmetry (94,

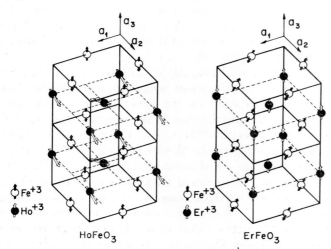

Fig. 63. Proposed magnetic structures for $HoFeO_3$ and $ErFeO_3$ at 125°K. (After Koehler, Wollan, and Wilkinson (355).)

450)], and (iv) canting of the antiferromagnetic rare earth sublattice as a result of interactions between the two sublattices. How many of these contributions are present in any compound depends upon the preparation and the magnetic easy axis for the Fe-sublattice spins. The spin configurations (355) for $HoFeO_3$ and $ErFeO_3$ are shown in Figure 63. The Curie temperatures $T_c \approx 569 \pm 10°K$ are all determined by the Fe^{3+} sublattice.

G. ORDERED ROCK SALT STRUCTURES

Several Li^+-substituted rock salt structures have been prepared in an attempt to find an example of Zener's (716) double exchange, a ferromagnetic cation-anion-cation interaction between cations of the same ion, but different valence state (see Section I-F-2-(b)). None of the oxides studied become ferromagnetic. Although a spontaneous magnetization was found (223) in the system $Li_x^+ Ni_{1-2x}^{2+} Ni_x^{III} O$ in the range of compositions $0.3 \leq x \leq 0.5$, it was due to ferrimagnetism resulting from preferential ordering of the Li^+ into alternate (111) planes. Since there is no static Jahn-Teller distortion about a Ni^{III} and electrostatic forces minimize the number of $Ni^{III}–O^{2-}–Ni^{III}$ interactions, all $Ni–O^{2-}–Ni$ interactions may be assumed antiferromagnetic. If only one such interaction is required to couple a Ni atom to the long-range magnetic order, the theoretical magnetization curve and fitted ordering parameters are those shown in Figure 64. Perakis, Wucher, and Parravano (512a) have found the ferrimagnetic phase present in samples with $x < 0.3$.

A preliminary study (264,523) of the system $Li_x Mn_{1-x} Se$ with $0 \leq x \leq 0.1$ indicates a complex magnetic behavior that has been interpreted (264) as evidence for Zener's double exchange. The composition $Li_{0.1} Mn_{0.9} Se$ appears to be ferromagnetic ($n_B \approx 0.7$) in the temperature interval $70°K < T < 110°K$, but to exhibit antiferromagnetic ordering of the third kind below $70°K$. Although a thermal hysteresis was noted in connection with the $70°K$ transition, no crystallographic or electrical data have been reported. A low μ_{eff} and μ (from neutron data) suggest that the trivalent manganese in this system is $Mn^{III}(t_{2g}^4 e_g^0)$. (However, the appearance of a second phase for $x > 0.1$ suggests that with a large enough concentration of trivalent manganese, the ion may be stabilized as Mn^{3+} by Jahn-Teller distortions. Jahn-Teller stabilizations and Li^+ ordering have been used to give a tentative structure, from powder-pattern data,

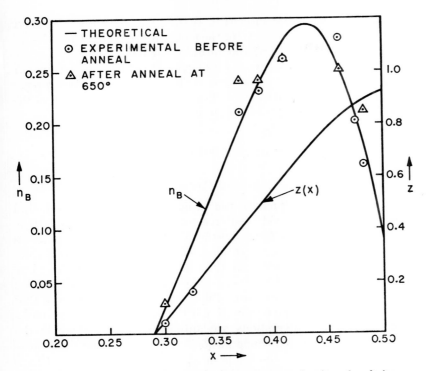

Fig. 64.   Magnetization n_B in Bohr magnetons per molecule and ordering parameter $z = 1 - (2y/x)$ for the system $(Li_{x-y}^+ Ni_{0.5-x}^{2+} Ni_y^{III})(Li_y^+ Ni_{0.5-x}^{2+} Ni_{x-y}^{III})O$, $x > 2y$.   (After Goodenough, Wickham and Croft (223).)

for $LiMnO_2$ (215).)   Since Mn^{III}–Se^{2-}–Mn^{2+} interactions are ferromagnetic according to Figure 42 and Table XII, the presence of 20% Mn^{III} + Li^+ would be sufficient to eliminate long-range antiferromagnetic order and to allow a small net moment from ferromagnetic clusters.   Although such a material would exhibit exchange anisotropy (430), no magnetic measurement has been made to distinguish this account of the spontaneous magnetization from the double-exchange proposal.   Thus the existence of pure double exchange, even in the presence of more covalent anions, appears to be still doubtful.   Nevertheless it undoubtedly contributes to the magnetic coupling, as indicated by the canted spins in $La_{1-x}Ca_xMnO_3$.

Although tetragonal $(c/a > 1)$ symmetry is generally associated with a Cu^{2+} octahedral interstice, Bertaut and Delorme (56) have reported an ordered structure for the rock salt compound $Cu_{0.25}Co_{0.75}O$ that is tetragonal ($c/a < 1$) and antiferromagnetic. The f.c.c. cation sublattice has the $CuAu_3$-type ordering; and the Cu^{2+} ions occupy one of its four simple-cubic sublattices. These facts can be interpreted (215) as due to cooperative Jahn-Teller distortions at the Cu^{2+} of the type found in $LaMnO_3$ (see Fig. 56(d)).

H. RUTILE STRUCTURES

1. *Normal Compounds*

(a) In the rutile structure, the cations occupy nearly octahedral interstices and form a body-centered-tetragonal ($c/a < 1$) sublattice. Packing considerations force shorter $O^{2-}-O^{2-}$ distances in the basal plane. Along the c axis the cation-occupied octahedra share a common edge (90° interactions), and the body-centered octahedra share common corners with the corner octahedra via a cation-anion-cation angle of $\sim135°$. It follows from the symmetry that the 90° and 135° interactions can only be cooperative if the 90° interactions are ferromagnetic. If all interactions are antiferromagnetic, there is the possibility of spiral-spin configurations as a result of the three competing exchange interactions illustrated in Figure 29(a). (See Chapter II, Section III-B). Such a spiral configuration has been observed for MnO_2, where the Mn^{4+}–anion–Mn^{4+} interactions are relatively weak because the e_g orbitals are empty. In MnF_2, on the other hand, the magnetic ordering is body-centered of the first kind, or $J^{c-c}/J^{c-a-c} < 1$, since the e_g orbitals at a Mn^{2+} ion are half filled. (The greater electronegativity of F^- weakens the cation-anion-cation interaction so that $T_N \sim 84°K$, but the greater $Mn^{2+}--Mn^{2+}$ separation along the c axis, 2.89 A for MnO_2 (714) and 3.31 A for MnF_2 (233) weakens the cation--cation interaction more rapidly. Note also that equation 174 calls for $R_c(Mn) \approx 2.85$ A, so that HL electrons are along the z axis. Recent nuclear magnetic resonance experiments (499) indicate that the 90° interactions along the c axis in MnF_2 are actually ferromagnetic, but with a strength of only 10% of the intersublattice interactions. This implies that the ferromagnetic $(sp^2)\sigma$, $(sp^2)\sigma'$ interactions are unexpectedly large, perhaps as a result of (sp^2) hybridization at the anion.

FeF_2, CoF_2, and NiF_2 also have body-centered ordering of the first kind, as is predicted since the t_{2g} orbitals are more than half filled. Because of the low Néel points, no crystallographic studies of the spin-orbit distortions about the octahedral Fe^{2+} and Co^{2+} ions have been reported.

(b) From crystal symmetry and equation 167, it follows that in the antiferromagnetic iron group difluorides MnF_2, FeF_2, and CoF_2, which have sublattice magnetizations parallel to [001], shear strains σ_{xz}, σ_{yz} will be accompanied by magnetizations along the y, x directions, respectively (161). Moriya (449) has pointed out that even a linear compression in the basal plane, say along the [110] direction, can produce different atomic moments on the two sublattices, and therefore piezoferrimagnetism, provided that the lifetime for interchange of $+$ and $-$ sublattices is sufficiently long. This effect is due to the 90° angle between the basal-plane, principal octahedral-site axes of the two different sublattices. The ligand fields around the two types of site are no longer the same in the presence of compression along an axis of the basal plane, and this gives rise to different g factors and to different anisotropic fine structure couplings. This effect is largest for CoF_2. Because the piezomagnetic moment reverses sign when the sublattice magnetizations of the antiferromagnet reverse their sign, Moriya makes the interesting suggestion that this effect may permit direct measurement of the relaxation time for this interchange.

2. Electron-Ordering Effects

(a) The compounds CrF_2 and $CrCl_2$ are complicated by the fact that octahedral $Cr^{2+}(3d^4)$ is a Jahn-Teller ion. A cooperative Jahn-Teller distortion of the rutile structure occurs above room temperature for each compound, but the cooperative character of the effect is different for the two cases. In each compound the Cr^{2+} octahedra become tetragonal ($c/a > 1$), but in CrF_2 the long axes have a large component parallel to the c axis (294) whereas in $CrCl_2$ they are perpendicular to the c axis (699). Therefore the c axis of monoclinic CrF_2 is relatively large (3.51 A), so that CrF_2 has body-centered magnetic ordering of the first kind, whereas the c axis of orthorhombic $CrCl_2$ is relatively small (3.48 A) given the larger size of the Cl^- ion. The very large cation--cation distances along the a and b axes of $CrCl_2$ (6.64 A and 5.98 A) mean that only the $\sim$135° cation-anion-cation interactions compete with the 90° interactions along the c axis. Nevertheless the observed (112) body-centered ordering of the third kind requires $J(90°)/J(135°) > 4$, which is improbable. This suggests that the $\sim 135°$ cation-anion-cation angles are not all equal, so that some of the interactions between corner and body-center cations are ferromagnetic corresponding to $\alpha > \alpha_c \sim 145°$, and some antiferromagnetic corresponding to $\alpha < \alpha_c \sim 145°$. (See Chapter II, Section I-A-4.)   The necessary small rotation of the octahedra about the long axes, though not reported, may be present.

Jahn-Teller ordering at Cu^{2+} distorts antiferromagnetic CuF_2 similarly to CrF_2 (70a).   The unpaired $d_{x^2-y^2}$ electron spins are presumably coupled via the shorter $\frown 135°$ cation-anion-cation links.

(b) Below $T_c = 121°C$, the rutile phase of CrO_2 is ferromagnetic with a nearly spin-only atomic moment $\mu_{Cr} = 2.07 \pm 0.03\mu_B$ (242).

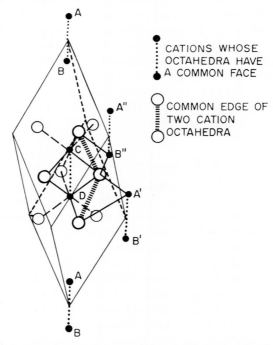

Fig. 65.   The corundum structure. A-B and C-D c-axis pairs share a common octahedral face, C-B'' and D-A' basal-plane near neighbors share a common octahedral edge, and there are A''-B and C-A' cation-anion-cation couplings between adjacent basal, "puckered" planes of cations.

From Table XIV it is apparent that ferromagnetic order can only be realized if the cation- -cation interactions along the c axis are eliminated by an ordering of the two Cr^{4+} d electrons away from the c axis (216). Such ordering simultaneously causes the intermediary anions to overlap half filled orbitals on one cation, empty orbitals on the other, so that the cation-anion-cation coupling would be ferromagnetic, corresponding to 180° Case 3. Since the crystalline fields are not cubic, but orthorhombic, the particular two-electron ground state requires a negative ligand-field contribution along the c axis. Such a field is possible because of the partial shielding of the cations from one another by the shorter O^{2-}–O^{2-} separations in the basal plane. Siratori and Iida (578) have observed that the temperature coefficient for the c axis is negative throughout the temperature range $0°C < T < T_t$, where $T_t > 200°C$, which is indicative of the required electron ordering away from the c axis throughout this interval. (Removal of electrons from the c axis permits smaller separation of the basal-plane O^{2-} ions.) Also, $c/a = 0.660$ (674) is larger than for most rutile structures. Further, CrO_2 is a relatively good electrical conductor ($\rho \sim 10^{-1}$ ohm-cm at room temperature). Because there is a pronounced maximum in the ρ vs. T curve at the Curie temperature (377), CrO_2 appears to have a metallic characteristic at room temperature. The conduction mechanism in CrO_2 is not understood. However, it seems reasonable to suspect that stacking faults of the type identified in Ti_5O_9 (see Chapter III, Section II-B-3) may be playing a role.

I. SOME HEXAGONAL STRUCTURES

1. *Corundum*

Information about the 90° interactions can be obtained from the magnetic structures of several hexagonal structures (corundum, ilmenite, $CdCl_2$, CdI_2). The corundum structure is illustrated in Figure 65. It has a unique threefold axis along which pairs of distorted, cation-occupied octahedra share a common face. In the basal plane these octahedra share a common edge with three similar octahedra. The strongest cation- -cation interactions occur along the c axis through the common octahedral face, but similar interactions may also occur perpendicular to the c axis. Cation-anion-cation interactions are also present. Cation-occupied octahedra share a common corner with one of the cation-occupied octahedra belonging to a neighboring c-axis pair. The cation-anion-cation angle is $\sim 135°$. These interactions couple, for example, A'' of Figure 65 with B and C, B'' with D and A'.

Two possible types of magnetic order are shown in Figure 18. In both types of order, the cation--cation interactions through a common face are antiferromagnetic. Given this interaction, it is apparent from Figure 65 that cation B'' cannot be simultaneously antiparallel to both D, to which it is coupled by a 135° cation-anion-cation linkage, and C, to which it is coupled by a 90° linkage. In corundum ordering of the first kind, the cation--cation C-B'' interaction is the stronger, and in ordering of the second kind the cation-anion-cation A-B' and B''-D interactions are the stronger. (Should the cation--cation A-B and the cation-anion-cation A-B' interactions be antiferromagnetic in both magnetic structures, the critical parameter ratio is $J_{B''-D}/J_{B''-C} = 1/2$, there being twice as many B''-D as B''-C linkages.) Ordering of the first kind is illustrated by α-Cr_2O_3. The $Cr^{3+}(3d^3)$ ions have no e_g electrons, so that cation-anion-cation interactions are relatively weak. Ordering of the second kind is illustrated by α-Fe_2O_3. The $Fe^{3+}(3d^5)$ ions have half filled e_g electrons so that the cation-anion-cation interactions are strong. The differences in the Néel temperatures given in Table VIII reflect the relative strengths of the interactions in the two compounds. [Osmond (496a) has argued for a ferromagnetic 135° cation-anion-cation interaction in α-Cr_2O_3. This is plausible, but not demonstrated (see Section III-C-3 for contradictory evidence), as $125° < \alpha_c < 150°$ represents the range of angle within which the sign changes from that of 180° to that of 90° coupling, and 90° Cr^{3+}-anion-Cr^{3+} interactions are ferromagnetic. Ferromagnetic 135° interactions would also lead to ordering of the first kind.]

Menyuk (433) has used the Luttinger-Tisza formalism of Chapter II, Section III-A to show that in the corundum structure the ground-state spin configuration is always a spiral, as in the case of a Bravais lattice. He has also derived the regions in parameter space for which the four alternative, collinear models that are possible for corundum are stable. [These regions have also been analytically defined by Bertaut (55). Although Bertaut's regions are correctly described, it should be pointed out that he asserts without proof that for any structure the Lagrange multipliers of equation 142 are equal for all sites of a given crystallographic sublattice. This is equivalent to assuming, *a priori*, that one of a restricted class of configurations will minimize the Heisenberg exchange energy. This restriction, which happens to be justified in the case of corundum, is not generally valid, so that failure to provide a sufficient criterion for testing the validity of the assumption prevents definite establishment of the ground state. The same limitation is not present in the Luttinger-Tisza approach.]

The compound α-Fe_2O_3 exhibits a weak, parasitic ferromagnetism in the temperature interval $-20°C < T < 675°C$. In this temperature range the atomic moments are nearly in the basal plane. From the symmetry, $\mathbf{D}$ of equation 167 is parallel to the c axis and anisotropic superexchange cants the spins in the basal plane in the same direction ($\mathbf{D} \cdot \mathbf{S}_1 \times \mathbf{S}_2 \neq 0$) to produce a net moment. Below $-20°C$, the spins are aligned parallel to the c axis, and the parasitic ferromagnetism disappears (446) since $\mathbf{D} \cdot \mathbf{S}_1 \times \mathbf{S}_2 = 0$ for any canting from the c axis. (Other contributions to parasitic ferromagnetism, such as weak ferrimagnetization due to a lack of stoichiometry, are not a fundamental property of the material.) In α-Cr_2O_3, the magnetic axis is the c axis for all $T < T_N$, and there is no parasitic ferromagnetism.

2. Ilmenite

(a) The ilmenite structure is similar to the corundum structure except that there is ordering of the two different cations into alternate (111) planes of the rhombohedral cell. The compounds $Ni^{2+}Mn^{4+}O_3$ and $Co^{2+}Mn^{4+}O_3$ have a magnetic order similar to that of α-Fe_2O_3. In each case this gives rise to ferrimagnetic moments per molecule of $\mu \sim 0.7\mu_B$ (59,97,119,608).

Spin-only moments would give $\mu = 1\mu_B$ and $0\mu_B$, respectively. Since the spins are in the (111) plane (303), a contribution to the ferrimagnetic moment should come from a canted-spin configuration. Orbital contributions to the g factor must also be playing a role, especially in the case of Co^{2+}. It was pointed out in the discussion on rock salt structures that Co^{2+} in CoO carries an atomic moment of $3.7\mu_B$ rather than the spin-only value of $3.0\mu_B$, and that this moment can be accounted for quantitatively if orbital considerations are included.

The magnetic order follows from the coupling rules. Since the t_{2g} orbitals of the M^{2+} ions are more than half filled, the M^{2+}–M^{2+} and M^{2+}–Mn^{4+} interactions are very small. The 90° interactions between Mn^{4+} ions within a (111) plane are ambiguous.   This means that the 90° C-B'' interactions are dominated by the cation-anion-cation A-B' and B''-D interactions, which are antiferromagnetic even though the e_g orbitals of one cation are empty, of the other half filled, because the cation-anion-cation angle is $\alpha < 135°$.

(b) In $MnTiO_3$, $FeTiO_3$, and $NiTiO_3$ the Ti cations appear to be diamagnetic Ti^{4+}.   This means that there are only two competing interactions present: a cation-anion-anion-cation interaction between A and A', D of Figure 65 and a 90° interaction between A' and D. If the $3d$ orbitals are half filled, the antiferromagnetic 90° interaction is probably the stronger (Case 1 of Fig. 43), but if the t_{2g} are more than half filled, the 90° interactions are ferromagnetic (presumably there is little quenching of the correlation $p\sigma$, $p\sigma'$ interactions) and cooperate with the antiferromagnetic cation-anion-anion-cation interactions.   This prediction has been substantiated by neutron diffraction studies (563,565), $MnTiO_3$ having antiferromagnetic A'-D interactions and $FeTiO_3$, $NiTiO_3$ having antiferromagnetic A-A' and A-D interactions (or ferromagnetic A'-D coupling).

3. Halogen Compounds

The transition element dichlorides crystallize in the $CdCl_2$ structure, and the dibromides have the hexagonal CdI_2 structure.   The $CdCl_2$ structure corresponds to rock salt with every other (111) cation plane removed.   The CdI_2 structure is formed by removal of alternate basal planes of a close-packed-hexagonal cation sublattice. Therefore these structures, like the ilmenites, contain cation-anion-anion-cation interlayer interactions that may compete with intralayer 90° interactions.   As in the ilmenites, the 90° interactions within the layers are antiferromagnetic if the $3d$ orbitals are half filled (Case 1 of Fig. 43), but are ferromagnetic if the t_{2g} orbitals are more than half filled.   Evidence for the sign of the intralayer interactions comes from Θ_a (see Table VIII).

In the trichlorides, one-third of the cations are removed from the dichloride layers, but 90° interactions are still present.   Therefore it is not surprising to find that the competing interactions produce a spiral configuration in $FeCl_3$.   (The hexagonal symmetry supports a spiral configuration even though it is not a Bravais lattice.)   The ferromagnetic layers of $CrCl_3$, on the other hand, indicate that the 90° intralayer interactions are ferromagnetic.   Negligible cation- -cation interactions are to be expected since the Cl^- ion is large, so that ferromagnetic 90° interactions are possible (see Fig. 43). That the intralayer interactions are ferromagnetic is indicated by $\Theta_a > 0$. This is in contrast to the strong antiferromagnetic Cr^{3+}– –Cr^{3+} interactions in the oxides where cation- -cation interactions are substantial. In $CrBr_3$ the chromium separations in the basal plane are even larger than in $CrCl_3$, and ferromagnetic 90° cation-anion-cation interactions must dominate. The ferromagnetism of $CrBr_3$ confirms this conclusion.

The orthorhombic oxides with $CrVO_4$ structure (see Table VIII) also have c-axis coupling that is compatible with the sign of the cation- -cation interactions: antiferromagnetic Cr^{3+}– –Cr^{3+} and ferromagnetic Fe^{2+}– –Fe^{2+}, Co^{2+}– Co^{2+}, Ni^{2+}– –Ni^{2+}.

Kanamori (320) has interpreted the magnetic properties of the iron group anhydrous chlorides with the aid of ligand-field theory. Since the crystalline anisotropy gives evidence for considerable spin-orbit coupling, he assumes that in $FeCl_2$ the Γ_5 triplet (one-electron problem with cubic fields splitting the ^5D atomic level into $\Gamma_5(t_{2g}^3)$ and $\Gamma_3(e_g^2)$) is split by the trigonal fields into a lower doublet ($\Gamma_{T3}^{1,2}$ of eq. 68) and an upper singlet (Γ_{T1}). Which level is stabilized depends sensitively on the magnitude of the effective point dipole moments induced on the chlorine ions. For $CoCl_2$ he assumes that the singlet Γ_{T1} is lower, which again permits large spin-orbit coupling. He further assumes that the trigonal-field splitting is large compared to the spin-orbit coupling. With this model it is possible to account for the principal susceptibilities both in the paramagnetic and in the antiferromagnetic states, and also for the parasitic-magnetization curve in the antiferromagnetic state.

J. INTERACTIONS BETWEEN CATIONS IN TETRAHEDRAL SITES

Arguments for the sign of the exchange interactions between tetrahedral-site cations are similar to those for octahedral-site cations. However, in this case cation- -cation interactions across a shared edge involve overlapping e_g orbitals. Correlation superexchange and cation- -cation interactions are both unambiguously antiferromagnetic for d^5-d^5 interactions.

There are two β-MnS phases, in each of which the $Mn^{2+}(3d^5)$ ions occupy half the tetrahedral interstices of a close-packed sulfur sublattice: one is cubic and the other hexagonal. The cation-occupied tetrahedra share a common corner. There are no cation--cation interactions, and the cation-anion-cation angle is 120°. Each anion has four neighboring cations, so that not all cation-anion-cation interactions can be antiferromagnetic simultaneously. The best compromise has two antiferromagnetic and one ferromagnetic linkage. Only nearest-neighbor cation interactions are present, so that the best collinear compromise leads to ordering of the third kind (Fig. 18). Although neutron-diffraction data (126) are compatible with this type of ordering, a difficulty remains for cubic β-MnS: The neutron data would call for a spin direction that gives a dipole-dipole energy of 1.3×10^6 erg/cm^3 above its minimum, and there are no known anisotropic forces of sufficient magnitude, in the case of Mn^{2+}, to force this orientation.

Keffer (341a) has pointed out that, if the anisotropic superexchange of equation 167 is included in the spin-dependent Hamiltonian, the ground state of cubic β-MnS (Mn^{2+} ions from a f.c.c. array) is a spiral ($\theta = 90°$) propagating along a [100], but with antiferromagnetic, collinear (001) planes. Whereas anisotropic superexchange (proportional to $\sin \theta_{ij}$) usually competes with normal superexchange (proportional to $\cos \theta_{ij}$), so that only the small cant angles of parasitic ferromagnetism are realized, it does not compete in cubic β-MnS because the compromise minimum-energy configuration for normal superexchange can be achieved in a variety of ways if noncollinear spins are allowed. Keffer's [100] spiral is one possibility that also permits considerable reduction of the anisotropic-superexchange energy, which is minimized by 90° coupling of neighboring Mn^{2+} spins. This spiral satisfies the neutron data as well as collinear ordering of the third kind, but it also gives a dipole-dipole energy of 1.3×10^6 ergs/cm^3 above the minimum. However, estimates (510a) of the magnitude of **D** indicate that the anisotropic-superexchange stabilization is of comparable magnitude, so that the spiral configuration is quite plausible.

Chalcopyrite, CuFeS$_2$, has the zinc blende structure, but with ordering of the Cu^+, Fe^{3+} ions within (001) layers so that the paramagnetic Fe^{3+} cation has only four tetrahedral Fe^{3+} near neighbors, but eight diamagnetic Cu^+ near neighbors. In this structure antiferromagnetic coupling between Fe^{3+} near neighbors can be propagated unambiguously over the Fe^{3+} sublattice. The tetragonal symmetry is presumably due to the cation ordering. The low-iron moment observed by neutron diffraction is not understood.

II. Ionic Compounds with Metallic Conductivity

A. DESCRIPTION OF THE OUTER ELECTRONS

As has been pointed out previously, ionic compounds are characterized by a Fermi level E_F that is located within an $s-p$-state energy gap E_g^{eff}. It is for this reason that ionic compounds are usually insulators. However, if the ionic compound contains transition element cations, electrical conductivity can take place via the d electrons. Two situations have been distinguished: the case where $R_{tt} > R_c(n,d)$ and that where $R_{tt} < R_c(n,d)$. Compounds corresponding to the first alternative have been discussed in Chapter III, Section I, where it was pointed out that the presence of similar atoms on similar lattice sites, but in different valence states, leads to low or intermediate mobility semiconduction via a hopping of d electrons over a lattice-polarization barrier from cations of lower valence to cations of higher valence. In this section it is shown how compounds that illustrate the second alternative, $R_{tt} < R_c(n,d)$, may lead to intermediate mobility, metallic conduction and to martensitic semiconductor $\rightleftharpoons$ metallic phase transitions.

1. Criteria for Metallic Conduction in Ionic Compounds

From the discussion of Chapter I, it follows that metallic conduction is to be associated with partially filled bands of collective-electron states. Since the $s-p$ bands of an ionic compound are either full or empty, metallic conduction implies partially filled d bands, and collective d electrons imply $R_{tt} < R_c(n,d)$. From the requirement $R_{tt} < R_c(n,d)$ it is apparent that the *metallic conduction in ionic compounds must be restricted either to transition element compounds in which the anions are relatively small or to compounds with a cation/anion ratio > 1.* Also $R_c(n,d)$ decreases, for a given n, with increasing atomic number, that is with increasing nuclear charge, and the presence of e_g electrons increases the "effective" size of an octahedral cation (627) (see Fig. 66) and similarly t_{2g} electrons the size of a tetrahedral cation. It follows that: *If the cation/anion ratio ≤ 1, MO d electrons are more probable in ionic compounds with octahedral-site cations if the cations contain three or less d electrons; MO d electrons are more probable in ionic compounds with tetrahedral-site cations if the cations contain two or less d electrons.*

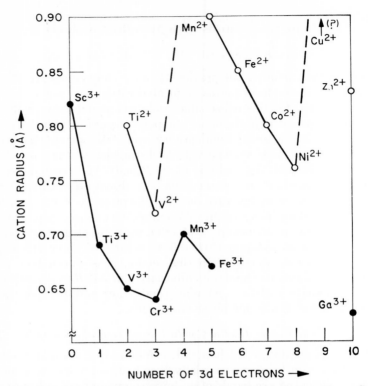

Fig. 66. Ionic radii for divalent and trivalent octahedral-site cations, Gold-schmidt values. (After Van Santen and Van Wieringen (627).)

The formation of collective-electron orbitals requires considerable overlap of the atomic wave functions of neighboring cations. Since the d wave functions are highly anisotropic (Fig. 2), the particular d electrons that may be collective are determined by the symmetry of the ligand fields. For octahedral-site cations, only t_{2g} electrons can directly overlap orbitals of neighboring cations (see Fig. 2). (For tetrahedral-site cations, only e_g electrons may be collective. These are illustrated in the Cu_2Sb compounds.)   Further, if occupied octahedra share a common face, as in corundum and NiAs, the ligand fields are trigonal and especially those electrons in Γ_{T1} of equation 68 may be collective. Similarly, given occupied octahedra that share a common edge, which of the t_{2g} electrons are more likely to be collective depends upon the local symmetry. Should the occupied octahedra (or tetrahedra) share only a common corner, as in ReO_3 (or β-MnS), there can be no collective-electron d bands.

2. Electron-Ordering Transformations

The melting point T_{mp} of an ionic compound is determined primarily by the s–p electrons and the Madelung energy, d-electron bonding playing only a secondary role. Therefore ordering of the d electrons into a configuration that optimizes d electron bonding may occur at a $T_t < T_{mp}$. It was pointed out in Chapter I, Section II-D that filled bonding bands, empty antibonding bands in a two-sublattice structure give greater stability at low temperature than partially filled metallic bands. Maximum binding occurs if each bond is an electron-pair bond (calculations of Mattheiss (415) and Slater (585) on the hydrogen chain, for example, show that the most stable configuration consists of H_2 molecules, as is known empirically), but core-core repulsive forces or the electrostatic forces due to the ionic character of a lattice may inhibit the formation of an "open" structure characteristic of electron-pair bonding. It follows that: *There are two principal types of electron ordering that may occur below $T_t < T_{mp}$ in ionic compounds with metallic conductivity: either the formation of electron-pair bonds at low temperatures, or the formation of a two-sublattice structure that orders metallic, collective electrons of a high-temperature phase into a bonding band in the low-temperature phase.* (Two other types of electron ordering that occur are illustrated by CrN and FeS.) Unless the cation sublattice already consists of cation pairs, as in the corundum structure, d-electron-pair bonding necessarily removes the cations from the center of symmetry of their anion interstice and reduces the crystal symmetry. The change in cation-cation binding energy due to the formation of $R_0 - \Delta R$ bond lengths within a pair (or a cluster), $R_0 + \Delta R$ bond lengths between pairs, is

$$\Delta E_{\text{binding}} \approx \left\{ n \frac{dV}{dR} \bigg|_{R_0 + \Delta R} - \alpha m \frac{dV}{dR} \bigg|_{R_0 - \Delta R} \right\} \Delta R = -A_B \Delta R$$

where n and m are the number per mole of cation-cation separations that are increased and decreased, respectively, by homopolar-bond formation, $V(R)$ is the cation-cation d-electron binding energy, and $\alpha > 1$ is the ratio of $V(R_0 - \Delta R)$ values for electron-pair vs. metallic bonding. This change in binding energy is accompanied by a change in elastic energy

$$\Delta E_{\text{elastic}} = A_{\text{el}}(\Delta R)^2$$

so that $\Delta R = A_B/2A_{\text{el}}$ and the total energy per mole gained by homopolar-bond formation is

$$NkT_t \approx A_B^2/4A_{\text{el}} = A_B\Delta R/2$$

Electron-pair bonding is therefore more probable if $R \approx R_c$, since the curvature of $V(R)$ has its maximum positive value at $R \approx R_c$. For R near the equilibrium for d-electron bonding, the curvature is negative and close-packed structures are more stable. Further, if the cations are small relative to the anion interstice, A_{el} is smaller and the transition temperature will be higher. (Conversely, if pressure is applied, A_{el} will generally increase faster than A_B^2, so that T_t decreases.) Electron-pair bonding is also more probable if homopolar, that is if between like cations, as there is then no ionic component, which favors close packing.

If electron ordering introduces a change in lattice symmetry, it is a cooperative phenomenon, and T_t is well defined, though it may exhibit considerable thermal hysteresis. If it introduces no change in the lattice symmetry, it need not be a cooperative phenomenon, and T_t may spread over a considerable ($\sim 100°C$) temperature interval.

3. *Electrical Conductivity*

Partially filled bands of collective-electron states support metallic conductivity. The electrical conductivity is defined as the ratio of current density $\mathbf{J} = ne\mathbf{v}$ to electric field strength, $\mathbf{E}$, where n is the number of carriers of charge e per unit volume and $\mathbf{v}$ is their average velocity. Since the average force on a charged particle is $e\mathbf{E} = m^*\mathbf{v}/\tau$, where τ is the mean time between collisions and m^* is the effective mass, it follows that

$$\sigma = ne^2\tau/m^* = ne\mu_e \qquad (173)$$

where $\mu_e = e\tau/m^*$ is known as the carrier mobility. For localized electrons that hop from lower valence to higher valence cations, τ is roughly the time required for an electron to jump from one cation to its neighbor, and from diffusion theory the mobility is given by equation 157. For collective s–p electrons, the assumption that electron-lattice interactions can be treated as a small perturbation is reasonable (provided the electronegativity difference of anions and cations is not too great), so that τ is much larger. The s–p carriers can be high-mobility carriers. There is apparently no change in τ on going from $R_{tt} > R_c(n,d)$ to $R_{tt} < R_c(n,d)$, the electron-lattice inter-actions remaining zero-order for narrow band electrons (279). In addition m^*, which is related to the band width by equation 33, is rela-tively large in the case of collective d electrons because the curvature of the $E_\mathbf{k}$ vs. $\mathbf{k}$ curve is smaller the narrower the band (see Fig. 6); and the smaller the overlap of atomic orbitals, the narrower is the band (see Fig. 7). Therefore, although the collective d electrons give rise to metallic conductivity, the mobility is of intermediate size ($\mu_e \sim 1$ to 10 cm^2/V-sec), so that $\sigma \sim 10$ to 10^3 ohm^{-1}-cm^{-1} is an-ticipated. Further for stoichiometric compounds having cations of a given atom in only one valence state, the number of charge car-riers may be temperature dependent if $R_0 \approx R_c$, since a small activa-tion energy may be required to separate a hole-electron exciton pair (see Chapter I, Section II-A-3).

If all the collective d electrons are ordered into homopolar, electron-pair bonds below some cooperative transition temperature $T_t < T_{mp}$, the low-temperature phase is semiconducting with an energy gap equivalent to the energy required to lift an electron from the homo-polar bond in which it is trapped to a collective state that belongs to the lattice as a whole. Therefore, *cooperative homopolar-bond ordering can give rise to a sharp, semiconducting $\rightleftharpoons$ metallic transition at T_t, σ changing by several orders of magnitude within a degree of temperature.*

If the low-temperature phase contains bonding and antibonding d bands, there will be a semiconducting $\rightleftharpoons$ metallic transition at T_t only if the bonding band is full and split from an empty antibonding band, and all other d electrons are localized. These semiconducting $\rightleftharpoons$ metallic transitions are to be distinguished from the metallic $\rightleftharpoons$ semiconducting transitions predicted from polaron theory (279) for $R = R_c(T_t)$. [The range $R_c(T_0) < R < R_c(T_m)$, where $T_0 = 0°$K and T_m is the melting point, should be small (~ 0.1 A).]

4. Magnetic Susceptibility

It should be possible to extrapolate the Heitler-London-Heisenberg description of the outer electrons from the case where the electrons are localized ($R > R_c$) to the collective-electron case ($R < R_c$), since there is nothing in this description that requires that the electrons be localized.   The difficulty with the method, once the atomic orbitals have been orthogonalized, is an adequate treatment of the polar terms.   At large internuclear separations $(R > R_c)$, it is sufficient to consider polar terms between nearest neighbors, as was done in the derivation of the cation- -cation exchange constants J_{ij} of equations 161–163.   *For collective electrons with R close to R_c, as is the case for ionic compounds that are metallic, the nearest-neighbor polar terms are probably still dominant, so that an extrapolation of the electron correlations reflected by the coupling rules of equations 161–163 should provide a correct, though qualitative, physical description of the dominant electron correlations among the collective electrons.*   It follows immediately that a two-sublattice structure with one electron per atomic orbital participating in the collective-electron bands has filled bonding states, empty antibonding states, and an electron correlation that reflects spin pairing of electrons occupying similar spatial regions; a two-sublattice structure with 1.5 electrons per atomic orbital participating in the collective-electron bands has filled bonding states, half filled antibonding states, and a potential electron correlation equivalent to ferromagnetic coupling of 0.5 localized electrons per atomic orbital. Although the electron-spin correlations are less sharply defined if the number of electrons per orbital is other than one or three-halves, the spin correlation rules of Chapter I, Section II-D appear to be a reasonable extrapolation.   Antiparallel-spin correlations cannot be propagated through the lattice in the case of collective electrons in metallic bands (two-sublattice criterion not fulfilled), so that parallel-spin correlations dominate.

The significance of these considerations for the magnetic susceptibility of the collective d electrons, given no localized electrons simultaneously present, is the following:

(a) For metallic bands, Pauli paramagnetism of equation 58 predominates.   Since the energy difference between the ground state and states of higher multiplicity are no larger than the width of the d bands (see Fig. 8), relatively high Pauli paramagnetism is to be expected if the bands are narrow.   Further, if the bands are so narrow that $kT \ll E_F(0)$ does not hold, the paramagnetic susceptibility becomes temperature-dependent.   However, μ_{eff} obtained from a linear portion of a χ_m^{-1} vs. T plot may be smaller than that predicted for localized d electrons, approaching the localized value asymptotically at high T.

(b) If there is a phase transformation below some T_t to a filled bonding band, and an empty antibonding band (or to electron-pair bonds), the low-temperature phase is diamagnetic. (Usually impurities and/or lack of stoichiometry introduce into experiment a small paramagnetism.) It follows that *one of the characteristic features to be associated with a semiconducting $\rightleftharpoons$ metallic transition is a marked discontinuity in the magnetic susceptibility.* This is in addition to the crystallographic changes and the specific-heat effects that are associated with the transition. Further, there should be no antiferromagnetic correlations visible to neutron diffraction below T_t so long as no localized electrons are simultaneously present.

(c) *If localized electrons are simultaneously present, a bonding-band $\rightleftharpoons$ metallic-band transition should coincide with (or lie above) a Néel temperature,* intraatomic exchange between localized and collective d electrons introducing an antiferromagnetic order of the localized electrons that reflects the antiparallel correlations of the collective electrons. *If the collective d bands are more than half filled, any magnetic ordering of localized electrons is ferromagnetic,* reflecting the parallel-spin correlations of the metallic or antibonding collective electrons. Because the intraatomic exchange interactions introduce a strong internal field that acts on the collective electrons, *there is a collective-electron contribution to the atomic moment, which may be equivalent to no spin-pairing of the collective-band holes (magnetic saturation) if the bands are narrow.*

B. ILLUSTRATIVE EXAMPLES

Only a few examples of metallic, ionic compounds are known that have a cation/anion ratio ≤ 1, but among these there are several that exhibit interesting transitions of the type anticipated above. These compounds are oxides and nitrides of titanium, vanadium, and chromium with three or less outer d electrons per cation. $TiCl_3$ exhibits magnetic properties that suggest it also belongs to this class of compounds. Metallic sulphides and selenides are encountered with Ti or partially filled $4d$ or $5d$ cation-sublattice bands. These materials are presently under study for possible thermoelectric applications, but the experimental data available are not yet adequate to be reported. Although compounds with the NiAs structure are generally metallic, these form a special group that will be considered separately.

Compounds with the Ni_2In and Cu_2Sb structure illustrate the situation for cation/anion ratio > 1.

1. *Compounds with Corundum Structure*

The most striking illustration of the ideas expressed in Chapter III, Section II-A is found in a comparison of Ti_2O_3 and V_2O_3, each of which, at high temperatures, is metallic with a corundum structure. This structure is illustrated in Figure 65, where it is seen that the pairs of cations along the c axis consist of two octahedral-site cations that share a common face. Each cation is linked with three neighboring cations in a basal plane via a common octahedral edge. Since the cation-cation distance R_{tt} is smaller along the c axis (shared face) than in the basal plane (shared edge), any bond formation would be stabilized in the c-axis pairs at a higher temperature than in the basal planes. Further, bond formation along the c axis would not require a change in lattice symmetry. Therefore it need not be cooperative and can be expected to take place over a range of temperature.

(*a*) In the case of Ti_2O_3 (Ti^{3+} has $3d^1$), which exhibits high conductivity at high temperatures, there are enough electrons for only one bond per cation, so that only the noncooperative (c-axis pairing) transition can occur. Further, at high temperatures the Γ_{T1} orbitals are stabilized relative to the $\Gamma_{T3}^{1,2}$ by the trigonal ligand fields, so that the compound should exhibit intrinsic semiconduction with a small ($\sim$100 cm^{-1}) energy gap. Stabilization of homopolar bonds along the c axis at lower temperatures would result in a sharp increase in the energy gap, the Γ_{T1} levels being further stabilized by bond formation. Since the bonding d electrons are spin-paired at low temperatures, there is no atomic moment to contribute to the paramagnetic susceptibility or to neutron scattering. With all the outer electrons tied up in the single c-axis bond, there should be a shift of the paired cations toward one another out of the center of symmetry of the anion interstice to give rise to a reduction in the c/a ratio. Since the transition is noncooperative, lack of stoichiometry would not influence appreciably the initial transition temperature. However, the presence of Ti^{4+} ions would guarantee the presence of unpaired Ti^{3+} electrons and therefore introduce acceptor levels and localized, paramagnetic moments into the low-temperature phase.

Experimentally a transition is observed in Ti_2O_3 near 200°C. Several physical parameters as a function of temperature are exhibited in Figures 67–71. All these parameters are compatible with

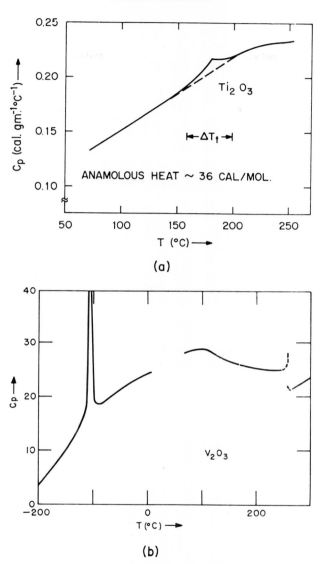

Fig. 67. Specific heat data for (a) Ti₂O₃ (after Nomura, Kawakubo, and Yanagi (482)—see also Naylor (468)) and (b) V₂O₃ (after Anderson (14) and Jaffray and Lyand (299)).

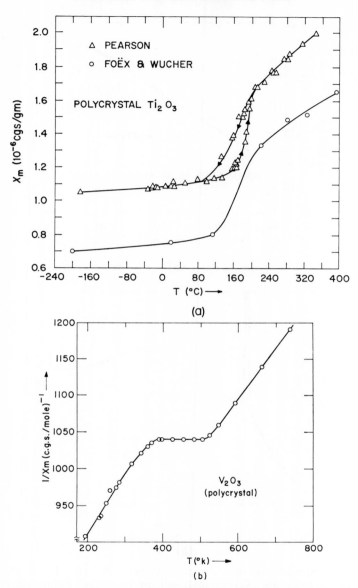

Fig. 68.   Polycrystalline magnetic susceptibility data for (a) Ti_2O_3.   (After Pearson (510); Foex and Wucher (182).)   (b) V_2O_3.   (After Foex and Wucher (183).)

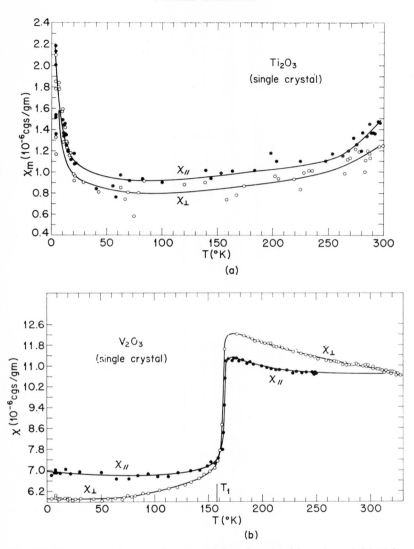

Fig. 69. Single-crystal magnetic susceptibility data for (a) Ti₂O₃ and (b) V₂O₃.
(After Carr and Foner (116).)

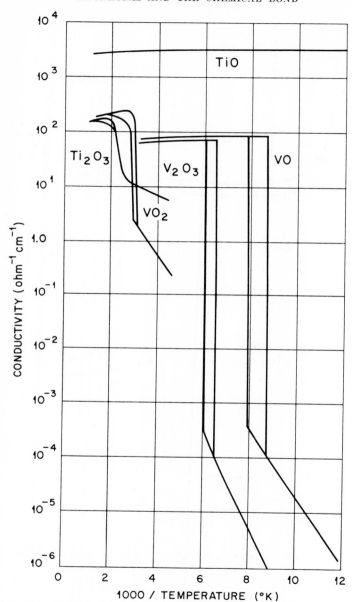

Fig. 70. Electrical conductivity vs. reciprocal temperature for several metallic
oxides.   (After Morin (448).)

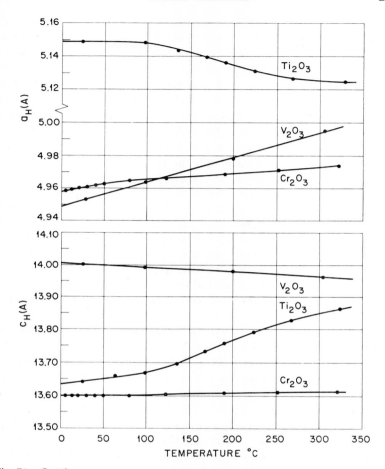

Fig. 71.   Lattice parameters vs. temperature for Ti_2O_3, V_2O_3, and Cr_2O_3.   (After Newnham and DeHaan (481).)

noncooperative, homopolar bonding of c-axis pairs in a low-temperature phase. Further evidence comes from the powder-pattern neutron data of Shirane and Pickart (564), which gave no noticeable magnetic peaks at 295°K and 4°K. Small ($< 5\%$) substitution of Ti^{3+} by $V^{3+}(3d^2)$ renders the material metallic (339), which is also consistent with the model since the additional d electrons from the V^{3+} occupy the basal-plane, $\Gamma_{7,3}^{1,2}$ bands.

(b) On the other hand, V_2O_3, which is metallic at high temperatures, can have two transitions (V^{3+} has $3d^2$): a noncooperative transition at higher temperatures due to c-axis pairing, and a cooperative transition at lower temperatures due to bonding in the basal plane. The high-temperature transition would have the following characteristics: (1) Below a critical temperature, homopolar, c-axis bonding sets in. Spin pairing results in a reduced magnetic susceptibility that is reflected by a break in the χ_m vs. T curves. The noncooperative character of the transition is reflected in a temperature interval for the transition. (2) Although metallic conductivity occurs via Γ_{T3} (basal-plane) electrons on either side of the transition, there should be a resistivity maximum in the transition-temperature interval where electron scattering is large both because of the large vibrations between nearly bonded pairs and because of the disorder caused by some bonded, some unbonded pairs. At lower and higher temperatures, the cation positions are stabilized. (3) Since the Γ_{T3} electrons do not permit closer packing between anion basal planes, any motion of the cations toward their c-axis mates away from the center of symmetry of their respective interstices would be manifest by an increase in c/a.

The low-temperature transition would be characterized by the following effects: (1) Cooperative $V^{3+}-$ $-V^{3+}$ bonding perpendicular to the c axis in but one of three possible directions so as to minimize the elastic energy. Many nucleation centers for the low-temperature phase would produce heavy twinning as a result of the three alternate axes. Such bonding would result in one short axis within the basal plane, a compensatory expansion within this plane occurring along the perpendicular axis. Although this would seem to give orthorhombic symmetry to the low-temperature phase, the cations of a c-axis pair move in opposite directions when basal-plane bonding occurs, so that a simultaneous tilting of the c axis reduces the symmetry to monoclinic. (2) A marked thermal hysteresis and sensitivity to both purity and stoichiometry, reflecting the cooperative character of the transition. (3) Elimination of the paramagnetic susceptibility, because of spin pairing of all the d electrons. Any small, residual paramagnetism would come from impurities and/or lack of stoichiometry. (4) A sharp change in electrical resistivity and in the type of conduction (semiconductor $\rightleftarrows$ metallic), since all of the d electrons of the low-temperature phase are trapped in homopolar bonds.

The experimental data for V_2O_3 are summarized in Figures 67–71. Both transitions are seen to exhibit the anticipated physical characteristics. The cooperative transition exhibits a thermal hysteresis of 18°C. The lowest temperature phase has monoclinic symmetry of the type described (c axis tilted), and single crystals cooled below the transition crumbled on heating to room temperature (645). The change in electrical resistance of over five orders of magnitude within a degree of temperature is the most dramatic phenomenon associated with the transition. The high-temperature transition is seen to extend over a considerable temperature interval, 110°C $< T <$ 260°C. The temperature-independent, small paramagnetism (116) and lack of any evidence of antiferromagnetic order at the lowest temperatures (500) supports strongly the concept that all d electrons are tied up in homopolar bonds in the low-temperature phase. However, it should be noted that the sensitivity of the neutron-diffraction experiments was such that small ($\lesssim 0.1 \mu_B$) atomic moments would not have been detected. Although the form factors for bonding s–p electrons drop off too rapidly to permit detection of any possible long-range collective-electron correlations, this is not necessarily true of d electrons with $R \rightarrow R_c$, and experiments of better resolution might reveal small ($< 0.1 \mu_B$) atomic moments associated with long-range correlations of the collective d electrons.

(c) Although Cr^{3+} has three outer d electrons, α-Cr_2O_3 is an insulator, indicating that $R_{tt} > R_c(3d)$ at least in the basal plane. Since the c-axis pairs are isolated from one another, an R_{tt} (c axis) $< R_c(3d)$ would not introduce metallic conductivity. Further, with two localized Γ_{T3} electrons, the internal exchange fields acting on the collective Γ_{T1} electrons would cause the collective electrons to contribute a major fraction of a Bohr magneton to the atomic moment. Thus the exchange fields tend to localize the electrons. Nevertheless, if R_{tt} (c axis) $< R_c(3d)$, below T_N there may be a variation in the fractional contribution of the Γ_{T1} electrons to the atomic moment with variations in R_{tt} (c axis). This variation can be brought about either by increased bonding with increased spin correlations below T_N or by dipole-dipole interactions that expand the A-B distance of Figure 65 with increasing c-axis component of the sublattice magnet-

izations.   Therefore an R_{tt} (c axis) $< R_c(3d)$ can be expected to
introduce variations in the atomic moment (or the apparent g factor)
with temperature.   Since the orbital angular momentum is essentially quenched by the cubic component of the ligand fields, marked
variations of the g factor from a spin-only value, especially if they are
temperature sensitive, would be evidence for an R_{tt} (c axis) $< R_c(3d)$
with induced localization of the Γ_{T1} electrons (or inhibition of homopolar bonding) via strong intraatomic-exchange fields.

Foner (186) has obtained a measure of $[2H_WH_A]^{1/2}$ vs. T, where
H_W and H_A are the exchange (or Weiss molecular) and anisotropy
fields, by observing antiferromagnetic resonance in high, pulsed
fields.   Since the Weiss fields are proportional to M_s and the anisotropy energy $M_sH_A \propto M_s^2$ if due to dipole-dipole interactions,
$[2H_WH_A]^{1/2} \propto M_s$ and should therefore have the temperature dependence of a Brillouin function.   In Figure 72 are shown $[2H_WH_A]^{1/2}$
vs. T curves for MnF$_2$, which is seen (Fig. 20) to be an antiferro-

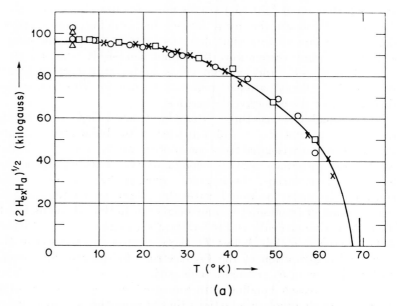

(a)

Fig. 72.   Critical field $H_c = (2H_{ex}H_a)^{1/2}$ vs. temperature from antiferromagnetic
resonance.   (a) MnF$_2$: Solid curve is Brillouin function for spin 5/2 and zero
applied field normalized at only $T = 0°$K, $T_N = 67.7°$K.   Triangles, circles, and

magnet that is described by the simple molecular field theory, and
for Cr_2O_3, which also should not be complicated by spin-orbit interactions.   The experimental points are seen to fall on the predicted
Brillouin curve corresponding to $S = 5/2$ for the case of MnF_2, but
to deviate markedly from the Brillouin curve for $S = 3/2$ in the
case of Cr_2O_3.   This is compatible with an R_{tt} (c axis) $< R_c(3d)$ in
Cr_2O_3.   However, it must be appreciated that deviation from a
Brillouin curve is common in antiferromagnets.   Such factors as an
easy plane, rather than an easy axis, of magnetization can cause
similar deviations from the Brillouin curve.   (In Cr_2O_3 the c axis is
the easy axis.   Color changes in the system $Al_2O_3 - Cr_2O_3$ (616a) also
indicate R_{tt} (c axis) $< R_c(3d)$ in Cr_2O_3.)

   (d) The room temperature R_{tt} distances of interest here, viz. A-B
and C-B'' (or D-A') of Figure 65 are the following: Ti_2O_3: 2.59,
2.99 A; V_2O_3: 2.70, 2.88 A; α-Cr_2O_3: 2.65, 2.89 A; α-Fe_2O_3: 2.89,
2.97 A (481).   In Ti_2O_3 and V_2O_3 both $R_{tt} < R_c$; and in α-Fe_2O_3 both

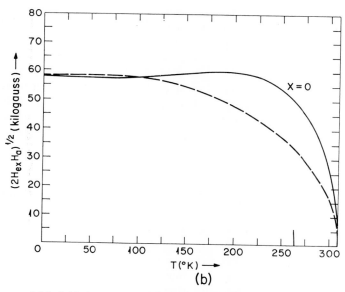

(b)

squares are high-field data at 35 kMc/sec (after Foner (186)) and crosses are
high-frequency data in zero applied field (after Johnson and Nethercot (306)).
(b) Cr_2O_3: Solid curve is experimental and dashed curve is Brillouin function for
$S = 3/2$.   (After Foner (188).)

$R_{tt} > R_c$. That $R_{\text{Ti–Ti}} = 2.99$ A $< R_c$ but $R_{\text{Cr–Cr}} = 2.89$ A $> R_c$ is possible because $R_0(3d)$ decreases with increasing nuclear charge by about 0.06 A on passing from titanium to chromium (see Fig. 66). Also, equation 27 fails to reflect any intra-atomic-exchange stabilization energy associated with localized electrons of total quantum number J. To this expression should be subtracted a term proportional to $\Delta(J(J + 1)) = J_l(J_l + 1) - J_c(J_c + 1)$, where J_l and J_c are the total quantum numbers for localized vs. collective electrons. This correction term is greater for chromium than titanium. However, $R_{\text{Cr–Cr}} = 2.65$ should be less than R_c, which is compatible with the anomalous behavior of the antiferromagnetic properties of Cr_2O_3. From this series of compounds it is therefore possible to draw the following tentative conclusion: *For similar octahedral-site cations in a close-packed oxygen sublattice, the critical cation-cation separation for localized versus collective electrons is*

$$R_c(3d) \approx [3.05 - 0.03(Z - Z_{\text{Ti}}) - 0.04\Delta(J(J + 1))] \text{ A} \qquad (174)$$

where Z_{Ti}, Z are, respectively, the atomic numbers of titanium and the transition metal cation in question. Although equation 174 is found to be consistent with the electric and magnetic properties of oxides, there are indications that R_c is somewhat larger if the anion is more polarizable. Derivation of a similar rule for the metals in Chapter III, Section III indicates that $R_c(\text{metal}) \approx R_c(\text{oxide}) + 0.2$ A. These estimates also give $R_c(4d) \approx R_c(3d) + 0.88$ A, $R_c(5d) \approx R_c(3d) + 1.36$ A. The critical distance for *dissimilar* atoms is somewhat smaller due to electronegativity differences between the atoms.

2. Compounds with Rock Salt Structure

(a) Metallic compounds with the rock salt structure are illustrated by TiN, ZrN, VN, NbN, CrN, TiO, and VO. Transition metal nitrides are usually considered interstitial alloys rather than ionic compounds. However, the rock salt nitrides listed above possess a markedly greater chemical stability than the perovskite nitrides like Fe_4N and Mn_4N, which suggests greater ionic character.

The rock salt nitrides are formed only if there are three or less d electrons on the formally ionic cation, so that the e_g orbitals are empty and the t_{2g} orbitals are half or less filled. In a simple ionic model, there is an effective energy gap due to an overlapping of the energy gaps of the split s bands and e_g-p bands. Within E_g^{eff} are nonbonding e_g-p and t_{2g} levels. With a large electronegativity difference of cation and anion sublattices, there is a large energy gap and the bonding electrons are associated with the anion sublattice, so that the bonding s and e_g-p electrons are primarily anion s and p, the nonbonding levels cation e_g and t_{2g}. With a smaller electronegativity difference between cation and anion, the greater association of the bonding electrons with the cation sublattice is reflected in a larger e_g character of the bonding electrons, a larger $s-p$ character of the nonbonding states. Greater covalent character of the bonding electrons can lead to different cation-anion-cation exchange correlations, as is pointed out in Chapter III, Section III-B-6, since in the extreme of no electronegativity difference the bonding electrons correlate parallel electron spins of the same sublattice (see Chapter I, Section II-D and Chapter III, Section III-A-1). If the covalent character of the bonds is sufficiently great that the correlations of Figure 86, rather than those of Figure 42, prevail, the compound must be classified as an interstitial alloy. Whereas the perovskite nitrides can only be properly discussed as interstitial alloys, the rock salt nitrides have sufficient ionic character that they are included with the ionic compounds. Nevertheless a partially covalent character of the intersublattice bonds give rise to a unique type of electron ordering in CrN. This unique electron ordering consists of an ordering of the covalent part of the bond along a single axis. In rock salt, the anion is octahedrally coordinated by cations, and vice versa. If the intersublattice bonds are 1/3 covalent, there is the possibility of electron ordering at a nitrogen anion that gives the formal, partially covalent outer-electron configuration: $N^-(p^4sp_z)$. This is possible because the s and p states for the principal quantum number $n = 2$ are not too different in energy.

(b) In the rock salt structure the cation sublattice forms a f.c.c. array, so that the t_{2g} orbitals, given $R_{tt} < R_c$, can only form a metallic band unless there is a distortion of the structure to lower symmetry. Of the rock salt structures listed, only CrN and VO are known to have a low-temperature transition to lower crystallographic symmetry. That transitions are found in the two cases where the t_{2g} orbitals are half filled is compatible with the fact that this condition is optimum for antiparallel-correlation stabilization and $R \approx R_c$. Why there is no electron ordering into (d_{yz}, d_{zx}) or into d_{xy} orbitals for two and one outer d electrons, respectively, is not clear, but it may be due to the fact that $R_{tt} \to R_0$ in these cases, the metal-metal separation being even smaller than in pure metals.

(c) At room temperature $R_{tt}(\text{CrN}) = 2.90$ A, which from equation 174 approximates the critical separation for formation of collective $3d$ electrons, nitrogen being more polarizable than oxygen. A neutron diffraction study (127) of CrN has revealed an antiferromagnetic low-temperature ($T < 0°\text{C}$) phase with ordering of the fourth kind (improved ordering of the second kind) in which (110) cation planes are ferromagnetic and the ordering of these planes on moving along the [110] direction is $\ldots + + - - + + \ldots$ (see Fig. 18). The structure is no longer cubic. The [110] axis is shortened, the [1$\bar{1}$0] axis is lengthened, and alternate (001) planes are shifted plus and minus along the [110] direction so that antiparallel cations are nearest neighbors, parallel cations have a greater separation. This distortion suggests bonding-band formation in the (1$\bar{1}$0) sheets via d_{yz}, d_{zx} orbitals and $R \approx R_c$ d_{xy} orbitals. The compound remains metallic through the transition. The atomic moment at 4.2°K is estimated to be $\mu_{\text{Cr}} = 2.36\mu_B$, which is considerably smaller than a spin-only value of $(3 + \epsilon)\mu_B$, whereas the high-temperature susceptibility gives a spin-only value for μ_{eff}. (Induced localization of bonding s and e_g–p electrons gives $\epsilon \ll 1$.) The sharp drop in χ_m on cooling through T_N is suggestive of some spin pairing as well as magnetic ordering.

A tentative interpretation of the physical properties of CrN rests on the assumption that the intersublattice bonding is partially covalent. In the low-temperature phase, there is ordering of the covalent part of the cation-anion bonding along the z-axis, and there is Cr––Cr bonding-band formation via d_{yz}, d_{zx} electrons. This gives cooperative electron correlations that are compatible with the magnetic order: Cation-anion-cation interactions within an xy plane are antiferromagnetic (Case 2, Fig. 42); along the z axis they are ferromagnetic, intraatomic exchange correlating the *covalent* electrons parallel within a sublattice and antiparallel between sublattices (see Fig. 86); cation- -cation interactions between $(d_{yz}d_{zx})$-bonded cations are antiferromagnetic. Only the localized d_{xy} electrons are forced to be antibonding. The atomic moment is

$$\mu_{\text{Cr}} = (1 + \delta_{yz} + \delta_{zx} + \epsilon)\mu_B$$

where δ_{yz}, δ_{zx} are the induced localizations of the bonding d_{yz}, d_{zx} electrons via intraatomic exchange with the localized d_{xy} electrons. Comparison with experiment requires that $\delta_{ij} \approx 0.6$ and $\epsilon \approx 0.16$, which compares favorably with what is usually encountered. Since $R_{tt} \approx R_c(Cr)$, the d electrons of the high-temperature phase occupy a narrow t_{2g} band $(E_F(0) < kT)$, so that the high-temperature susceptibility closely approaches the spin-only value. The origin and nature of the electrical conductivity above and below T_N is not clear at the present time.

(*d*) Stoichiometric VO has a sharp $(\Delta\rho \sim 10^6$ ohm-cm according to Fig. 70) semiconducting $\rightleftharpoons$ metallic transition at 114°K on cooling, at 121°K on heating. Here the lattice is ionic and clearly $R_{tt} = 2.89 < R_c(V)$. Therefore the semiconducting character of low-temperature VO indicates a phase in which all three t_{2g} electrons participate in homopolar bonding. One possible configuration for this phase can be imagined easily. It consists of paired (111) cation sheets, the distance between sheets varying alternately on going along a [111] axis. In such a phase there should be no evidence of antiferromagnetic order from neutron diffraction experiments since $\mu_V \rightarrow 0$. The low-temperature structure, magnetic susceptibility, and neutron diffraction data have not been reported.

(*e*) The compounds LiVO₂ and NaVO₂ consist of a rock salt struc-

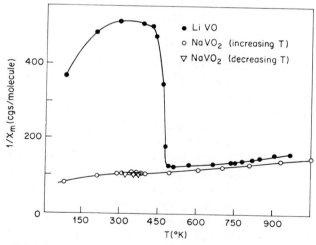

Fig. 73.   Polycrystalline magnetic susceptibility data for LiVO₂ and NaVO₂. (After Bongers (82).)

ture with ordering of M^+ and V^{3+} on alternate (111) cation planes to introduce a unique [111] axis and rhombohedral ($\alpha < 60°$) symmetry (82,159). Bongers (82) has found that both samples have a high-temperature susceptibility that approaches the spin-only value for V^{3+}. With $\alpha < 60°$, the sign of the trigonal fields would stabilize the $\Gamma_{T3}^{1,2}$ orbitals to partially quench spin-orbit effects. Cation- -cation interactions would also stabilize the $\Gamma_{T3}^{1,2}$ orbitals. In LiVO₂, $R_{tt} = 2.84$ A $< R_c(V)$ and in NaVO₂, $R_{tt} > 2.95$ A $= R_c(V)$. Therefore the sharp drop in χ_m (see Fig. 73) that occurs in LiVO₂ at $T_t = 463°K$, which is in sharp contrast to the small change at about 330°K in NaVO₂, is reasonably attributed on the one hand to molecular-orbital formation in the basal plane, on the other to antiferromagnetic coupling. However, the close-packed basal planes are not two-sublattice structures. Therefore, antiferromagnetic order probably consists of a noncollinear configuration, and molecular-orbital formation probably consists of triangular-cluster formation (the symmetry of LiVO₂ is rhombohedral below the transition). With no localized electrons simultaneously present, the molecular electrons should exhibit Pauli paramagnetism. Evidence for bonding in the basal plane in LiVO₂ comes from a comparison of c/a (hexagonal basis) for LiNiO₂ ($c/a = 4.930$) with LiVO₂ ($c/a = 5.22$) (667). Also Bongers (83) reports $a = 2.845$ A, $c = 14.84$ A below $T_t = 463°K$ and $a = 2.912$ A, $c = 14.65$ A above T_t.

3. Compounds with Rutile Structure

Of the rutile structures containing $3d$ transition metal ions, only TiO₂ and VO₂ can have $R_{tt} < R_c(3d)$. In this structure cation octahedra share a common edge along the c axis (see Fig. 29). Rutile (TiO₂) is an insulator. The Ti^{4+} ion has no outer d electrons and is located at the center of its anion interstice. With no outer d electrons, no d-band conductivity can occur. With only a few anion vacancies, $R_{tt}(c$ axis$) = 2.96$ A $< R_c(3d)$. Experimental reports are conflicting. Von Hippel et al. (642) report metallic c-axis conductivity for photoexcited electrons in stoichiometric TiO₂. Hollander and Castro (278) found that conductivity takes place via excitation to the antibonding $s–p$ bands and a hopping of localized electrons along the c axis, but that as the anion vacancies are increased, a composition is reached for which $R_{tt}(c$ axis$) < R_c(Ti)$. Experimentally this happens at a relatively low anion-vacancy concentration

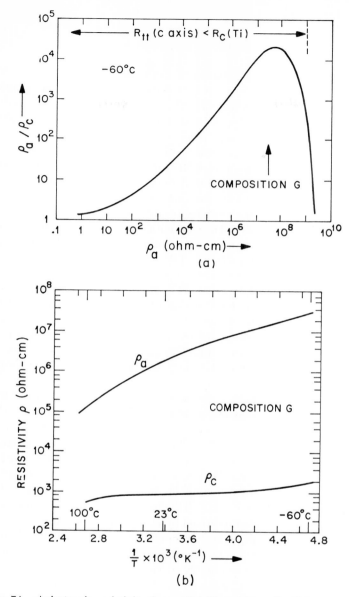

Fig. 74. Anisotropic resistivity in nonstoichiometric rutile $TiO_{2-\lambda}$, where ρ_a and ρ_c are a- and c-axis resistivities, respectively. (a) Anisotropy ratio ρ_a/ρ_c at $-60°C$ vs. ρ_a, where ρ_a and R_{tt} decrease with increasing oxygen deficiency λ. $R_{tt}(c \text{ axis}) < R_c(Ti)$ for $\rho_a <$ approx. 10^9 ohm-cm. The sharpness of the breakdown in ρ_a with $R_{tt}(a \text{ axis})$ is not apparent from this type of plot. (b) The a-axis and c-axis resistivities vs. temperature for composition G, a nonstoichiometric rutile. (Adapted from Hollander and Castro (278).)

(specimens not analyzed chemically, but a-axis resistivity $\rho_a \propto 1/N_{Ti^{3+}}$ is down by only factor ~ 10 over nearly stoichiometric samples). In samples with $R_{tt}(c \text{ axis}) < R_c(Ti)$, a large anisotropy in the resistivity occurs, ratios of a-axis to c-axis resistivity in excess of 20,000 to 1 being observed (see Fig. 74).

Careful x-ray work by Andersson (20a) provides a possible clue to some of the experimental difficulties. He finds that Ti_5O_9 does not contain randomly distributed oxygen vacancies, rather the vacancies tend to order so as to provide a stacking fault. The structure consists of slabs of rutile that are of infinite extension in two dimensions, but are only five TiO_6 octahedra thick. Across the common surface to adjoining slabs, TiO_6 octahedra share a common face. With a cation distribution $Ti^{3+} - Ti^{4+} - Ti^{4+} - Ti^{4+} - Ti^{3+}$ across any slab, there can be a pair of d electrons across each shared octahedral face to give homopolar Ti^{3+}- -Ti^{3+} bonding. Thus stoichiometric Ti_5O_9, with perfectly ordered stacking faults, would presumably be a semiconductor at lower temperatures. This type of stacking fault, which can be expected in oxides with a fractional d electron per cation, obviously has significant consequences for transport properties and may be partly responsible for the conductivities of the bronzes (Na_xWO_3, etc.).

The structure of VO_2 (V^{4+} has $3d^1$) is rutile only above 340°K. At room temperature the chains of octahedra along the [001] axis are puckered, and the V^{4+} ions are shifted so as to form metal-metal pairs within the chains (410). The bonded V–V pairs are separated by 2.65 A whereas the other V–V distance along the chain is 3.12 A. Such bonding within the chains is cooperative, and it traps all the available d electrons into homopolar bonds so as to quench metallic conductivity along the c axis. This means that the crystallographic transition should be characterized by (1) a semiconducting $\rightleftharpoons$ metallic transition with a $\Delta\rho$ of several orders of magnitude since the bonding and antibonding portions of the high-temperature c-axis d band are not split by the crystal symmetry; (2) a diamagnetic $\rightleftharpoons$ paramagnetic transition with $\mu_{eff} \rightarrow 1.73\mu_B$ (Curie-Weiss law not obeyed) at high temperatures; and (3) no magnetic peaks in low-temperature neutron diffraction patterns.

The experimental data for this compound are summarized in Figures 70 and 75. The semiconducting $\rightleftharpoons$ metallic transition at 340°K has a 10°C hysteresis, μ_{eff} increases above the transition to $1.58\mu_B$

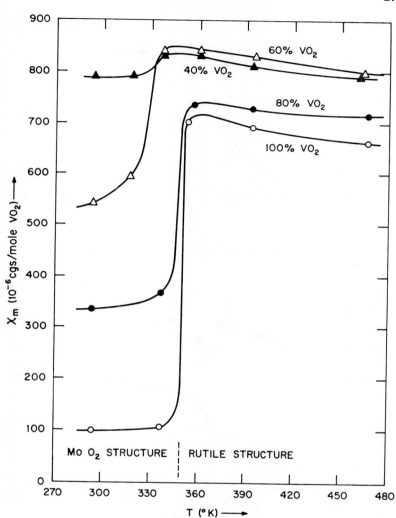

Fig. 75. Polycrystalline magnetic susceptibility data for samples from the system VO_2–TiO_2. (After Rüdorff, Walter, and Stadler (547).) Note that $Ti^{4+}(3d^\circ)$ cations have no d electrons for cation- -cation bonding.

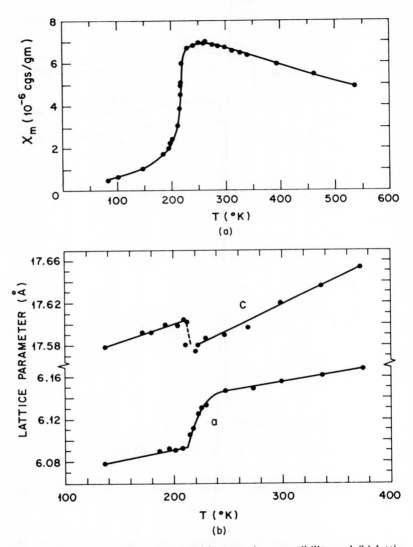

Fig. 76.   Temperature dependence of (a) magnetic susceptibility and (b) lattice parameters for TiCl₃.   (After Ogawa (486).)

by 466°K. Kasper (333) found no magnetic scattering in neutron diffraction experiments below room temperature. The fact that MoO_2, WO_2, TcO_2, and ReO_2 have a similar distorted-rutile structure at room temperature (410) appears to eliminate the possibility that the Jahn-Teller effect is responsible for the distortions. So does the shift of the cations from the center of anion-interstice symmetry.

4. The Compound TiCl₃

The compound $TiCl_3$ has the trigonal $FeCl_3$ structure, which consists of close-packed Ti^{3+} layers with one-third of the cations removed in an orderly manner so that each Ti^{3+} ion has three Ti^{3+} near neighbors via a shared octahedral edge. Thus the layers compose a two-sublattice structure. These layers are separated by two anion layers. Although the Ti^{3+}–Ti^{3+} distance within the layers is $R_{tt} = 3.07$ A, Ogawa (486) has found evidence for bonding-band formation within the layers below $217 \pm 2°K$ (see Fig. 76). The difference between $\chi_{\parallel}$ and $\chi_{\perp}$ (relative to c axis) was estimated to be less than 3×10^{-7} egs/gm in the interval $77°K < T < 370°K$. Electrical data were not reported.

This result is significant because it implies that equation 174 is only valid for the oxides, and the $R_c(3d)$ must be increased in the presence of anion sublattices of greater polarizability. It also implies that any extrapolation of equation 174 to transition metals must allow for some increase in $R_c(3d)$ from that given in equation 174.

5. Compounds with Cu₂Al Structure

In this structure the cation/anion ratio is greater than one, and c-axis-directed orbitals form a band of collective states. The ferromagnetic coupling along the c axis that is observed in $MnSn_2$ is presumably due to the presence of more than one electron per manganese atom in this band (extrapolation of equation 163). This is consistent with the fact that these d states are most strongly stabilized by the ligand fields. However, the relative positions of the d and $s–p$ bands and levels in these compounds cannot be given in any simple, qualitative scheme in this case, so that more detailed discussion is not meaningful.

C. COMPOUNDS WITH THE NiAs STRUCTURE

1. *General Considerations*

The ideal NiAs structure consists of a close-packed-hexagonal anion sublattice with cations in the octahedral interstices, which form a simple-hexagonal sublattice. Along the c axis the octahedral sites share common faces both above and below, so that the cations are arranged in linear chains with optimum conditions for cation- -cation interactions via Γ_{T1} orbitals, each octahedral-site cation seeing a trigonal ligand field (see Fig. 77). Whether the Γ_{T1} electrons are

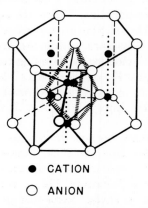

● CATION

○ ANION

◉ AN INTERSTITIAL SITE

Fig. 77. Schematic diagram of the NiAs structure.

collective or localized depends both upon the size (and polarizability) of the anions and upon the c/a ratio. For perfect close packing of the anions, the axial ratio is $c/a = 1.63$. Within the basal plane the octahedra share a common edge, so that cation- -cation interactions are also possible within the basal plane; however, these interactions are weaker than those along the c axis, just as in the case of corundum. What makes the NiAs structure difficult to characterize experimentally is the fact that the tetrahedral interstices of the anion sublattice also share a common face, and this means that each tetrahedral-site pair forms a single, trigonal-bipyramidal hole where the coordination is five (see Fig. 77). These holes are sufficiently large, especially if the anions themselves are large, that interstitial cations can be readily accommodated. In fact, it is usually difficult to order all of the cations into the octahedral sites. The octahedral and bipyramidal holes share a common face, so that an interstitial cation can interact directly (cation- -cation interactions) with its six neighboring octahedral-site cations; and for an ideal ($c/a = 1.63$) close-packed anion sublattice, the ratio of this cation- -cation distance to that along the c axis is $(1 + \sqrt{2})/2\sqrt{2} = 0.85$. Therefore *the presence of interstitial cations may introduce collective d electrons and metallic conductivity even if $R_{tt}(c\ axis) > R_c(3d)$*. Finally, the large interstitial sites not only make it difficult to order all cations into the octahedral interstices, but also permit considerable excess metallic component to be absorbed into the phase. Therefore the NiAs phase usually extends over a considerable range of composition. In this respect it is more like an alloy than a compound. The compositional range may be on either side of stoichiometry; that is there are both defect structures and interstitial structures. In fact it is often impossible to obtain the stoichiometric composition in the NiAs phase.

2. *Electrical Properties*

If all the cations are ordered into the octahedral interstices, the c-axis electrostatic interactions would favor $c/a > 1.63$. However, an interstitial cation favors $c/a = 1.63/\sqrt{2} = 1.15$. Therefore the presence of interstitial ions forces $c/a < 1.63$. Thus the magnitude of the axial ratio may serve as an indicator of the number of interstitial cations that are present. Since cations with outer-electron configuration d^3 or d^8 are especially stabilized in octahedral sites by ligand fields, stoichiometric (or defect) compounds containing Cr^{3+}, V^{2+}, Ni^{2+}, or Pd^{2+} cations might be anticipated to have fewer interstitial cations. Since cation- -cation bonding stabilizes the interstitials, it is more probable that of these compounds only those with $n_{2g} > 3$ (Ni^{2+} and Pd^{2+}) have $c/a > 1.63$ and semiconducting properties. Usually $c/a \sim 1.3$ to 1.5, which is indicative of many interstitials, and the conductivity is metallic. Metallic d-band conduction can occur via the interstitials because the NiAs structure is only found in compositions having cations with partially filled d shells. These facts also imply that cation- -cation d-electron interactions are usually important for stabilization of the structure. However, strong ligand-field stabilization into octahedral sites and a relative ion size that is too small for the rock salt structure ($R_{cat}/R_{an} < 0.414$)

may force the NiAs ($c/a > 1.63$) structure without benefit of strong cation- -cation interactions via large numbers of interstitials.*

3. Magnetic Interactions

(a) Given no interstitial cations, the predominant cation-anion-cation and cation- -cation exchange interactions are between basal-plane layers, weaker cation- -cation interactions existing within a plane. With a cation-anion-cation angle of $\sim 135°$, it is not obvious whether the magnetic interactions carry the sign of 180° interactions (Fig. 42 and Table XII) or of the $R \gg R_c$ 90° interactions, which are represented by the chlorides of Figure 43(c). It is assumed that the sign corresponds to the 180° interactions, which are all antiferromagnetic with the exception $3d^4$ cations (Cr^{2+}, Mn^{3+}, Fe^{4+}) in interstices that have no static Jahn-Teller distortion. It will be seen below that the magnetic data are compatible with this assumption. If the d shell is half or less filled (high-spin-state cation), the c-axis cation- -cation interactions are also antiferromagnetic; and if the d shell is more than half filled, the cation-anion-cation interactions are strong, and hence predominate. Therefore, *except in the case of $3d^4$ cations, the magnetic order of stoichiometric nickel-arsenides should consist of ferromagnetic basal planes coupled antiparallel to one another* (hexagonal ordering of the first kind, Fig. 18). Of course more complicated configurations may occur in ordered-vacancy structures, as was pointed out for corundum, which may be treated as an ordered-vacancy NiAs structure.

Interstitial ions always favor ferromagnetic ordering of the principal cation sublattice. If the principal sublattice is antiferromagnetic, the interstitials are undoubtedly shifted from the center of symmetry of their bipyramidal interstice into the tetrahedral environment nearer one of the two neighboring cation basal planes. The

---

* Relatively high conductivity may also be due to lack of stoichiometry in the presence of polarizable (heavy) anions. The origin of the metallic conductivity in these compounds is not established, even though the present discussion emphasizes the possible role of interstitials. Hall-mobility measurements should provide a significant test; intermediate (1 to 10 cm^2/V-sec) mobilities would indicate d-band conductivity via the interstitials, high (10^2 to 10^3 cm^2/V-sec) mobilities would indicate s–p-band conductivity. Hall effect measurements (198) of nominally (chemistry and structure not specified) NiTe, FeS, and FeTe give Hall mobilities 0.2 to 2 cm^2/V-sec, indicative of d-electron charge carriers, as here assumed.

magnitude of the atomic moment, as measured by neutron diffraction, is reduced by the presence of interstitials, which introduce some collective electrons. At high temperatures, μ_{eff} approaches a localized-electron model with orbital momentum largely quenched by the ligand fields. [The possibility of spin quenching by the ligand fields must also be kept in mind.]

Direct confirmation of these conclusions has been obtained by neutron diffraction for CrSb, MnTe, FeS and by susceptibility measurements (see Table VIII). It is significant that the titanium compounds show Pauli paramagnetism, indicative of collective electrons, since 3.15 A $< R_{tt}(c$ axis$) <$ 3.23 A. This is in agreement with equation 174, which calls for $R_c \approx 3.2$ A in the more polarizable anion sublattices.

(b) If the outer-electron configuration at the cations is $3d^4$, the situation may be quite different. First it is noted that: *With the exception of monoclinic CrS (305), no static Jahn-Teller distortions are associated with $3d^4$ cations in a NiAs structure.* (Although the B31 structure of MnP is a distorted NiAs structure, the distortions are not due to the Jahn-Teller effect.) Apparently a static, cooperative distortion of the structure to monoclinic symmetry (the structure being midway between NiAs and PtS) is relatively unstable. However, this does not mean that the vibrational modes are uninfluenced by the presence of Jahn-Teller ions. In fact it is reasonable to suppose that there is quasistatic coupling between the single e_g electrons and the lattice vibrations, so that by Table XII and Figure 57 *the $\sim135°$ cation-anion-cation interactions are ferromagnetic.* Since the cation- -cation interactions are all antiferromagnetic, this introduces competitive interactions that may lead to spiral configurations if no one competitor predominates. If this view is correct, then any antiferromagnetic NiAs structures that contain $3d^4$ cations should be those with smaller anion and lighter $3d^4$ cation, any ferromagnetic NiAs structures should have a larger anion and heavier $3d^4$ cation. Spiral-spin configurations may occur in materials with intermediate specifications. Since interstitials would couple antiparallel to a ferromagnetic matrix, the saturation magnetization must be especially sensitive to the number of interstitials that are present. At high temperatures, however, μ_{eff} should approach a spin-only value of $4.9\mu_B$ per $3d^4$ cation.

Experiment appears to confirm the essential features of this model.

1. All the ferromagnetic NiAs compounds contain $3d^4$ cations (CrTe, MnAs, MnSb, and MnBi).

2. Of the Cr^{2+} compounds, $CrS_{1+\delta}$ is antiferromagnetic (or ferrimagnetic if defects are ordered), CrTe is ferromagnetic, and the intermediate CrSe has a complex spin configuration (see Table VIII). [Only stoichiometric CrS is distorted to monoclinic symmetry, and its conductivity changes by three orders of magnitude on passing through the monoclinic $\rightleftharpoons$ hexagonal transition (317). It should also be noted that the peculiar spin configuration of CrSe cannot be accounted for with competing exchange interactions alone. Some other effect, such as crystalline anisotropy, must be playing a role. The particular anisotropy terms that must be introduced have not been worked out.]

3. The low saturation moment reported for CrTe ($\bar{\mu}_{Cr} = 2.4\mu_B$) is probably due either to interstitial ions, or to a ferromagnetic-spiral configuration. This point has not been checked by neutron diffraction experiments. The low moments generally reported for MnAs, MnSb, MnBi ($\bar{\mu}_{Mn} \approx 3.5\mu_B$) are almost certainly due to the presence of interstitial ions (540). Heikes (262) found that a MnBi sample quenched from above 445°C to room temperature had a saturation moment of only $1.7\mu_B$ per Mn atom whereas annealing the same specimen above 200°C gave a magnetization corresponding to $\bar{\mu}_{Mn} = 3.95\mu_B$.

4. The paramagnetic susceptibility of MnAs gives $\mu_{eff} \approx 4.9\mu_B$ per $3d^4$ cation.

MnAs and MnBi exhibit a first-order phase change at T_c, which is accompanied by discontinuous changes in a and c. In MnAs the c/a ratio increases (decrease in a) on heating through the Curie temperature, in MnBi it decreases. Roberts (540) has shown that in MnBi this transition is due to a movement of about 10% of the Mn atoms into interstitial sites. The origin of the phase change at T_c in MnAs has been attributed (44) to an exchange energy (or Curie temperature) that is a strong function of interatomic spacing and to a compressible lattice. It is conventional to assume that the exchange parameters J_{ij} are weak functions of interatomic spacing, and this leads to second-order phase changes at the Curie temperature, that is to no discontinuity in entropy or volume at T_c. However, if direct cation- -cation interactions are dominant in J_{ij} and $R \gtrsim R_c$, then it is clear that this assumption is suspect since the strength of the superexchange is strongly dependent upon the amount of orbital overlap. Collective electrons ($R < R_c$) have spin correlations that are less sensitive to this parameter. Bean and Rodbell (44) assumed a volume-dependent Curie temperature of the form

$$T_c = T_0[1 + \beta(V - V_0)/V_0]$$

where the parameter β could be positive or negative. The Gibbs free energy per unit volume contains five terms: exchange energy, elastic energy, entropy, and energies induced by application of an external magnetic field and an external pressure. Since the exchange term is now volume-dependent, minimization of the free energy with respect to volume shows that the volume change is due to a simple sum of the effects of magnetization and pressure. The dependence on magnetization is known as the volume *exchange striction*. Minimization of the free energy with respect to the magnetization, subject to the minimum-energy–volume conditions, gives the temperature dependence of the spontaneous magnetization. This relation contains a parameter $\eta = (3/2)NkT_0K\beta^2/(1 - q\beta)$, where K is the compressibility, P is the pressure, α the coefficient of thermal expansion, and $q \equiv (PK - \alpha T)$. If $\eta < 1$, the transformation at the Curie temperature is second-order; but if $\eta > 1$, then it is first-order. Although such an isotropic model cannot be a correct description for MnAs, the basic concept is important for the description of first-order transformations at magnetic-phase changes. This same physical concept was introduced by Kittel (349) to account for the first-order antiferromagnetic $\rightleftharpoons$ ferrimagnetic transition in $Mn_{2-x}Cr_xSb$ (see Chapter III, Section II-D-3).

In MnAs, $T_c = 45°C$ and there is an upper magnetic transition at $\sim130°C$. Although it has been suggested that MnAs is antiferromagnetic in the interval $45°C < T < 130°C$, it has been established that this is not the case (336). However, it is possible that short-range antiferromagnetic clusters are being formed about the interstitial Mn cations (this is the shortest cation--cation distance). The observation (336) of small distortions to orthorhombic symmetry in the interval $45°C < T < 130°C$ supports this suggestion. It is also compatible with the basic notion of Bean and Rodbell, but it complicates any quantitative description of the transformation.

The orthorhombic MnP structure is similar to the NiAs structure. Within a basal plane, alternate rows of Mn atoms are shifted towards one another, so that each Mn atom has only two nearest neighbors within the plane. Optimum packing is achieved by staggering the pairs of bonded rows from plane to plane, so that along the hexagonal c axis the chains of cations zigzag slightly. There are four $R_{tt} < R_c(\text{Mn})$: two along the c axis (b axis of orthorhombic cell) and two within the basal plane (b plane). This implies one localized Γ_{T_3} orbital and the formation of bonding bands from the Γ_{T_1} and a Γ_{T_3}. If the trivalent manganese in MnP were in a high-spin state, antiferromagnetic order via the bonding electrons and $n_B^A = 2 + 2\delta$ would be anticipated. However, MnP is metamagnetic with $n_B^A = 1.3$ in saturating fields (41,172,238–240,283). This is compatible with two bonding d orbitals only if trivalent manganese is in a low-spin state, so that the antibonding collective d bands are half filled and $S \approx 1$. There is a small discrepancy between the $S_{\text{eff}} = 0.65$ obtained from n_B^A and an $S \approx 1$ inferred from n_{eff}, which suggests that the spin configuration at $T = 0°\text{K}$ and $H > H_c$ is a ferromagnetic spiral. Antiferromagnetic next-near-neighbor Mn- -Mn and Mn-P-Mn interactions are presumably responsible for metamagnetism and the ferromagnetic spiral in high fields. Similarly ferrimagnetic FeP appears to be partially spin quenched. Further experimentation on these compounds is needed.

4. The System $\square_\delta Fe_{1-\delta}S$

The system $Fe_{1-\delta}S$ illustrates the type of complexity that can be encountered in systems with the NiAs structure. Interest in (49, 53,54,252,273,274,276,315,316,402,441,458,596,624,654,717) this system was originally stimulated by the observation of a spontaneous magnetization of the mineral pyrrhotite (654).

(a) Nominally stoichiometric FeS exhibits two transitions on heating, sometimes three transitions on cooling. Magnetic susceptibility and electrical resistivity data of Murakami and Hirahara (274,458) are shown in Figure 78. The two transitions for the heating cycle occur at $T_\alpha \uparrow = T_s \uparrow$ and at T_N, where T_α marks a crystallographic phase change, T_s a spin-axis change, and T_N the Néel point. In the cooling cycle the anomalous susceptibility can be interpreted as indicating $T_s \downarrow > T_\alpha \downarrow$, as will be discussed below. High-temperature susceptibilities obey a Curie-Weiss law (eq. 96) that gives $\Theta_a \approx -875°\text{K}$ and $\mu_{\text{eff}} \approx 5.24\mu_B$ (49). In the temperature interval $T_s \leq T \leq T_N$ the magnetic easy axis is in the

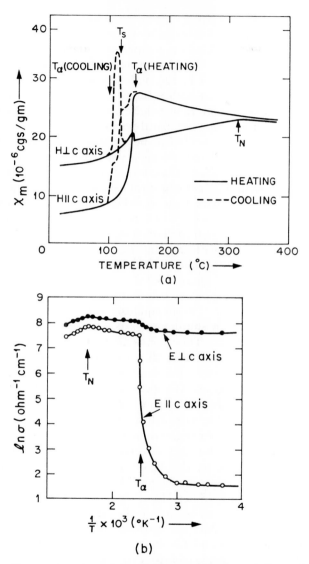

Fig. 78.   Temperature dependence of (a) magnetic susceptibility and (b) electric conductivity (natural logarithm) for a single crystal of nominally $FeS_{1.00}$ with magnetic and electric fields **H, E** applied parallel and perpendicular to the *c* axis.   (After Hirahara and Murakami (274, 458).)

basal plane; in the interval $T < T_s$ it is along the c axis.   At 465°K the shortest cation- -cation distance in the high-temperature phase is R_{tt} (c axis) = 2.90 A.   The low-temperature phase has been characterized by Bertaut (54).   The iron atoms of a basal plane, which are separated by about 3.5 A in the high-temperature phase, form triangular clusters such that within the plane each iron atom has two neighbors at 3.00 A and four neighbors at 3.73 A.   Clustering is identical in alternate pairs of basal-plane layers.   Within a pair of basal planes, R_{tt} (c axis) = 2.94 A; between pairs the layer separation is 2.97 A and R_{tt} = 3.04 A.   There is a sharp change both in χ_m and in c-axis resistivity at T_α.   That the change in c-axis resistivity is not associated with T_s has been established (273) by measurements on samples with δ = 0.05 to 0.08.   Throughout this range T_s decreases from -30°C to -150°C whereas T_α, which is associated with a narrow field about δ = 0, remains near 100°C for $\delta > 0.04$.   Thus the effects associated with T_α and T_s can be separated.   Neutron diffraction results (596) indicate an increase in the g factor of Fe^{2+} in the low-temperature phase.

Interpretation of these data depends upon a proper description of the $3d$ electrons of Fe^{2+}.   From equation 174, the critical intercation separation for iron in a sulfur matrix is $2.9 < R_c < 3.1$, which suggests that $R_c \approx 3.0$ A.   This means that the intercation distances found in FeS are compatible with a ligand-field model for $T > T_\alpha$, but with relatively strong cation- -cation interactions along the c axis that broaden the energy level for c-axis-oriented orbitals into a narrow band of collective-electron states.   At $T < T_\alpha$, the intercation distances are compatible with collective-electron orbitals within the basal planes for the "triangular molecule" of a cluster.   However, again the band width for the collective-electron states may be assumed small relative to the ligand-field splittings.   Therefore a qualitative energy-level scheme may be obtained with the Hamiltonian of equation 61.   Since Hund's rule applies, $V_{el} > V_c$ and the energy level diagram can be obtained from the one-electron model.   However, the ground state is a six-electron state.

Whereas the trigonal-field component V_t of the ligand field favors stabilization of a nondegenerate Γ_{T1}, which quenches the orbital angular momentum and concentrates the "extra-electron" charge along the c axis, spin-orbit coupling would stabilize the twofold-degenerate $\Gamma_{T3}^{1,2}$, which concentrates this charge in the basal plane.

Therefore the ground state at temperature T of the high-temperature phase is $\alpha\Gamma_{T1} + \beta\Gamma_{T3}$, where $\alpha + \beta = 1$ and V_t favors α, V_{LS} favors β. In addition, the magnetic-exchange term consists of two parts, an antiferromagnetic cation-anion-cation interaction between basal planes, which is independent of the magnitudes of α and β, and a c-axis cation--cation interaction between basal planes that, from equations 163 and 161, is ferromagnetic for $\alpha \neq 0$, is antiferromagnetic for $\alpha = 0$. This latter statement is really a postulate, not a statement of fact, as it is based on an extrapolation of the super-exchange coupling rules for localized electrons to obtain the spin correlations of narrow-band $(R \approx R_c)$ collective electrons. This extrapolation gives the following rules: *Half filled, overlapping localized orbitals that satisfy the two-sublattice criterion are stabilized by antiferromagnetic coupling and are repulsive if coupled ferromagnetically. More than half filled, overlapping localized orbitals are stabilized by ferromagnetic coupling.* Support for the postulate will be seen to reside in the fact that it permits a consistent, though qualitative, interpretation of a great many magnetic compounds and systems. (For a further discussion of electron correlations when $R \approx R_c$, see Chapter III, Section III-A.) Since the magnetic-exchange energy of FeS is optimum if the cation--cation and cation-anion-cation interactions are cooperative, cation--cation spin correlations favor $\alpha = 0$. Further, the cation--cation interactions are especially sensitive to $R(c$-axis$)$, increasing exponentially with decreasing c. (The relative sensitivity to lattice-parameter changes of cation--cation to cation-anion-cation interactions gives an *exchange-inversion-temperature* in $Mn_{2-x}Cr_xSb$. See Chapter III, Section II-D.) Since the c parameter varies as the temperature, this means that so long as $\alpha \neq 0$, both α and the intersublattice coupling parameter n, which from equation 112 is measured by $\chi_\perp = 1/n$, must decrease with temperature. However, once $\alpha = 0$ the two magnetic-exchange contributions add, and n increases with decreasing c parameter, or temperature. These facts have led (220) to the following interpretation of the properties of nearly stoichiometric FeS.

(*i*) The paramagnetic susceptibility should obey a Curie-Weiss law, but with $\mu_{eff} > \mu_{.ff}$ (spin only) $= 4.90\mu_B$ both because of the presence of an orbital-momentum contribution $(\beta \neq 0)$ and a $\Theta_a = \Theta_{a0} + aT$.

(*ii*) In the interval $T_\alpha \leq T \leq T_N$, $\chi_\perp = 1/n$ increases with decreasing temperature because $\alpha \neq 0$. The discontinuous increase in $\chi_\perp$ on cooling through T_s reflects an added lowering of α and c due to strong spin-orbit coupling below T_s, where $\mathbf{L}$ and $\mathbf{S}$ are parallel.

(*iii*) For $T < T_\alpha$, $\alpha = 0$ and a discontinuous decrease in $\chi_\perp = 1/n$ on cooling through T_α reflects the fact that below T_α the two magnetic-exchange terms add, above they subtract.

(*iv*) There are two principal contributions to the magnetic anisotropy: dipole-dipole interactions, which stabilize the spins in the basal plane, and spin-orbit coupling, which stabilizes the spins along the c axis. The spin-orbit coupling increases with decreasing α (or decreasing T), so that the dipole-dipole term predominates for $T > T_s$, the spin-orbit term for $T < T_s$. Since $\alpha = 0$ below T_α, it follows that $T_\alpha \leq T_s$.

(*v*) Below T_α, where $\alpha = 0$, the four atomic $\Gamma_{T3}^{1,2}$ orbitals are three-fourths filled, which is compatible with ferromagnetic cation- -cation exchange within the basal planes. (See rules above.) Since R (basal plane) $\approx R_c$, there exists the possibility of stabilizing the system via the formation of cation- -cation molecular orbitals to give $R < R_c$ for bonded cations and $R > R_c$ for nonbonded cations. Such a bonding distorts the structure; if this distortion lowers the crystalline symmetry, the elastic coupling V_λ of equation 61 induces a cooperative phenomenon. The most stable cation- -cation bond would be a homopolar bond, the Γ_{T3} hole of neighboring cations being ordered into the same bond. Such ordering would require antiferromagnetic coupling between bonded cations, or a new magnetic order, and it would give rise to a sharp decrease in the symmetry from hexagonal to orthorhombic or monoclinic. Less cation- -cation binding energy is realized by three-membered-ring formation (three-membered ozone is less stable than O_2), which contains three-electron bonds compatible with ferromagnetic basal planes, but the induced crystallographic distortion is more compatible with the close-packed-hexagonal anion matrix. The fact that three-membered-ring formation is observed below T_α indicates that the sum of the elastic and cation- -cation binding energies stabilizes the structure with the smaller binding energy.

(*vi*) The angular momentum associated with the Γ_{T3} "hole" is larger for the molecular orbital, with larger radius, than for the atomic orbital, so that the c axis remains the easy axis. Through the cooperative transition at T_α, a discontinuous change in the orbital contribution to the moment can be expected. Further, the spin contribution to the moment remains the same for the Γ_3 and Γ_{T3} electrons, but may be slightly reduced for Γ_{T1} below T_α due to some tendency to homopolar bonding between pairs of basal planes. The net result would give an atomic moment that is roughly the same as the spin-only value at all temperatures, but noticeable changes in the g factor in the temperature interval $T_\alpha \leq T \leq T_s$.

(*vii*) Interpretation of the electrical conductivity versus temperature is dangerous without a knowledge of the number of interstitials that are present. Ordering of the electrons below T_α to give $\alpha = 0$ is compatible with the observed c-axis resistivity changes, but conductivity can only be sustained below T_α if interstitial Fe^{2+} are present to provide "bridges" between the "triangular" molecules (Hall mobilities (198) of < 1 cm^2/V-sec indicate d-electron charge carriers.)

Thus the data for FeS are compatible both with an $R_c \approx 3.00$ A for Fe^{2+} in a sulfur lattice and with the rules for narrow-band $(R \approx R_c)$, collective-electron correlations that are extrapolated from the theory of localized-electron $(R > R_c)$, cation--cation superexchange. This fact gives the interpretation of FeS even more significance than a recognition of an additional class of electron ordering at a $T_t < T_{mp}$.

(*b*) Compositions in the range $\sim 0.10 < \delta < \sim 0.125$ have a spontaneous magnetization with a Curie temperature $T_c = 300°C$ for Fe_7S_8 that decreases with decreasing δ. Bertaut (53) determined from a natural crystal of Fe_7S_8 that the vacancies order into every other cation layer in a way that maximizes the distance between them. An ordering of the Fe^{3+} ions probably takes place simultaneously at the vacancy-ordering temperature T_V. Since the crystallographic features of the ordered and disordered structures are different, the average exchange energy for the two need not be the same. Therefore if $T_V \geq T_N$, there is only one magnetic transition T_c, but if $T_V < T_N$, there are two. Below T_c the specimen is ferrimagnetic since the vacancies (and Fe^{3+}) ions order into just one cation sublattice. Further, if $T_c < T_V < T_N$, then on heating the sample the spontaneous magnetization disappears at T_c, the specimen is paramagnetic in the range $T_c < T < T_V$, becomes antiferromagnetic in the range $T_V < T < T_N$, and is paramagnetic again in the range $T > T_N$. Lotgering (402) has found $T_V \approx T_N = 330°C$ and $T_V > T_N$ in samples with $\delta = 0.124$ that were given different heat treatments.

(c) Compositions in the range $0.07 < \delta < \sim 0.10$ are characterized by an antiferromagnetic $\rightleftharpoons$ ferrimagnetic transition temperature T_γ that has been called an anti-Curie point (252). Lotgering (402) has argued that since the Bragg-Williams (684) order-disorder theory calls for a first-order transition at T_V (ordering in $\square Fe_7$ sublattice) whereas spin-ordering transitions are of second order, it is possible for the free energy of a magnetically ordered, vacancy-disordered phase to be less than that of the magnetically ordered, vacancy-ordered phase at some $T_\gamma < T_c$. Thus the anti-Curie point T_γ is interpreted as a vacancy and Fe^{3+} disorder $\rightleftharpoons$ order transition temperature that occurs below $T_c < T_V$. The disordered phase is, of course, antiferromagnetic.

5. Cation-Excess Nickel Arsenides

With a cation excess, there are necessarily a large number of interstitial ions present, and the magnetic interactions between the two cation sublattices become competitive with those within the octahedral-site sublattice. With $R < R_c$, the dominant interactions are probably the cation--cation interactions; and for $c/a < 1.33$, R_{tt} (c axis) $< R_{tt}$ (inter), where R_{tt} (c axis) is the octahedral-site separation along the c axis and R_{tt} (inter) is the intersublattice separation. In all cases discussed below, R_{tt} (c axis) $< R_{tt}$ (inter) $< R_c$, so that all the electrons on octahedral-site cations are collective, all but one (that in the c-axis-directed orbital) are collective for bipyramidal-site cations. (The cation-anion-cation angles through shared faces are $\alpha < 60°$, so that even anion-directed orbitals are collective via π bonding.) The two-sublattice criterion is only fulfilled if the c-axis interactions within the octahedral-site sublattice are ferromagnetic. However, there should be a critical fraction of bipyramidal sites such that if more than this fraction f_c are occupied, the spin correlations between sublattices dominate those along the c axis. For $f = 1/3$, each octahedral-site cation has as many bipyramidal-site as octahedral-site neighbors, so it is reasonable to anticipate $f_c \sim 1/3$. Since the cation symmetries differ, the band of collective, intersublattice d states is split in two: a lower band of bonding states and an upper band of antibonding states each containing four orbitals per cation. The c-axis-directed orbitals on the octahedral-site sublattice are forced by these correlations to be antibonding, and hence to appear localized. (For further discussion of bonding, antibonding, and metallic bands, refer to Chapter III, Section III-A.) Given parallel-spin correlations within the sublattice, the most stable bonding would occur with 3/2 electrons per c-axis orbital as this gives optimum ferromagnetic coupling along this axis. (This follows from extrapolation of equation 163.) These considerations lead to the following predictions.

In the systems Fe_xGe and Fe_xSn having the Ni_2In (cation-excess nickel-arsenide) structure, there can be only antiferromagnetic coupling within and between sublattices if $x \leq 4/3$ since the d orbitals of every cation are then half or less filled. For $4/3 < x \leq 3/2$, intersublattice correlations dominate, and with more than five d electrons per iron core the octahedral-site c-axis orbitals are more than half filled. The formal, localized-electron valences would be $Fe_{1-3\zeta}^{3+}Fe_{3\zeta}^{2+}[Fe_{1+\zeta}^{3+}]X$ where X is Ge or Sn and the brackets enclose bipyramidal cations. Therefore ferrimagnetism with ferromagnetic intrasublattice and antiferromagnetic intersublattice interactions are anticipated, with a maximum ferrimagnetic moment of $(3.3 - 8\zeta)\mu_B$/mol, where $\zeta = x - 4/3$. The observed moment will be reduced by $10\epsilon\mu_B$/mol, where ϵ is the fraction of octahedral sites with reverse spin. Thus with $\epsilon \approx 0.1$ for x near $4/3$ the spontaneous magnetization found (26) in $\gamma Fe_{1.3}Sn$ is accounted for. Since this phase is unstable at higher temperatures, it was not possible to determine from susceptibility measurements whether the magnetic interactions are ferro- or antiferromagnetic. If, on the other hand, $x > 3/2$, the intersublattice bands are also more than half filled. (It is assumed that the c-axis bands of the octahedral-site sublattice are stabilized at 3/2 electron per c-axis orbital.) Therefore the rules of electron correlation, as extrapolated from the cation- -cation superexchange rules, call for all cation- -cation interactions to be ferromagnetic. Chemical inhomogeneities will cause some ferromagnetic, some ferrimagnetic regions in the vicinity of $x = 3/2$, but for $x \gtrsim 1.7$ the entire structure is probably ferromagnetic with a maximum spontaneous magnetization corresponding to $[0.5 + ((1/3) + \zeta)]\mu_B$/mol. from the c-axis-directed orbitals on the two sublattices and $[3\zeta - 0.5 + 4((2/3) - \zeta)]\mu_B$/mol. from the other orbitals, where the term $4((2/3) - \zeta) = 4(2 - x)$ comes from the imbalance in the number of cations on the two types of sites. This gives a constant spin-only spontaneous magnetization of $3.0\mu_B$/mol. For $x < 2$, this will be reduced by $7.5\epsilon\mu_B$/mol., where $\epsilon \ll (2 - x)$ is the fraction of vacancies on the octahedral-site sublattice. Thus a $\mu_s = [3 - 7.5\delta(2 - x)]\mu_B$/mol., where $\delta \ll 1$, is anticipated.

Striking support for this model comes from the system Fe_xGe, where $1.5 \leq x \leq 2.0$ (703,704). In the compositional range $1.67 \leq x \leq 2.0$, the system is ferromagnetic and the spontaneous magnetization appears to be described by the formula $\mu_s = (1 + x)\mu_B$/mol, which corresponds to $\delta = 2/15$. Further, for $x = 1.5$, $\mu_s = 2.1\mu_B$, which is only slightly greater than the $2.0\mu_B$ predicted for ferrimagnetism with $\epsilon = 0$. With $\epsilon > 0$, some ferromagnetic regions within a mostly ferrimagnetic matrix is anticipated. The rapid increase in μ_s that is observed throughout the range $1.5 < x < 1.67$ would be a result of the growth with x of the ferromagnetic regions.

In the systems Mn_xSn and Mn_xGe, on the other hand, there can only be antiferromagnetic coupling between sublattices for all x in the range $1.5 \leq x \leq 2.0$. Further, intersublattice correlations predominate only for $(x - 1) > f_c \sim 1/3$. Again chemical inhomogeneities will probably mean full intersublattice correlations only for $x \gtrsim 1.5$, but ideally this calls for a ferrimagnetic moment for $4/3 < x < 5/3$ of $\mu_s = (4 - x)\mu_B$/mol, and for $5/3 < x < 2$ of $\mu_s = 7(2 - x)\mu_B$/mol, given a Mn^{3+} preference for bipyramidal sites. The system Mn_xSn with $1.45 \leq x \leq 2.0$ has been shown (27,705) to be ferrimagnetic with $2.4\mu_B$/mol $< \mu_s < 2.6\mu_B$/mol in the range $4/3 < x < 5/3$ and a $\mu_s \approx (1/3)(19 - 7x)\mu_B$/mol for $5/3 < x < 2.0$. Although the decrease with x in μ_s is observed to be much smaller than predicted for the range $4/3 < x < 5/3$, it was noted that there is considerable substitution of manganese on the anion sublattice in this compositional range. Such substitutions would tend to increase μ_s. For the proposed concepts and model, the significant feature of these experimental results is the striking confirmation of the criterion for antiferromagnetic versus ferromagnetic coupling in the manganese and iron systems.

D. COMPOUNDS WITH THE Cu_2Sb STRUCTURE

1. *General Considerations*

The tetragonal Cu_2Sb structure contains two types of cation position, I and II (see Fig. 18(j)). Cations of type I are tetrahedrally coordinated by anions, cations of type II are octahedrally coordinated. Cations of a given type occupy a basal plane, and along the c axis the types of planes vary in the sequence

$$-I-II_a-II_b-I-II_a-II_b-I-.$$

The shortest cation- -cation distance R_1 is between type I and type II cations, which occupy octahedral and tetrahedral interstices that share a common face. Thus for $R_1 < R_c$, there are bonding and antibonding t_{2g} bands associated with cation- -cation bonds of a three-layer II–I–II block. The next-shortest distance R_2 is within a type I plane, where the tetrahedral interstices share a common edge. If $R_2 < R_c$, there are bonding and antibonding e_g bands associated with the type I planes. The third shortest distance $R_3 = II_a-II_b$ is between type II cations. Their octahedra share a common edge. Since $R_1 < R_3$, the t_{2g} electrons tend to concentrate in the R_1 bonds, especially if $R_1 < R_c < R_3$. There are three important cation-anion-cation interactions to be considered: 180° II_i-anion-II_i, $\sim$125° II_i-anion-I, and $\sim$90° II_a-anion-II_b.

2. Mn_2Sb

Guillaud (235) measured the saturation moment of Mn_2Sb in 1943. He found a $\bar{\mu} = 0.936$ μ_B per Mn atom, or $n_B = 1.87$ per molecule, and he postulated that the two types of manganese atoms were coupled antiparallel to one another with atomic moments $3\mu_B$ and $5\mu_B$. Subsequent neutron experiments (676) have verified the type of order, but the measured moments $\mu_{MnI} = 2.13 \pm 0.20\mu_B$ and $\mu_{MnII} = -3.87 \pm 0.40\mu_B$ are considerably smaller. The Curie temperature is $T_c = 550°K$, and there is a change in the direction of the easy axis at $T_s = 240°K$, the spins being parallel to the c axis for $T_s < T < T_c$, perpendicular to the c axis for $T < T_s$ (241).

Since $R_1 < R_c$, there is a filled t_{2g} bonding band (empty antibonding band) that correlates any localized atomic moments of any three II–I–II layers antiparallel to one another. (Refer to Figure 2 for anisotropy of hybridized t_{2g} orbitals.) Since the strong $(R_1 < R_c)$ cation- -cation interactions can be expected to have stronger spin correlations than any cation-anion-cation interactions, any magnetic order should be composed of ferromagnetic layers that are strongly coupled antiparallel to one another within the three-layer units II–I–II. Therefore three alternatives can occur in Mn_2Sb: antiferromagnetism due to an antiparallel coupling between type II layers, ferrimagnetism due to a ferromagnetic coupling between these layers (these alternatives are illustrated in Figure 18(j)), or a complex configuration with repeat axis the c axis and spin angles or alternating spin coupling only between type II layers. Further, within a type I plane $R_2 \approx R_c$, but the parallel-spin correlations that are forced by the bonding t_{2g} insure "localized" electrons. Since antimony is tri-valent, one manganese cation is monovalent, the other divalent; and since the antibonding e_g states of type I manganese are more stable than the antibonding t_{2g} band of a II–I–II triple layer $(R_1 < R_2)$, the formal charge configuration must be $Mn_I^+ Mn_{II}^{2+} Sb^{3-}$. Therefore the atomic moments are given by

$$\mu_{Mn_I} = (1 + \delta_{xy} + \delta_{yz} + \delta_{zx})\mu_B$$
$$\mu_{Mn_{II}} = (2 + \delta'_{xy} + \delta'_{yz} + \delta'_{zx})\mu_B \tag{175}$$

where δ_{ij} and δ'_{ij} are induced localizations of the bonding t_{2g} electrons. Since the Mn_{II}^{2+} have the larger localized atomic moment, it is reason-able to expect $\delta'_{ij} > \delta_{ij}$. It is always difficult to estimate the fractions δ_{ij}, which may vary from ~ 0.3 to ~ 0.6. The upper bound was found in CrN, Chapter III, Section II-B-2. The lower bound is found in metal alloys, Chapter III, Section III. From the experi-mental data, a $\delta'_{ij} = 0.6$ and a $\delta_{ij} = 0.4$ are indicated for ferrimagnetic Mn_2Sb.

There are three interactions that determine the sign of the coupling between type II layers: (a) two 180° II-anion-II interactions and (b) eight 90° II_a-anion-II_b plus II_a- -II_b (via $R_3 > R_c$) interactions that stabilize antiparallel coupling, and (c) eight $\sim 125°$ II-anion-I interactions that stabilize parallel coupling. Whether antiferromag-netism, ferrimagnetism, or a complex-spin configuration prevails depends upon the relative strengths of the competitive interactions. It is not possible to predict from qualitative considerations alone which alternative should prevail. However, it is possible to say that antiferromagnetic coupling must accompany the shorter c parameter since the cation-anion-cation interactions are relatively insensitive to intercation distance whereas the antiferromagnetic II_a- -II_b inter-actions are extremely sensitive to R_3. Also, complex-spin configura-tions can only occur if the competing interactions are comparable, or c is intermediate. Thus there may be a critical c parameter c_c such that the compound is ferrimagnetic for $c > c_c$, has a complex-spin configuration for $c \approx c_c$, and is antiferromagnetic for $c < c_c$. From experiment, it is apparent that $c > c_c$ in Mn_2Sb.

3. Antiferromagnetic $\rightleftharpoons$ Ferrimagnetic Transition

Kittel (349) has given a thermodynamic theory for antiferromagnetic $\rightleftharpoons$ ferromagnetic (antiferromagnetic $\rightleftharpoons$ ferrimagnetic in Mn_2Sb) transitions at an exchange-inversion lattice parameter c_c, the parameter varying with temperature and pressure. For Mn_2Sb the exchange energy per unit volume between type II layers is

$$\epsilon_{ex} = -\rho(c - c_c)\mathbf{M}_A \cdot \mathbf{M}_B$$

where $\mathbf{M}_A$, $\mathbf{M}_B$ are the magnetizations of alternate sets of II–I–II blocks and $\rho = \partial W / \partial c$ is the rate of change of the Weiss molecular field constant W with lattice parameter c. (If an additional term in the Taylor expansion is used, so that

$$\epsilon_{ex} = -[\rho(c - c_c) + \tfrac{1}{2}\rho'(c - c_c)^2]\mathbf{M}_A \cdot \mathbf{M}_B$$

it is possible to determine experimentally a unique c_c for compounds $Mn_{2-x}M_xSb$ or $Mn_2Sb_{1-x}M'_x$ (302a).) Kittel neglects the intrinsic dependence of the $\mathbf{M}_i$ on c and T. At zero pressure, this gives, to the lowest relevant order, a free-energy density

$$f = \tfrac{1}{2}R(c - c_T)^2 - \rho(c - c_c)\mathbf{M}_A \cdot \mathbf{M}_B \qquad (176)$$

where R is the c-axis stiffness constant divided by c^2 and c_T is the lattice parameter for $\mathbf{M}_A \perp \mathbf{M}_B$, that for zero *exchange striction* (474). (Exchange striction gives a change in lattice parameter due to exchange stabilization with magnetic order. Since the associated strain must change with the sign of the coupling, this strain energy must be included in the relevant free-energy term. Refer to the discussion of the first-order phase change at T_c in MnAs, Chapter III, Section II-C-3.) The equilibrium parameter obtained from minimizing f with respect to c at a fixed temperature is

$$c = c_T + (\rho/R)\mathbf{M}_A \cdot \mathbf{M}_B \qquad (177)$$

and the difference in c at constant temperature between the states with ferromagnetic and antiferromagnetic coupling is

$$\Delta c = c_F - c_{AF} = 2\rho M^2/R \qquad (178)$$

In the case of Mn_2Sb, it was shown that $c_F > c_{AF}$ is anticipated, or that compatibility with the model requires $\rho > 0$.

Substitution of equation 177 into 176 gives

$$f = -(\rho^2/2R)(\mathbf{M}_A \cdot \mathbf{M}_B)^2 - \rho(c_{T'} - c_c)\mathbf{M}_A \cdot \mathbf{M}_B \qquad (179)$$

Since the sign of the first term is invariant with the sign of the interaction and $\rho > 0$, $\mathbf{M}_A$ is parallel to $\mathbf{M}_B$ if $c_T > c_c$ and $\mathbf{M}_A$ is antiparallel to $\mathbf{M}_B$ if $c_T < c_c$. *There occurs a first-order antiferromagnetic $\rightleftharpoons$ ferrimagnetic phase transition at a temperature T_e such that*

$$c_T = c_c \qquad (180)$$

Note that the sign of the interaction depends upon c_T, not c.

If ϕ is the angle between $\mathbf{M}_A$ and $\mathbf{M}_B$, the term in $\cos^2 \phi$ in equation 179 acts as a potential barrier separating the two states. It may introduce thermal hysteresis at the transition as large as

$$\Delta T = 2c_0 \rho M^2/\gamma C_L \qquad (181)$$

where C_L is the lattice heat capacity per unit volume, c_0 is the lattice parameter at zero temperature, and γ is the Grüneisen constant.

The effect of hydrostatic pressure p on T_e can be simply determined with the aid of the Clausius-Clapeyron equation. Kittel derives

$$dT_e/dp \approx (\gamma C_L)^{-1} \qquad (182)$$

Such an antiferromagnetic $\rightleftharpoons$ ferrimagnetic transition has been observed (120,122,609) in the system $Mn_{2-x}Cr_xSb_{0.95}In_{0.05}$. Apparently the decrease in lattice parameter with increasing Cr content is sufficient that a T_e is observed for $x > 0.03$, T_e increasing from about 120°K to nearly 400°K at $x = 0.2$. For $x = 0.1$, the change in lattice parameter at T_e is $\Delta c = 0.014$ A. From equation 178 and reasonable estimates of the stiffness constant R it follows that

$$\rho = \partial W/\partial c \sim 10^4 \text{ ergs/gauss}^2 \text{ A}$$

which is a large rate of change that supports a model in which cation--cation wavefunction overlaps are involved (see eq. 161). This is provided by the II--II interactions. The atomic moments were also observed to change at the transition. With increasing temperature, $\Delta\mu_{Mn_I} \approx 0.4\mu_B$, $\Delta\mu_{Mn_{II}} \approx -0.5\mu_B$. From the model, there should be no change in the number of localized electrons at the atoms. However, a $\Delta\delta_{ij} \sim 0.15$ is reasonable and would be of the correct sign.

Spiral-spin configurations were reported for compositions with

$0 < x \leq 0.03$ (70). However, it is more probable that the II–II interactions alternate in sign along the c axis.

4. Mn_2As, Cr_2As, and Cu_2Sb

The compound Mn_2As is similar to Mn_2Sb except that the smaller lattice parameter stabilizes *only the antiferromagnetic state*. Yuzuri and Yamada (711) have examined the system Mn_xAs, $1 \leq x \leq 2.5$, and found that a sample of $Mn_{2.3}As$ has the Cu_2Sb structure with $T_N = 573°K$.

The compound Cr_2As should have the charge configuration $Cr_I^+Cr_{II}^{2+}As^{3-}$. Since the octahedral interstices have tetragonal ($c/a > 1$) symmetry, the single e_g electron at a Cr_{II} occupies a d_{z^2} orbital oriented parallel to the c axis. This ordering increases the axial ratio (Jahn-Teller effect). With $c/a = 1.76$, $R_2 = 2.53$ A $< R_1 = 2.75$ A $< R_c(Cr)$. This indicates that the tetragonal distortion of the interstices stabilizes a $Cr_I^+(3d^5)$ e_g bonding band relative to the t_{2g} bonding band, so that the Cr_I moments are correlated antiparallel to one another within a basal plane. (Note that with fewer d electrons, there are no antibonding e_g electrons.) This means that cooperative t_{2g} bonding between type I and type II layers is inhibited. Although $R_3 = 3.28$ A $> R_c(Cr)$, cooperative antiferromagnetic correlations between type II layers are possible. Therefore it is predicted that Cr_2As is antiferromagnetic and that the magnetic order is different from that found in antiferromagnetic Mn_2As. Yuzuri (710) has reported that Cr_2As is indeed antiferromagnetic with $T_N = 393°K$. Measurements of the magnetic order have not been reported.

The compound Cu_2Sb should have the charge configuration $Cu_I^+Cu_{II}^{2+}Sb^{3-}$. Since the octahedral interstices have tetragonal ($c/a > 1$) symmetry, the Cu_{II} e_g hole is concentrated in the basal plane. This means that the Cu_I atoms should carry no atomic moment, $\mu_{Cu_{II}} \approx 1\mu_B$, and the Cu_{II} atoms are coupled antiparallel *within* a basal plane via 180° cation-anion-cation interactions. Cu_2Sb is reported (710) to be antiferromagnetic with a $T_N = 373°K$.

III. Metals and Alloys

A. DESCRIPTION OF THE OUTER ELECTRONS

In the transition metals and their alloys, the outer s and p electrons occupy partially filled, overlapping s and p bands. These give rise to high mobility, metallic conductivity. The character of the d electrons, on the other hand, is not so obvious. It was pointed out in Chapter I that whereas all the $5d$ electrons of the Pt metals are undoubtedly collective and all of the $4d$ electrons of the Pd metals are probably collective, both collective and localized $3d$ electrons may be simultaneously present in the metals of the first transition series. In Chapter II, Section II-B-1 an empirical relationship, equation 174, was given for the critical intercation separation in oxides for collective versus localized d electrons, and it was pointed out that this distance is somewhat larger if the anion sublattice is more polarizable. The maximum critical distance probably occurs in metals and alloys. To obtain an estimate for the metals, it is noted that dilute concentrations of substitutional iron in palladium induce localized moments on neighboring Pd atoms (138). This implies that $R_c(\text{Pd}) \approx R_{nnn}(\text{Pd}) = 3.89$ A, and this fact was used to obtain equation 27. From equations 26′ and 27 it follows that for metals, with correction term proportional to $\Delta(J(J + 1))$ neglected,

$$R_c(3d) \approx 2.5R_{nnn}(\text{Ni})/2.96 \ = \ 3.06 \text{ A}$$
$$R_c(4d) \approx 2.5R_{nnn}(\text{Pd})/2.47 \ = \ 3.94 \text{ A} \qquad (183)$$
$$R_c(5d) \approx 2.5R_{nnn}(\text{Pt})/2.21 \ = \ 4.42 \text{ A}$$

Comparison of equations 174 for the oxides and 183 for the metals gives

$$2.2R_0 \lesssim R_c^{nd} \lesssim 2.5R_0$$

where the lower limit applies to the oxides and fluorides, the upper limit to metals. This means, for example, that

$$R_c(\text{metals}) \approx R_c(\text{oxides}) + 0.2 \text{ A},$$

where $R_c(\text{oxides})$ is given by equation 174 for $3d$ electrons, and $R_c(4d) \approx R_c(3d) + 0.88$ A, $R_c(5d) \approx R_c(3d) + 1.36$ A. Although these numbers are crude, being based on semiempirical physical arguments, their internal consistency is significant. Further, since the empirical numbers for the metals come from one side of the periodic table, those for the oxides from the other, the result that

$$(\text{oxides})3.02 \text{ A} \lesssim R_c(\text{Ti}) \lesssim 3.22 \text{ A}(\text{metals})$$

probably represents an upper limit for the difference in R_c for oxides versus metals.

In this chapter, Section III, it is shown that the magnetic order and the magnitudes of the atomic moments that are found in the transition metals and their alloys may be interpreted in a consistent manner with the aid of the electron-correlation considerations of Chapter I (217). Although these ideas can only be proposed in a postulatory manner, it should be appreciated that all of the postulates are based on but one assumption: *The configuration interaction appropriate for localized d electrons, which gives the cation- -cation super-exchange rules [eqs. 161–163], remains the principal configuration interaction responsible for electron correlations among collective d electrons, where $R \rightarrow R_c$.* The fact that these postulates follow from the superexchange mechanisms already discussed in Chapter III, Section I makes desirable their inclusion in the present discussion. However, the reader should be aware that a great many theoretical investigations on the character of the collective d bands is not being reviewed here. Much of this work has unfortunately involved laborious calculations that have been based on questionable simplifying assumptions. Present experimental results are forcing a hard relook into the assumptions on which d-band calculations are based, and it is premature to say whether the particular physical ideas expressed below, which will be seen to be quite qualitative, can form a firm basis for a quantitative theory of these materials. These ideas are illustrated below with reference to cubic and tetragonal structures only.

1. *Body-Centered-Cubic Structures*

(a) Figure 79(a) shows the most reasonable configuration for a Cartesian reference frame relative to the b.c.c. structure. This reference frame is used to orient the highly anisotropic d orbitals, for the following assumption is explicitly made: *The collective d electrons retain the same symmetry relative to the lattice as the overlapping atomic orbitals that form the collective-electron states.* The b.c.c. structure contains two sublattices, and from Figure 2 it follows that the t_{2g} electrons, which are directed towards nearest neighbors, are collective $(R_{nn} \approx 2.09R_0^{3d} < R_c(3d) \approx 2.5R_0^{3d}$, see Chapter I, Section II-A-4). Nevertheless *with $R_{nn} > R_0$ and a two-sublattice structure, extrapolation of the cation- -cation superexchange spin correlations for localized electrons to the t_{2g}-band collective-electron spin correlations is reasonable.* This extrapolation is possible because in a two-sublattice structure it is advantageous to relax the requirement that orbitals of different

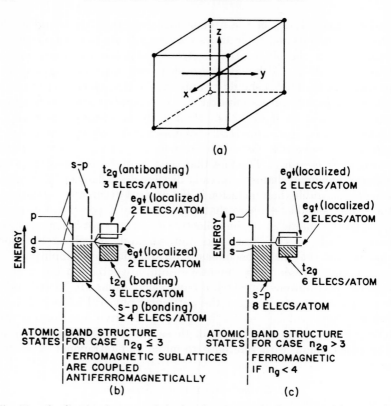

Fig. 79.   Qualitative features of the band structure for b.c.c. transition metals.

spin are identical.   As has been emphasized already, this says that for a two-sublattice structure the near-neighbor-directed orbitals form a band in which the bonding states, corresponding to antiparallel spin correlations within the bonds, are more stable than the antibonding states.   Parallel-spin correlations dominate the antibonding electrons.   Therefore antiparallel-spin correlations between the two sublattices predominate if the t_{2g} orbitals are half or less filled ($n_{2g} \leq 3$), and parallel-spin correlations predominate if the t_{2g} orbitals are more than half filled ($n_{2g} > 3$).   Since these electrons are collective, there is no correlation of bonding electrons of a given spin with a particular sublattice unless localized electrons with unpaired spins are simultaneously present.   Further, long-range antiparallel-spin correlations should occur if the bonding states are filled, but need not occur if they are only partially filled. This point is particularly significant for dilute concentrations of transition metal atoms in a nontransition metal solvent, such as Cu or Au, and for the rare earth metals. In these materials localized d or f electrons are coupled to one another via $s-p$ electrons in partially filled bands. Two somewhat different models have been developed for this case to describe the $s-p$ spin correlations that are induced and that are manifest by the magnetic order (497,722).

The e_g orbitals, see Figure 2, are directed along the axes of the Cartesian reference frame towards next-nearest neighbors. Since intraatomic-exchange interactions and nearest-neighbor spin correlations are both stronger than next-nearest-neighbor correlations, it follows that whether antiparallel or parallel correlations dominate the t_{2g} electrons, the e_g electrons are forced to have a parallel-spin correlation. Therefore if the intraatomic-exchange splitting is greater than the width of an e_g band, the e_g electrons act like localized electrons that obey Hund's rule. The splitting of the e_g subband containing positive spins from that containing negative spins is $(E_{ex} - \Delta E_g)$, where E_{ex} is the intraatomic exchange energy and ΔE_g is the width of an e_g subband. The fact that $R_{nnn} \approx R_c$ suggests narrow e_g bands that are split by intraatomic exchange into two subbands. Since the electrons of these split subbands are similar to localized electrons, they are referred to as "localized" electrons in the following discussion.

From the rules for stability that were developed in Chapter I, it follows that the bonding states are more stable than antibonding states, and that next-near-neighbor antibonding states are more stable than near-neighbor antibonding states. Therefore the lower e_g subband, which is stabilized to some extent by intraatomic exchange, should have an energy between the bonding and antibonding portions of the t_{2g} band. In Figure 79 are shown schematically the relative energies of the various bands and subbands. In an antiferromagnet there are two atoms per unit cell, and the t_{2g} bands may be split in two. In a ferromagnet or paramagnet there may be no splitting, but the bonding and antibonding portions of the t_{2g} band should be distinguishable, the density of states curves $N(E)$ vs. E having a bimodal character. In Figure 79 the e_g subbands are drawn as localized energy levels. Narrow bands, rather than sharp levels, are physically more reasonable; and the lower e_g subband may overlap the bonding t_{2g} band. Where overlap occurs, there is mixing of the states of the two bands, especially where the overlapping bands both come from d states. The broad s–p bands must overlap the relatively narrow d bands as shown.

From these simple considerations, it is possible to give sharp criteria for the existence of Pauli paramagnetism, antiferromagnetism, and ferromagnetism in b.c.c. transition metals.

(*i*) *If* $n_{2g} \leq 3$ *and* $n_g = 0$, *b.c.c. transition metals are Pauli paramagnetic.*

(*ii*) *If* $n_{2g} \leq 3$ *and* $n_g \neq 0$, *b.c.c. transition metals are antiferromagnetic with an atomic moment*

$$\mu = (n_g + \delta n_{2g} + \delta n_{sp})\mu_B. \tag{184}$$

Whereas long-range antiferromagnetic order should occur for $n_{2g} = 3$, a breakdown of simple antiferromagnetic order may occur if $n_{2g} < 3$, that is, if the collective electrons responsible for coupling the localized spins occupy partially filled bonding bands.

(*iii*) *If* $n_{2g} > 3$, *b.c.c. transition metals are ferromagnetic with an atomic moment* $\mu = (n_{2g} - 3 + n_{g1} - n_{g2} + \delta n_{sp})\mu_B$ *for* $3 < n_{2g} \leq 4.5$ *and*

$$\mu = (6 - n_{2g} + n_{g1} - n_{g2} + \delta n_{sp})\mu_B \, for \, 4.5 \leq n_{2g} < 6. \tag{185}$$

Here δn_{2g} and δn_{sp} are the fractional number of t_{2g} and s–p bonding-band spins that are correlated with a given atomic site as a result of the intraatomic, parallel-spin correlations between localized e_g and collective t_{2g}, s–p electrons. The symbols n_{g1} and n_{g2} refer to the number of electrons in the lower and upper e_g subbands, respectively.

In order to make contact with experiment, it is necessary to know to what extent the s–p bands overlap the d bands. Since the symmetry is compatible with (sp^3) bonding-band formation, considerable overlap of the d bands by both p and s states is expected in the b.c.c. structure; extra stabilization over that usually calculated by MO methods comes from the antiparallel spin correlations made possible by the two-sublattice character of the structure. In the absence of adequate calculations, it is necessary to take an empirical estimate of n_{sp}, the number of s–p electrons, that are present in the b.c.c. transition metals. Although the relative positions of the d and s–p

bands must vary from element to element (the relative stability of the s–p bands must decrease with increasing atomic number), the relatively large density of states $N(E)$ in the narrower d bands permits qualitative conclusions to be drawn with a *fixed* value of n_{sp} for the entire b.c.c. 3d series from Ti to the Fe–Co alloys. *The value $n_{sp} \approx 3$ is chosen* as this permits a consistent interpretation of the transition metals and their alloys in terms of the sharp criteria for paramagnetism, antiferromagnetism, and ferromagnetism that have been given.

(*b*) Since previous MO calculations for the b.c.c. transition elements have assumed $n_{sp} \approx 0.22$ to 1.0, it is necessary to cite additional experimental evidence in support of $n_{sp} \approx 3$.

(*i*) Soft x-ray K emission does occur in V, Cr, and Fe even though transitions to the K shell are forbidden for 3d and 4s electrons. This fact can be accounted for by the strong admixing of p states into the occupied MO states that is implied by $n_{sp} \approx 3$.

(*ii*) If $n_{sp} = 3$, nontransition solute elements with the largest solid solubility in the b.c.c. phase should be those with $n'_{sp} \sim 3$ to 4. (*Primed symbols always refer to solute atoms.*) The range of solid solubility is limited in most b.c.c. transition elements because of the stability of the A15 structure. [In the A15 structure, formula M_3S', the M atoms have four to six outer electrons and form linear chains suggestive of strong linear bonding via $(d_{z^2}p_z)$ σ bonds, $(d_{yz}d_{zx},\ p_xp_y)$ π bonds.] Since iron, with more than six outer d electrons, does not stabilize the A15 structure, it provides the most interesting case study, and the solid solubility of the elements in α-Fe is presented in Table XVII. Given $n_{sp} = 3$, the predicted characteristics indicated for the phase diagram, size effects neglected, can be immediately obtained. (*α*) With $n'_{sp} \leq 2$, phase stability is determined by the radius of the closed-shell core. (*β*) With $n'_{sp} = 3$ or 4, the solute readily participates in the s–p band of the α phase, but it has too many electrons for the s band of the γ phase. Therefore the α phase is favored provided $n'_d \leq 3$. With $n'_d > 3$, phase stability is largely determined by the magnetic energy, the α phase being favored if the average atomic moment $\bar{\mu}$ is increased, the γ phase if $\bar{\mu}$ is decreased. (*γ*) If $n'_{sp} > 4$, the solute will stabilize the α versus the γ phase, but it is increasingly insoluble as a substitutional element as the electronegativity difference between it and iron is increased.

TABLE XVII

Solid Solubility of Elements in α-Fe and on Magnetization of Disordered b.c.c. Fe Alloys[a]

Order of Entries

1. Size factor (fav. = favorable if within 15% atomic size of Fe; unf. = unfavorable; mar. = marginal)
2. Atomic % solid solubility in α-Fe.
3. Characteristics of phase diagram (cl. γ = closed γ loop; α fav. = α phase favored; γ fav. = γ phase favored; no fav. = neither phase favored; ins. = insoluble; int. = interstitial).
4. Measured rate of change in magnetization per solute atom of disordered alloy.
5. Predicted rate of change in magnetization per solute atom (in parentheses).

IA	IIA	IIIB	IVB	VB	VIB	VIIB	VIII	VIII	VIII	IB	IIB	IIIA	IVA	VA	VIA	VIIA
Li Unf. Ins.	Be Fav. 5–8% Cl. γ $(-2.2\mu_B)$											B <0.1%				
Na Unf. Ins.	Mg Unf. Ins.											Al Mar. 50% Order >18% Cl. γ $-2.3\mu_B$ $(-2.2\mu_B)$	Si Fav. 26% Order >10% Cl. γ $-2.2\mu_B$ $(-2.2\mu_B)$	P Fav. 1–4% Cl. γ $(\sim-2\mu_B)$	S Mar. Ins.	Cl Small Ins.
K Unf. Ins.	Ca Unf. Ins.	Sc Unf. $(-2.2\mu_B)$	Ti Unf. 3–14% Cl. γ $-3.45\mu_B$ $(<-2.2\mu_B$ & $>-4.2\mu_B)$	V Fav. 100% (high T) Cl. γ $-2.2\mu_B$ $(<-2.2\mu_B$ & $>-3.2\mu_B)$	Cr Fav. 100% (high T) Cl. γ $-2.9\mu_B$ $(<-2.6\mu_B)$	Mn Fav. ~10% γ fav. $-2.0\mu_B$ (?) $(<-3.5\mu_B)$	Fe	Co Fav. 75% No fav. $1\mu_B$ $(1\mu_B)$	Ni Fav. ~8% γ fav. $-0.5\mu_B$ $>0\mu_B$ & $<2\mu_B$	Cu Fav. <1% γ fav. $(-2.2\mu_B)$	Zn Fav. 3–15% γ fav. $(-2.2\mu_B)$	Ga Fav. b $(-2.2\mu_B)$	Ge Fav. 18% Cl. γ $(-2.\ \mu_B)$	As Fav. ~8% Cl. γ $(-2\mu_B)$	Se Fav. Ins.	Br Fav. Ins.
Rb Unf. Ins.	Sr Unf. Ins.	Y Unf.	Zr Unf. Ins.	Nb Unf. <1% α fav. $<2.2\mu_B$ & $>-3.2\mu_B$	Mo Fav. 4–20% Cl. γ $(-2.2\mu_B)$	Tc	Ru Fav. ~10% γ fav. Max $\bar{\mu} \sim 0\%$ (Max $\bar{\mu}$ at 0%)	Rh Fav. 50% No fav. $\sim0.9\mu_B$ $(<1\mu_B)$	Pd Fav. ~4% γ fav. $\sim0\mu_B$ $>0\mu_B$ & $<2\mu_B$	Ag Mar. Ins.	Cd Unf. Ins.	In Unf.	Sn Unf. 8% Cl. γ $-2.2\mu_B$ $(-2.2\mu_B)$	Sb Unf. ~5% (?) Cl. γ $(\sim-2\mu_B)$	Te Mar. Ins.	I Fav. Ins.
Cs Unf. Ins.	Ba Unf. Ins.	La Unf.	Hf Unf.	Ta Unf. <0.5% α fav. $(<-2.2\mu_B$ & $>-3.2\mu_B)$	W Fav. 4% Cl. γ $(-2.2\mu_B)$	Re Fav.	Os Fav. ~8% γ fav. Max $\bar{\mu} \sim 0\%$ (Max $\bar{\mu}$ at 0%)	Ir Fav. ~12% γ fav. $-0.8\mu_B$ $(<1\mu_B)$	Pt Fav. ~10% γ fav. $\sim2\mu_B$ $>0\mu_B$ & $<2\mu_B$	Au Mar. <1.5% γ fav. $(-2.2\mu_B)$	Hg Unf. Ins.	Tl Unf. Ins.	Pb Unf. Ins.	Bi Unf. Ins.	Po Unf. Ins.	At

Small ions enter interstitially

Predicted characteristic of phase diagram, neglecting size effects

Cl. γ	Cl. γ	Cl. γ	Cl. γ	Cl. γ	γ fav.	Larger μ favors α smaller μ favors γ	γ fav.	γ fav.	γ fav.	Cl. γ	Cl. γ	Cl. γ	Cl. γ	Int. or Ins.

[a] Data from refs. (89,250).
[b] Alloys easily.

It therefore seems significant that the nontransition elements of greatest solid solubility in α-Fe are Al and Si, and this in spite of the fact that Si crystallizes in an extremely stable diamond structure because both its s and p electrons are active in bonding.

(*iii*) Careful x-ray measurements of the atomic scattering factors can be used to determine the number of $3d$ electrons in the transition metals. The technique is to measure the absolute scattering factors and to subtract the "argon core," as calculated by self-consistent techniques, for the free atom. Since the radial extension of the collective $4s$ and $4p$ electrons is such that their scattering factors are negligible at all Bragg angles, subtraction of the "argon core" leaves only the contribution of the outer $3d$ electrons. If $n_{sp} = 3$, then the outer-electron configurations for b.c.c. Cr and Fe are, respectively, $n_{sp}^3 n_{2g}^{3-\delta} n_g^\delta$ and $n_{sp}^3 n_{2g}^{3+\epsilon} n_g^{2-\epsilon}$, and the number of $3d$ electrons is 3 and 5. Original experiments by Weiss and DeMarco (659) claimed to find only 2.3 ± 0.3 and 0.2 ± 0.4 $3d$ electrons associated, respectively, with b.c.c. Fe and Cr. These results may reflect the fact that the three bonding t_{2g} electrons of Fe and Cr have a greater extension than the electrons that contribute to the localized atomic moment. The experiments require extreme care and large-angle scattering data. Subsequent measurements by Batterman (42) gave approximately six $3d$ electrons for Fe. Komura, Tomiie, and Nathans (358) investigated the number of $3d$ electrons at the Fe_I atoms (all near neighbors Fe_{III}, and next-near neighbors Al) in ordered Fe_3Al and obtained results compatible with $n_d = 5 \pm 1$. The present consensus of opinion among those workers is that in α-Fe, definitely $n_d < 7$ and $n_d = 5$ falls within experimental error (43).

(*c*) In order to obtain a more quantitative $N(E)$ vs. E curve, it is assumed that the major peaks and valleys of such a curve are described by a knowledge of the relative widths and positions of the individual bands and subbands. Therefore the detailed configurations are ignored, and a simple parabolic-energy-band approximation (see eq. 48)

$$\epsilon_i = a_i [N(\epsilon_i)]^2 \qquad (186)$$

is assumed for both the electrons at the bottom and the holes at the top of the bands. Only in the case of a t_{2g} band that is not resolved into bonding and antibonding subbands is it necessary to assume a bimodal character. The a_i, which depend upon the empirical parameter m^*, are determined from a knowledge of the total number of electrons Nz_e, or holes Nz_h, in an energy interval ΔE_i, since by equation 50

$$Nz_i = \zeta_s \int_0^{\Delta E_i} N(\epsilon)d\epsilon = \frac{2}{3}\zeta_s\Delta E_i \left(\frac{\Delta E_i}{a_i}\right)^{1/2} = \frac{2}{3}\zeta_s\Delta E_i N(\Delta E_i) \quad (187)$$

where $\zeta_s = 1$ or 2 reflects the spin degeneracy of the band. There are two types of experimental information that give a number for a_i providing a numerical relationship between Nz_i and ΔE_i: the total width of the occupied portions of the overlapping s–p and d bands from x-ray absorption data and the electronic specific heat. The x-ray absorption data fixes the Fermi level E_F relative to the bottom of the s–p band at $\sim$7 eV for V and Cr (288). With the aid of Fermi statistics and the assumption that $kT \ll E_F$, where E_F is the Fermi energy, it is possible to show (556) that the electronic specific heat for a paramagnetic metal with a single conduction band is

$$C_{el} = \gamma_{el}T \qquad \gamma_{el} \approx \frac{1}{3}\pi^2 k^2 N(E_F) \qquad (188)$$

If there is more than one conduction band and the metal has a net magnetization, the expression for γ_{el} becomes more complicated (688). However, in rough approximation

$$\gamma_{el} \sim 1.7 \times 10^{-4} \sum_i N_i(\Delta E_i) \text{ cal/mole-deg}^2 \qquad (189)$$

where the $N_i(\Delta E_i)$ are the densities of states (in units of eV^{-1}). Given the contribution from the s–p bands, as estimated from the x-ray absorption data and the assumption $n_{sp} = 3$, $N_i(\Delta E_i)$ for the various d subbands can be obtained from γ_{el}. With this procedure and the γ_{el} data of Table VIII, the density of states curves of Figure 80 were constructed. A very small overlap (or mixing) of the t_{2g} and e_g bands, which was anticipated by the qualitative discussions, is suggested by the existence of a small atomic moment, $\mu_{Cr} \approx 0.4\mu_B$, on antiferromagnetic Cr, but a small γ_{el}. [The magnetic order probably represents a spin-density wave, but the exceptionally large amplitude is consistent with the presence of localized e_g states near the Fermi surface.] The simplest possible construction, which is shown, is based on a maximum γ_{el} at V and δ-Mn. The bottom of the upper t_{2g} subband must fall between antiferromagnetic δ-Mn and ferromagnetic α-Fe.

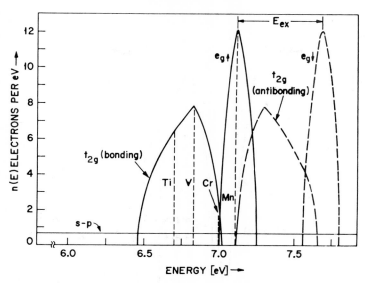

Fig. 80. Simplified density of states curve for metallic chromium. Energy scale is referred to bottom of s–p band. The Fermi level relative to the d bands is also shown for b.c.c. Ti, V, and Mn given the same relative positions of d and s–p bands. Ferromagnetic, simple-cubic sublattices are coupled antiferromagnetically in b.c.c. Cr–Mn alloys.

In the case of ferromagnetic iron, the t_{2g} band need not be split in two, and the electron correlations between ferromagnetic e_g and t_{2g} electrons should be optimized.   This means that in the ferromagnetic materials, the antibonding t_{2g} subband tends to be split in two by intraatomic exchange.   The more stable portion overlaps the lower e_g subband to form a single subband (e_g and t_{2g} states admixed) of parallel spin; the less stable portion overlaps the upper e_g subband to form a single subband of antiparallel spin.   The ratio of e_g to t_{2g} states in each subband is 4:3, so that the ferromagnetic electrons of α-Fe can be expected to display e_g versus t_{2g} character in about that proportion.   (Spherical symmetry corresponds to 2:3.)   The magnetization data of the Fe–Co alloys suggests that the two e_g subbands are not completely resolved by the exchange energy, as is indicated in Figure 81.   (X-ray absorption data give 5 eV for the energy difference between E_F and the bottom of the s–p band in α-iron.)

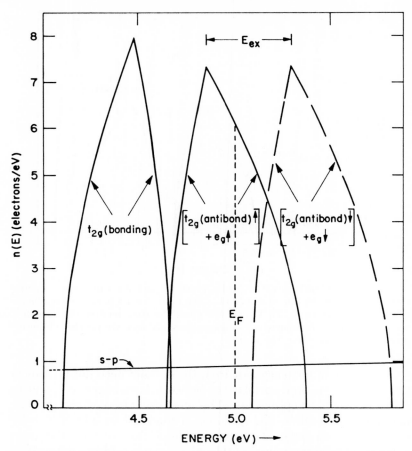

Fig. 81. Simplified density of states curve for ferromagnetic α-Fe. Energy scale is referred to bottom of $s–p$ band. The $[e_g + t_{2g}$ (antibonding)$]$ bands each contain 3.5 electrons per atom. Bonding t_{2g} band held same as in Figure 80 and magnetic-electron band drawn to give $10^4\gamma_{el} = 12$ cal/mole/deg^2.

2. Face-Centered-Cubic Structure

(a) The Cartesian reference frame may be reasonably placed into the f.c.c. structure either as in Figure 82(a) or as in Figure 83(a). It is immediately obvious that Figure 83(a) has tetragonal, not cubic, symmetry. Cubic symmetry is only achieved by a transformation to the b.c.c. structure via a simultaneous contraction along [001] and an expansion within (001). This relationship between f.c.c. and b.c.c. phases was first pointed out by Bain (36). The driving force for the b.c.c. $\rightleftharpoons$ f.c.c. martensitic phase change essentially comes from changes in band structure that are associated with a 45° rotation of the Cartesian reference frame.

In f.c.c. Ni and Co, $R_{nnn} \approx 3.5$ A $> R_c$ and $R_{nn} \approx 2.5$ A $< R_c$ (see eq. 183). Since the f.c.c. structure is not a two-sublattice structure, it follows that the collective t_{2g} electrons occupy a metallic band. The localized e_g electrons occupy two levels that are split by intra-atomic exchange (Hund's rule). These levels tend to be broadened into a narrow band through interactions with the overlapping t_{2g} states. Since the repulsion between filled orbitals is smaller for next-near-neighbor-directed than for near-neighbor-directed orbitals, the upper e_g level should fall below the top of the metallic t_{2g} band. Although the exact placement of the lower e_g level is not critical for

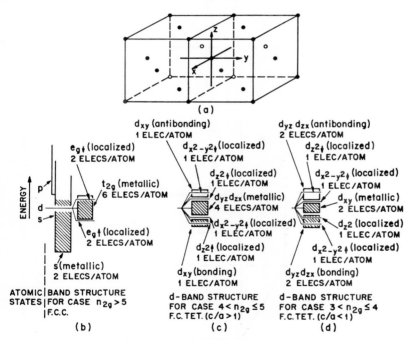

Fig. 82. Qualitative features of the band structure for face-centered transition metals of the first long period.

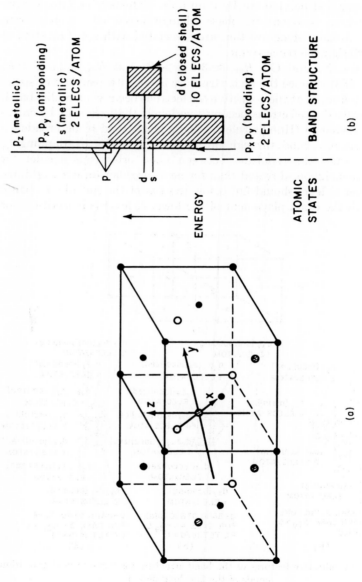

Fig. 83. Qualitative features of f.c. tet. $(c/a > 1)$ indium. Tetragonal $(c/a > 1)$ symmetry is a two-sublattice structure compatible with ordering of outer electrons into bonding s and $p_x p_y$ bands.

most of the arguments to follow, magnetization data for the Ni–Cr alloys suggest that it falls below the bottom of the metallic t_{2g} band. This leads to a density of states curve with the principal features similar to those of the celebrated Krutter– (375) Slater (581) curve for copper. Unlike the b.c.c. structure, the f.c.c. symmetry is not compatible with bonding-band stabilization of the p states, so that the number of occupied s–p states is $n_s \sim 1$. This number must decrease with increasing relative stability of the d bands; that is, with increasing atomic number. In order to obtain a model that is consistent with experiment, *the following choice is made: $n_s = 0.55$, 0.75, 0.95, 1.15, respectively, for f.c.c. Ni, Co, Fe, Mn* (see eq. 195 for rationalization).

Since bonding-band stabilization (see Chapter III, Section I-C-5) should occur whenever possible, *the f.c.c. structure can only be stable to lowest temperatures if $n_{2g} = 0$ or $5 < n_{2g} \leq 6$.* If $4 < n_{2g} \leq 5$ or $3 < n_{2g} \leq 4$, for example, there are one or two t_{2g} holes, respectively, that can order among the t_{2g} electrons. One hole would order into the d_{xy} orbitals to permit formation of a bonding d_{xy} band, two holes would order into d_{yz}, d_{zx} orbitals. Such ordering would be accompanied by a cooperative lattice distortion to tetragonal symmetry; in the former case to $c/a > 1$, in the latter to $c/a < 1$. Such ordering would also introduce a two-sublattice structure and antiferromagnetic correlations. In the former case, localized electrons would couple antiferromagnetically within (001) planes, in the latter case between (001) planes. These qualitative ideas lead to the following sharp criteria for the existence of Pauli paramagnetism, antiferromagnetism, and ferromagnetism in f.c.c. transition metals.

(*i*) *If $5 < n_{2g} \leq 6$, f.c.c. transition metals remain cubic to lowest temperatures and are ferromagnetic if a 3d metal with $n_g < 4$, Pauli paramagnetic otherwise.*

(*ii*) *If $4 < n_{2g} \leq 5$, f.c.c. transition metals may become tetragonal ($c/a > 1$) with antiferromagnetic coupling within (001) planes if of the first long series.*

(*iii*) *If $3 < n_{2g} \leq 4$, f.c.c. transition metals may become tetragonal ($c/a < 1$) with antiferromagnetic coupling between (001) planes if of the first long series.* It is assumed that localized e_g electrons occur only in the first long series since, as was pointed out in Chapter I, $R_{nnn} \approx R_c(4d)$ and $R_{nnn} < R_c(5d)$.

(*b*) Construction of a semiempirical density of states curve for the f.c.c. structures is difficult. From x-ray absorption data (288), E_F is 5.0 eV above the bottom of the s band in nickel. To determine n_s, it is noted that $\mu_{\mathrm{Ni}} = 0.60\mu_B$ (93), $g_{\mathrm{Ni}} = 2.193$ (435). Since nickel has 10 outer electrons, the total number of d-band holes is $n_h = \mu_{\mathrm{Ni}}/((1/2)g_{\mathrm{Ni}}\mu_B) = 0.55 = n_s$. If the e_g electrons are localized, they do not contribute to γ_{el}. Therefore subtraction of the s-electron contribution to the experimental (280) $10^4\gamma_{el} = 17.4$ cal/mole-deg^2 gives $N(E_F)$ for the t_{2g} band. To obtain the number of t_{2g} holes per atom that this corresponds to, it is necessary to have an estimate of the relative number of e_g to t_{2g} holes in nickel. Polarized neutron experiments (464) indicate that the magnetic electrons have an anisotropic form factor, from which the e_g/t_{2g} hole ratio is estimated to be 1/3. This gives 0.41 t_{2g} holes and 0.14 e_g holes. Since measurements (661) of γ_{el} for Ni–Co alloys indicate that γ_{el} is a maximum for pure nickel, the simplest construction has the maximum $N(E)$ at E_F for

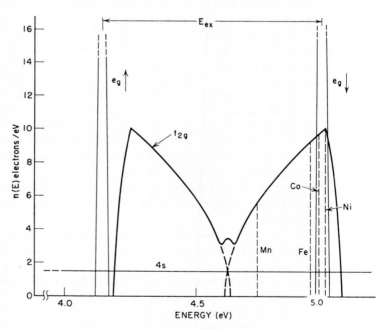

Fig. 84. Schematic density of states curve for f.c.c. nickel, where $n(E)$ for 4s band is enlarged by a factor of ten. The Fermi level E_F is 5 eV above the bottom of the 4s band. E_F's for Mn, Fe, and Co are also indicated.

pure nickel, as shown in Figure 84.   The lower e_g and t_{2g} states shown are entirely schematic.

B. COMPARISON WITH EXPERIMENT

A proper description of the band structure of a metal has much broader implications than for magnetic and crystallographic properties.   Among these, as was seen from the constructions of Figures 80, 81, and 84, is the electronic specific heat.   Reassurance concerning the qualitative features of Figure 80 comes from measurements of γ_{el} for b.c.c. Cr–Fe, Cr–Mn, V–Fe, TiFe–TiCo, and Fe–Co alloys (117a, 598a).   It is found that γ_{el} vs. electron/atom ratio has a sharp maximum of (40 to 50) $\times$ 10^{-4} cal/mole-deg^2 at 6.5 electrons per atom, a maximum which appears to reflect the lower e_g subband.   It suggests that this subband may be considerably narrower than shown in Figure 80, where it was given its maximum width for simplicity.   The γ_{el} curve also has a sharp minimum at $\sim$8.35 electrons/atom in the ferromagnetic Fe–Co system.   Since the system has partial ordering toward the CsCl structure for higher electron/atom ratios, this may reflect only the change in band structure that must accompany this ordering.   However, it is reasonable to assume that ordering itself reflects overlap of positive spin and negative spin subbands for higher Co concentrations in the disordered alloy, as is shown in Figure 81.   Further, CsCl-type ordering does not appear to introduce any significant changes in the d-band structures of alloys with lower electron/atom ratio.

Walmsley (643a) has performed an ingenious experiment in which he claims to measure the fraction of electrons at the Fermi surface of αFe that have spins parallel or antiparallel to an external field.   From the model of Figure 81, it is predicted that the moments associated with the spins of the $3d$ electrons at the Fermi surface will *all* be parallel to an external saturating field.   This is opposite to the prediction from a conventional rigid-band model with d bands more than half filled (see Figure 8, but consider the band is being filled with holes and reverse the sign of the external field).   Therefore such a measurement would provide a sharp distinction between the model of Figure 81 and the various conventional models extant in the literature.   Walmsley reports that the spins at the Fermi surface are those predicted in Figure 81.

The sign of the Hall constant indicates whether the charge carriers have a positive or negative effective mass m^*.   From Figure 80, the bonding s–p band, which is three-fourths full, makes a small positive contribution.   Since the magnitude of a positive contribution is inversely proportional to the number of holes in the band, there should be a large positive contribution from the t_{2g} band in Cr, a smaller positive contribution from this band in V and from the e_g plus antibonding t_{2g} band in ferromagnetic iron.   Positive Hall constants have been observed (185) in V, Cr, and low-temperature Fe, much the largest occurring in Cr as expected.

Such qualitative comparisons, though important, do not disclose the sharp predictions about crystal symmetry, magnetic order, and atomic moments that are the significant contribution inherent in the simple constructions of Figures 80, 81, and 82.   These are the topics that are relevant here and that are discussed below.

1. *Crystal Structures*

In a pure metal, phase stability is determined by the comparative band-forming energies for various symmetries and by the repulsive forces from closed inner shells.   The various metallic phases found in the first three long periods are given in Table XVIII.

With one outer s electron, there is little difference in band-forming energy between the b.c.c. and f.c.c. phases.   The two-sublattice structure of the b.c.c. phase permits bonding states to be formed, and this is presumably responsible for the occurrence of this phase in Column Ia.   In the Column Ib metals the d-shell cores have relatively large radial extension, and strong repulsive forces between cores favor close packing.

With a larger number of outer electrons, simple Brillouin-zone considerations are complicated by interactions between the Fermi surface and the Brillouin-zone surface (212,307).   However, it should be noted that with partially filled d states, a bonding $(p_z d^5)$ band can be formed provided $c/a < 1.63$.   Such stabilization would be more pronounced among the heavier atoms, and it may account for the preference for c.p.h. versus f.c.c. phases that occurs in metals with eight or fewer outer electrons.   With more than eight outer electrons, it is clear that antibonding states must be occupied in both the f.c.c. and c.p.h. symmetries.   As antibonding states become occupied, binding energies are reduced.   Therefore the melting points of the close-packed phases can be expected to decrease with more than seven outer electrons per atom $(s^1 p_z d^5)$.

TABLE XVIII

Some Physical Properties of Elements of the First Three Long Periods of the Periodic Table

$R_0[10^{-13}$ V-cm/amp-gauss] = ordinary Hall constant (185); $\gamma_{el}[10^{-4}$ cal/mole-deg^2] = electronic-specific-heat constant (199,280,660); $d\chi/dt$ = rate of change of paramagnetic susceptibility with temperature (374). Atomic magnetic moments expressed in Bohr magnetons per atom (93); data on strontium (559); phase boundaries for titanium (429,357), for all others (387,357); melting points (606). Axial ratio c/a for c.p.h. structures are given in parentheses. Stability ranges for each phase are given below the phase identification.

Ia (s^1)	IIa (s^2)	IIIa ($d s^2$)	IVa (d^2s^2)	Va (d^3s^2) / (d^4s^1)	VIa (d^5s^1) / (d^4s^2)	VIIa (d^5s^2) / (d^6s^1)	VIIIa (d^6s^2) / (d^7s^1)	VIIIb (d^7s^2) / (d^8s^1)	VIIIc (d^8s^2) / (d^9s^1)	Ib ($d^{10}s^1$)
K b.c.c. 0-336°K	Ca f.c.c. 0-723°K γ_{el} = 2.9 c.p.h.(1.63) 723-1123°K	Sc c.p.h.(1.585-8) 0-?°K f.c.c. ?-1673°K	Ti c.p.h.(1.587) 0-1153°K γ_{el} = 8.0 $d\chi/dt > 0$ b.c.c. 1153-1950°K	V b.c.c. 0-2190°K γ_{el} = 15(22.2) $d\chi/dt < 0$ R_0 = +8.20	Cr b.c.c. 0-2176°K γ_{el} = 3.8 $d\chi/dt > 0$ ↑↓: ~0.4μ_B R_0 = +36.3	Mn α: A12 0-1000°K γ_{el} = 42 ↑↓: complex β: A13 1000-1364°K paramag. (?) γ: f.c.c. tet. ⇌ f.c.c. 1364-1410°K γ_{el} = 11.2 ↑↓: 2.3μ_B δ: b.c.c. 1410-1517°K γ_{el} = 22.5 ↑↑: ~1μ_B	Fe α: b.c.c. 0-979°K γ_{el} = 12.0 ↑↑: 2.22μ_B R_0 = +2.45 γ: f.c.c. 979-1674°K ↑↓: (?) δ: b.c.c. 1674-1812°K	Co c.p.h.(1.623) 0-723°K γ_{el} = 12.0 ↑↑: 1.72μ_B R_0 = -13.3 f.c.c. 723-1768°K ↑↑: 1.75μ_B	Ni f.c.c. 0-1728°K γ_{el} = 17.4 ↑↑: 0.6μ_B	Cu f.c.c. 0-1356°K γ_{el} = 1.6-1.8
Rb b.c.c. 0-312°K	Sr f.c.c. 0-488°K c.p.h.(1.63) 488-878°K b.c.c. 878-1043°K	Y c.p.h.(1.585-8) 0-1773°K	Zr c.p.h.(1.592) 0-1140°K γ_{el} = 6.92(3.92) $d\chi/dt > 0$ b.c.c. 1140-2125°K	Nb b.c.c. 0-2770°K γ_{el} = 17.5-20.4 $d\chi/dt < 0$	Mo b.c.c. 0-2880°K γ_{el} = 5.1 $d\chi/dt > 0$	Tc c.p.h.(1.604) 0-2408°K	Ru c.p.h.(1.583) 0-2700°K γ_{el} = 8.0 $d\chi/dt > 0$	Rh f.c.c. 0-2239°K γ_{el} = 10-11.7 $d\chi/dt > 0$	Pd f.c.c. 0-1828°K γ_{el} = 31.0 $d\chi/dt < 0$	Ag f.c.c. 0-1234°K γ_{el} = 1.45-1.6
Cs b.c.c. 0-302°K	Ba b.c.c. 0-983°K	La c.p.h.(1.61) 0-1644°K γ_{el} = 16-21	Hf c.p.h.(1.587) 0-2250°K γ_{el} = 6.3-6.8 $d\chi/dt > 0$	Ta b.c.c. 0-3270°K γ_{el} = 13.0-14.0 $d\chi/dt < 0$	W b.c.c. 0-3650°K γ_{el} = 1.8-2.5 $d\chi/dt > 0$	Re c.p.h.(1.615) 0-3453°K γ_{el} = 5.85	Os c.p.h.(1.579) 0-3000°K γ_{el} = 5.62 $d\chi/dt > 0$	Ir f.c.c. 0-2727°K γ_{el} = 7.5-7.6 $d\chi/dt > 0$	Pt f.c.c. 0-2043°K γ_{el} = 16.0 $d\chi/dt < 0$	Au f.c.c. 0-1336°K γ_{el} = 1.67

More significant is the occurrence of the b.c.c. structure in Columns IVa, Va, VIa. From Figures 80, 81 it follows that the most stable b.c.c. configuration must occur in VIa, where there are six bonding electrons per atom. Additional electrons occupy the antibonding e_g states and therefore reduce the melting point of the b.c.c. phase. This prediction is consistent with Table XVIII, since evidence for a few e_g electrons first appears in Cr, but not yet in Mo and W, and a reduced melting point, noted in Cr, is marked for δ-Mn.

Manganese is famous for its peculiar structure. With $n_s = 1.15$, it follows from Figure 84 that $3 < n_{2g} < 4$ in γ-Mn, and therefore that below some critical temperature t_{2g}-hole ordering should induce a f.c.c. → f.c.tet. $(c/a < 1)$ transformation. The existence of such a transformation and the magnetic properties of the low-temperature phase can be extrapolated from Mn-rich Mn–Cu alloys (35,432).

2. Magnetic Properties of b.c.c. Metals

From Figures 79 and 80, it follows that b.c.c. metals of Columns IVa and Va should, as observed, be Pauli paramagnetic, of VIa should be marginal between Pauli paramagnetism and antiferromagnetism, of VIIa should be antiferromagnetic, and of VIIIa should be ferromagnetic. That Cr is just at the transition to antiferromagnetism is suggested not only by its low atomic moment ($\sim 0.4\mu_B$), but also by its temperature-independent susceptibility (424) and by the sensitivity of its Néel point to impurities (152). [T_N drops sharply with small additions of V, increases sharply with small additions of Mn.] It also exhibits complex magnetic order (33,255,677). Small additions of Mn seem to stabilize simple, collinear magnetic order. The physical origin of the complex magnetic phases is not known.

If there are no localized electrons present, equation 58 gives $\chi \propto N(E_F)$. Plots (611a) of χ vs. the number of outer electrons for $3d$, $4d$, and $5d$ elements and alloys all reflect the qualitative features of Figures 80 and 84. Further, $d\chi/dT > 0$ if E_F is at a minimum in the $N(E)$ curve, $d\chi/dT < 0$ if E_F is at a maximum (374). Comparison of Figure 80 with the b.c.c. elements of Table XVIII shows consistency.

The atomic moments of antiferromagnetic metals are given by equation 184. From the moment of Cr it appears that $(\delta n_{2g} + \delta n_{sp}) \sim 0.3\mu_B$. It follows that $\mu_{Mn} \sim 1.3\mu_B$ and that for a 50-50 Mn–Cr alloy, which should be antiferromagnetic, $\bar{\mu} =$

$(\mu_{Mn} + \mu_{Cr})/2 \sim 0.85\mu_B$. Neutron diffraction measurements (335) of disordered MnCr confirm the predicted antiferromagnetic coupling and give a $\bar{\mu} = (0.85 \pm 0.04)\mu_B$.

If $n_{sp} \approx 3$, the transition from antiferromagnetism to ferromagnetism must occur at or before α-Fe since iron has eight outer electrons. From equation 185, the atomic moment of ferromagnetic α-Fe is $\mu_{Fe} = (2 + \delta n_{sp})\mu_B$, where $\delta n_{sp} < 0.3$.

Thus with the assumption $n_{sp} = 3$ for all b.c.c. transition metals, the model provides a consistent interpretation of the type of magnetism encountered, the magnetic order, and the magnitude of the atomic moment. [The fact that vanadium has an anomaly at $\sim 250°K$ in several physical parameters suggests that there may be long-range electron correlations below this temperature among the collective t_{2g} electrons. The fact that there is no specific-heat anomaly (140a) indicates an extremely small entropy change associated with any long-range $\rightleftharpoons$ short-range correlation transitions in this temperature range.]

3. Magnetic Properties of b.c.c. Alloys

The measured and predicted rate of change in magnetization per solute atom in disordered, b.c.c. iron alloys are listed in Table XVII. The predicted rates of change in average atomic moment $\bar{\mu}$ with solute concentration c follow from the fact that the model distinguishes four types of solute atom:

(a) Nontransition elements ($n'_d = 0$). Solute carries no moment so that

$$d\bar{\mu}/dc = -(2.2 + \Delta n_{sp})\mu_B \qquad (190)$$

where Δn_{sp} is the increase in the number of outer iron electrons in the s-p bands and is a measure of any relative shift of the s-p bands with c.

(b) Columns IVa, Va, VIa except Cr ($n'_{2g} \leq 3, n'_g = 0$). Solute carries no moment, but its participation in the t_{2g} bonding band may alter the number of $3d$ electrons at the iron atoms, so that

$$d\bar{\mu}/dc = -(2.2 + \Delta n_{sp} + \delta'_i)\mu_B \qquad (191)$$

where δ'_i is the number of antibonding t_{2g} electrons of iron that have been donated to the bonding t_{2g} band. (For Ti, $\delta'_i \leq 2$; for V, Nb, and Ta, $\delta'_i \leq 1$; and for Mo and W, $\delta'_i = 0$.)

It is noteworthy that small additions of Fe to b.c.c. Ti, V, Nb introduce no localized electrons with unpaired spins; but localized spins are introduced by additions of Fe to $Nb_{1-x}Mo_x$ alloys if $x > 0.5$ (109,416,417,418).

(c) *Cr and column VIIa* $(n'_{2g} \leq 3,\ n'_g > 0)$. Solute carries a moment; but with no antibonding t_{2g} electrons at the solute, this moment (if only iron near neighbors) is antiparallel to the ferromagnetic matrix and

$$d\bar{\mu}/dc = -(2.2 + n'_g + \delta'_{2g})\mu_B \qquad (192)$$

where δ'_{2g} represents the induced localization of the bonding, solute t_{2g} electrons due to intraatomic exchange.

(d) *Columns VIIIa, VIIIb, and VIIIc* $(3 < n'_{2g} < 6,\ n'_g < 4)$. Solute atoms contribute antibonding t_{2g} electrons, so that coupling is ferromagnetic and

$$d\bar{\mu}/dc = -\Delta n_{sp}\mu_B \qquad \text{for Column VIIIa}$$

$$d\bar{\mu}/dc = (1 - \Delta n_{sp})\mu_B \qquad \text{for Column VIIIb} \qquad (193)$$

$$0\mu_B < d\bar{\mu}/dc < 2\mu_B \qquad \text{for Column VIIIc}$$

where $\Delta n_{sp} \geq 0$ increases on going down a column. Given solute states that match the solvent bands, an VIIIb solute may carry a moment of $\sim 3\mu_B$. The maximum atomic moment can only be $3.5\mu_B$, which may force the two extra d electrons on an VIIIc to be spin-paired. Thus an VIIIc solute will cause $d\bar{\mu}/dc \approx 0$ if $n'_d > 6.5$, but it may cause $d\bar{\mu}/dc = 2\mu_B$ if there is sufficient adjustment of the bands to give $n'_d \leq 6.5$ and $\Delta n_d \geq 0.5/c$. Larger band adjustments are more probable going down the column.

The ordered alloys also provide important information. In the CsCl structures FeAl, CoAl, and NiAl there are no d electrons on the Al so that there are no near-neighbor t_{2g} correlations to force the e_g electrons to be antibonding. Since $R_{nnn} < R_c$, a bonding e_g band must form within the simple-cubic iron sublattice. If the t_{2g} are localized, they are correlated antiparallel via intraatomic exchange with the bonding e_g electrons. Given $n_{sp} \approx 3$ in the ordered alloys, this would give $\mu_{Fe} \approx 3\mu_B$, $\mu_{Co} \approx 2\mu_B$, $\mu_{Ni} \approx 1\mu_B$.

Neutron diffraction experiments (522) indicate that there is *no* localized atomic moment in ordered FeAl. This result implies that $s-p$ bonding between *unlike* atoms is considerably less stable relative to the iron d levels than that between like atoms, so that the localized, iron t_{2g} orbitals are filled. Since aluminum is electropositive with respect to iron, such a conclusion is quite reasonable. However, if it is valid in this case, then it is necessary to question an $n_{sp} \approx 3$ for other *ordered*, b.c.c. alloys. It should be noted that Arrott and Sato (24) and Kouvel (364) found definite evidence of antiferromagnetic coupling between next-near-neighbor irons in ordered (FeAl-type) alloys with 28 to 40 atomic per cent aluminum.

In sharp contrast to FeAl, the ordered FeV alloys with CsCl structure are ferromagnetic. Preliminary measurements by Chandross and Shoemaker (566) on a sample that was 80% ordered give $\bar{\mu} \approx 0.91\mu_B$ and $\approx 0.1\mu_B$ for the two sublattices, which implies $\mu_{Fe} \sim 1.14\mu_B$ and $\mu_V \sim 0\mu_B$. In this case ferromagnetism follows from the model since there are d electrons on the vanadium, so that the t_{2g} correlations remain. With $n_{sp} \approx 3$ and $n_{2g} \approx 3$, the moment on the iron atoms would be reduced by $\sim 1\mu_B$ since iron contributes four electrons to the bonding t_{2g} band. This gives a predicted ferromagnetic moment at the iron atoms $\mu_{Fe} \sim (1 + \delta_{sp})\mu_B$ and a zero vanadium moment $\mu_V \sim 0\mu_B$, in good agreement with experiment. Lack of a large adjustment in the relative stabilities of the bands on ordering may be attributed to the closeness of V and Fe in the periodic table.

Ordered TiFe apparently contains no localized moment, or $\mu \leq 0.061\mu_B$ (480a), which is anticipated for an electron/atom ratio of 6 if the relative positions of the d and $s–p$ bands are similar to that found in metallic chromium.

In the case of ordered FeCo, the model calls for ferromagnetic coupling and, given $n_{sp} \approx 3$, a $\mu_{Fe} \sim 2\mu_B$ with $\mu_{Co} \sim 3\mu_B$ and $\bar{\mu} \sim 2.5\mu_B$. Measurements indicate that in the compositional range $0.33 < c < 0.5$ there is a small adjustment of n_{sp} with increased ordering that is reflected in a change of slope in $d\bar{\mu}/dc$, in γ_{el}, and in the Hall effect. In fact $\bar{\mu}$ decreases slightly with ordering from $2.52\mu_B$ at $c = 0.33$ to $2.42\mu_B$ at $c = 0.5$ (656). Neutron diffraction experiments (566a) on the ordered alloy reveal an atomic moment of $\sim 2.0\mu_B$ for one sublattice and $\sim 2.9\mu_B$ for the other, in excellent agreement with the model. (Although it was not possible to say whether the larger moment was on the iron or the cobalt sublattice, the band adjustments on ordering indicate that $n_{sp} \approx 2$, which leads to $\mu_{Fe} \backsim 3\mu_B$ and $\mu_{Co} \backsim 2\mu_B$, is more probable than an $n_{sp} \approx 3$ with $\mu_{Fe} \backsim 2\mu_B$ and $\mu_{Co} \backsim 3\mu_B$.) It is significant that $d\bar{\mu}/dc = -1\mu_B$ for $c > 0.5$, which indicates occupancy of the antiparallel e_g and antibonding t_{2g} states at the higher cobalt concentrations, or higher electron/atom ratio. Unfortunately a $d\bar{\mu}/dc = -1\mu_B$ does not distinguish whether $n_{sp} \approx 3$ or $n_{sp} \approx 2$ for $c > 0.5$. If all the cobalt atoms already have an antiparallel e_g electron at the ordered FeCo composition and $n_{sp} \approx 2$ so that $\mu_{Fe} \sim 3\mu_B$ and $\mu_{Co} \sim 2\mu_B$, then a $d\bar{\mu}/dc = -1\mu_B$ follows immediately for $c > 0.5$. This interpretation requires a continuous adjustment of n_{sp} and the number of cobalt atoms with antiparallel e_g spin through the transitional range $0.33 < c < 0.5$. A $d\bar{\mu}/dc = -\mu_B$ is also seen to be consistent with Figure 81, especially as ordering can be expected to make critical the 50-50 composition. For $c > 0.5$, cobalt atoms are forced into the second sublattice, and cobalt atoms on this sublattice have $\mu_{Co} \sim 1\mu_B$. Note that the e_g bands associated with the two sublattices would, due to ordering, be at different energies.

In the case of ordered FeRh, where unlike atoms come from different rows of the periodic table, the relative stability of bonding states between *unlike* atoms is certainly reduced considerably relative to localized d levels, or to next-near-neighbor-bonding states between *like* atoms. The fact that below a critical $T_t < T_c$ the ordered alloy contains antiferromagnetic simple-cubic sublattices and a 0.3% smaller lattice constant (143,65) indicates that indeed next-near-neighbor bonding has become competitive in this case. Further, the number of d electrons on the two sublattices need not be the same: the larger radial extension of the $4d$-electron potential can be expected to favor more d electrons on the rhodium sublattice. Charge neutrality can be maintained via a similar imbalance, but toward the opposite sublattice, in the s–p bands. Observation of $\mu_{Fe} \approx 3.1\mu_B$ and $\mu_{Rh} \approx 0.7\mu_B$ in the ferromagnetic phase suggests that $\bar{n}_{sp} \approx 2.5$ and that the bonding t_{2g} states are primarily associated with the rhodium sublattice, the antibonding t_{2g} states with the iron sublattice. If the bonding t_{2g} electrons were to become completely associated with the rhodium sublattice and the e_g electrons of each sublattice were to form bonding bands, thus removing one rhodium e_g electron to the t_{2g} bands, the reported antiferromagnetic phase would result: antiferromagnetic coupling within sublattices. If, further, there was a simultaneous change in $\bar{n}_{sp}$ to $\bar{n}_{sp} \approx 2$, this would give $\mu_{Fe} \approx 3\mu_B$, $\mu_{Rh} \approx 0\mu_B$ and $n_{sp}^{Fe} \approx 3$, $n_{sp}^{Rh} \approx 1$. Thus the observed magnetic properties of this alloy are compatible with the model even though it is not possible to make sharp predictions for the case of ordered alloys where n_{sp} is uncertain.

Ordered Fe_3Al and Fe_3Si carry two types of iron atoms: Fe_I occupies an ordered rock salt-type FeAl sublattice and Fe_{II} occupies an all-iron simple-cubic sublattice. According to the model, the system is ferromagnetic and the e_g states at an Fe_I atom, which has only Al or Si next-near neighbors, are more stable than those at an Fe_{II} atom, so that the optimum parallel-spin correlations occur if the magnetic electrons at an Fe_I atom are e_g electrons, those at an Fe_{II} atom are t_{2g} electrons. Evidence that such ordering takes place has been found by Pickart and Nathans (520) in recent polarized neutron beam experiments that suggest (granted the dubious assumption of equal radial distributions of e_g and t_{2g} electrons) that of the magnetic electrons $\sim 70\%$ are e_g on Fe_I and $\sim 12\%$ on Fe_{II}. Further, the relative stability of the outer s—p electrons at the Al or Si atoms can be expected to increase $n_{sp}^{Fe_{II}} = 3 + \delta_{II}$ so that $\mu_{Fe_I} \approx 2.2\mu_B$ and $\bar{\mu}_{Fe_{II}} \approx [(2.2 - \delta_{II})(1 - 4x) - 4x(3 - \delta_{II})]\mu_B = [(2.2 - \delta_{II}) - 4x(5.2 - 2\delta_{II})]\mu_B$, where $\delta_{II} \leq 1$ and x is the fraction of Fe_I atoms that are disordered over the Fe–Al sublattice. It is assumed that an Fe_{II} atom couples antiparallel if it has five or more Al or Si near neighbors. (There must be some critical number of Al or Si nearest neighbors at which an e_g bonding band is more stable than a t_{2g} bonding band.) To obtain the observed (see Table XXIII) $\bar{\mu}$ for the ordered alloys, it is necessary to assume $x \approx 0.035$ for Fe_3Al and $x \approx 0.05$ for Fe_3Si in the limit $\delta_{II} = 0$, or $\delta_{II} = 0.7$ and 1.0, respectively, for the limit $x = 0$. These values are quite reasonable.

4. Magnetic Properties of Close-Packed Metals

It is interesting to compare the face-centered-cubic and close-packed-hexagonal metals. Whereas ferromagnetism was seen to result essentially from the spin correlations within the bands of a b.c.c. metal, in the case of close-packed metals the criterion for ferromagnetism versus Pauli paramagnetism is the existence of partially filled, localized-electron states. In *f.c.c. structures of the second and third long periods* $R_{nnn} \approx R_c(4d)$ *and* $R_{nnn} < R_c(5d)$, *so that Pauli paramagnetism prevails* (see Chapter I, Section II-A-4). *In c.p.h. structures of the second and third long periods, bonding* $(p_z d^5)$ *orbitals are probable, so that Pauli paramagnetism prevails.*

In the first long period, $R_{nnn} > R_c(3d)$ so that e_g electrons should be localized in the f.c.c. structure, d_{z^2} electrons in the c.p.h. structure. (It is assumed that no $(p_z d^5)$ bonding band is formed in the c.p.h. metals of the first long period.)   The collective electrons are in metallic states, and therefore the close-packed metals are ferromagnetic provided $n_g < 4$ (f.c.c. case) or $n_{z^2} < 2$ (c.p.h. case); they are Pauli paramagnetic otherwise.   From Figure 84 it appears that if there are $n_h > 0.4$ holes in the d bands of a f.c.c., first transition series metal, then $n_g < 4$.   The density of states curve for the c.p.h. metals should be qualitatively similar to Figure 84 except that the localized e_g levels are replaced by d_{z^2} levels that are less widely split by intraatomic exchange.   This means that there must be a larger number of d-band holes present in order to have $n_{z^2} < 2$.   Since the overlapping s bands are broad relative to the d bands, $n_s(\text{c.p.h.}) \approx n_s(\text{f.c.c.})$.   It follows that: *A metal with nearly filled d bands may have $n_g < 4$ to be ferromagnetic in a f.c.c. phase, but have $n_{z^2} = 2$ to be Pauli paramagnetic in a c.p.h. phase.*   Finally the atomic moment of the close-packed 3d metal is, according to the model,

$$\mu = \tfrac{1}{2}g(n_s + m)\mu_B \qquad (194)$$

where $m = 0, 1, 2, 3$ for Ni, Co, Fe, Mn, respectively.   This means that measurements of the magnetization provide a direct measure of the number of d-band holes $n_h = n_s + m$.

Magnetization measurements (93,136) of f.c.c. and c.p.h. Co and Ni give $n_s^{\text{Co}}(\text{c.p.h.}) = 0.72 \approx n_s^{\text{Co}}(\text{f.c.c.}) = 0.75$ and $n_s^{\text{Ni}}(\text{f.c.c.}) = 0.55 \ (g_{\text{Ni}} \neq 2)$.   *At room temperature c.p.h. nickel is paramagnetic* (391,614).   (The "c.p.h." Ni samples were thin films, and there is some possibility that the paramagnetic phase was "amorphous" Ni rather than c.p.h. Ni.)   The possibility that c.p.h. Ni is Pauli paramagnetic has been anticipated by the model, since the probability is high that in the c.p.h. metals $n_{z^2} = 2$ for $n_s \approx 0.6$.   With $n_h = 1.7$ as in cobalt, on the other hand, the probability is high that $n_{z^2} < 2$, or that the metal is ferromagnetic.

Since the 4s band becomes increasingly stable relative to the 3d band on passing from Ni to Co to Fe to Mn, the estimates $n_s^{\text{Ni}} = 0.55$, $n_s^{\text{Co}} = 0.75$ suggest that $1 < n_s^{\text{Mn}} < 2$.   This implies $4 < n_h^{\text{Mn}} < 5$, or that $3 < n_{2g} < 4$, so that the stable low-temperature form is f.c.tet. ($c/a < 1$) and antiferromagnetic (face-centered ordering of the first kind, Fig. 18).   The existence of a f.c.tet. $\rightleftharpoons$ f.c.c. transition in γ-Mn has already been mentioned.

Because bonding tends to spin-pair the electrons of the $(d_{yz}d_{zx})$ bonding band, these electrons will only contribute a fractional number of Bohr magnetons to the atomic moment. Therefore in place of the ferromagnetic moment of equation 194, the atomic moment becomes

$$\mu_{Mn} \approx [n_s^{Mn} + m - (2 - \Delta)]\mu_B \qquad m = 3$$

where $\Delta \sim 0.3$ measures the induced localization of the d_{yz}, d_{zx} electrons. Neutron diffraction measurements confirm the predicted magnetic order for $T < T_t$ and reveal a $\mu_{Mn} = (2.4 \pm 0.1)\mu_B$ (see Table VIII). Since $m = 3$ for Mn, this is compatible with $n_s^{Mn} \approx 1.15$, or with the consistent progression:

$$n_s^{Ni} = 0.55 \qquad n_s^{Co} \approx 0.75 \qquad n_s^{Fe} \approx 0.95 \qquad n_s^{Mn} \approx 1.15 \qquad (195)$$

This fact is important not only because it demonstrates the internal consistency of the model and its power to distinguish between antiferromagnetic, ferromagnetic, and Pauli paramagnetic elements, but also because it has important implications for f.c.c. iron. At high temperatures $(T > T_t)$, γ-Fe should be cubic, ferromagnetic with $\mu_{Fe} = (2 + n_s^{Fe})\mu_B$. Direct evidence in support of a $\mu_{Fe}^{\gamma} \approx \mu_{Fe}^{\alpha}$ comes from the observation (675) of no significant change in the diffuse neutron scattering on passing through the $\alpha \rightleftharpoons \gamma$ transition temperature $T^{\alpha \rightarrow \gamma}$. Resistivity vs. temperature measurements (659a) also indicate this since there is no change in resistivity at either $T^{\alpha \rightarrow \gamma}$ (1183°K) or $T^{\gamma \rightarrow \alpha}$ (1665°K), which indicates a similar high-temperature magnetic contribution to the resistivity

$$\rho_\mu(T) = C_\infty S(S + 1), \qquad C_\infty = \text{const.} \sim 30$$

for the two iron phases. This in turn implies either that $n_s^{Fe\gamma} \approx 0.2$, which is much smaller than is anticipated by equation (195), or that μ_{Fe}^{α} increases with increasing temperature due to a shift in the relative stabilities of the d and s–p bands. Evidence for $\mu_{Fe}^{\alpha} = \mu_{Fe}^{\alpha}(T)$ was discussed in Chapter II, Section I-B. Evidence that $n_s^{Fe\gamma} \sim 1$ comes from the fact that low-temperature γ-Fe, which is stabilized by precipitation in f.c.c. copper (480b), has a low, temperature-independent susceptibility indicative of either antiferromagnetism or Pauli paramagnetism (338). Neutron-diffraction studies (2a) of iron precipitates in copper over the range 1.5–4.6°K also indicate an antiferromagnetic order similar to that in γ-Mn, but with $\mu_{Fe} \approx 0.7\mu_B$. This antiferromagnetic structure is also indicated by extrapolation from the magnetic order and moments found (613) in iron-rich, f.c.c. Mn-Fe alloys. That this implies $n_s^{Fe\gamma} \sim 1$ follows from Figure 82.

If $n_s^{\text{Fe}} > 1$ so that $n_{2g} < 5$, then a low-temperature f.c. tet $(c/a > 1)$ phase would be stabilized by d_{xy} — bonding-band formation. But a tetragonal distortion would split the e_g level, lowering the d_{z^2} level below the Fermi surface. Hence the low temperature phase to be anticipated is f.c. tet $(c/a < 1)$ with a filled $d_{x^2-y^2}$ level and a $d_{yz}d_{zx}$ bonding band that causes a magnetic order like that in γMn (f.c. ordering of the first kind). Such a configuration calls for an iron moment

$$\mu_{\text{Fe}} = (n_s^{\text{Fe}} + \Delta)\mu_B.$$

Although consistency with data for other systems calls for $\Delta \sim 0.3$ and therefore $n_s^{\text{Fe}} \sim 0.4$, the magnetic order would indicate two t_{2g} holes (or $n_s^{\text{Fe}} \sim 1$), bonding-band formation, and f.c. tet. $(c/a < 1)$ symmetry. Tetragonal symmetry has not been reported. It is concluded that the general qualitative arguments represented by Figure 82 are able to account for the anomalous increase in atomic moment with temperature and the magnetic order that are observed, but that the difficulties and uncertainties associated with the low-temperature measurements make the assignment of an n_s^{Fe} quite uncertain. It will be seen below that in f.c.c. alloys, a $\mu_{\text{Fe}} \sim 2.9\mu_B$ is encountered, which is compatible with the value for n_s^{Fe} that is given in equation 195.

5. Magnetic Properties of Close-Packed Alloys

With the exception of a few tetragonal, antiferromagnetic elements (low-temperature γ-Mn and γ-Fe), close-packed, transition element solvents have been found to be either ferromagnetic or Pauli paramagnetic. These will be referred to, respectively, as solvents of class (1) or class (2). In the class (1) solvents the d-band holes all have the same spin in the ferromagnetic state (see Fig. 8). It is therefore possible to discuss the close-packed, class (1) alloys with the collective-electron model originally proposed by Stoner (601) and later developed by Stoner (603) and Wohlfarth (688). However, it must be kept in mind that this formalism is valid, within the framework of the model presented here, only so long as $n_g < 4$. At solute concentrations for which $n_g = 4$, the d-band holes need not all have the same spin, since there are no localized unpaired spins present to induce a spontaneous magnetization of the collective electrons.

If $n_h < 3$ is the number of holes in the d bands of a class (1) solvent,

v' is the number of outer electrons on a gaseous solute atom, and n_d' is the total number of d electrons on the solute when present in the solvent, then the average number of Bohr magnetons per atom in a ferromagnetic alloy is

$$\bar{n}_B = (1 - c)(\mu/\mu_B) + c(\mu'/\mu_B)$$

$$= (1 - c)(n_h + \delta_s) - c(v' - n_g' - n_{2g}' - n_z)$$

$$+ c \begin{cases} n_g' + n_{2g}' + \delta_s' & \text{for } n_d' \leq 5 \\ 10 - n_g' - n_{2g}' + \delta_s' & \text{for } 5 \leq n_d' \leq 10 \end{cases}$$

(196)

where the first two terms represent the contribution from the solvent d-band holes reduced by the number of solute electrons that enter the solvent d bands and the last term gives the atomic moment on the solute. The quantities δ_s', δ_s represent any induced magnetization of the s electrons. Implicit in equation 196 is the assumption that the orbital angular momentum is completely quenched. This cannot be correct so long as $0 < n_{2g} < 6$, but it should not introduce an error greater than $\sim 10\%$ and is therefore neglected in this simplified treatment.

If n_{hp}, δ_{sp} refer to the pure solvent, it is reasonable to assume that $(n_{hp} + \delta_{sp}) - (n_h + \delta_s) = \Lambda_0 c$, where the proportionality constant Λ_0 is a small fraction, positive or negative, that measures the solute-induced alteration of relative d- and s-band stability. With this assumption, it follows that

$$\bar{\mu} = \bar{n}_B \mu_B = \mu(p) - cn\mu_B$$

(197)

where $\mu(p)$ is the atomic moment of the pure class (1) solvent, and that

$$-\frac{d\bar{n}_B}{dc} = n = (v' + m + \Lambda) - \begin{cases} 2(n_g' + n_{2g}') & \text{for } n_d' \leq 5 \\ 10 & \text{for } 5 \leq n_d' \leq 10 \end{cases}$$

(198)

where $\Lambda = (\Lambda_0 + \delta_s - \delta_s')$ and $m = n_h - n_s$ is an integer.

Application of equations 197 and 198 requires explicit consideration of two factors, the relative energies of solvent and solute d states and bonding-band (or homopolar-bond) stabilization that induces, wherever possible, t_{2g}-hole ordering at low temperatures. These two considerations require the distinction of four separate situations.

Case (a). $n_g' = n_{2g}' = 0$ (*nontransition element or ionized solute*)

$$d\bar{n}_B/dc = -(v' + m + \Lambda)$$

(199)

Early experimental information, which is summarized in Table XIX, would show that in most Ni alloys $\Lambda \approx 0$. However, more

TABLE XIX

Variations in Average Atomic Moment with Concentration
of Nontransition-Element Solute in f.c.c. Ni and Co

Solute	Solvent	$-d\bar{\mu}/d(c\mu_B)$ (theory)[a]	$-d\bar{\mu}/d(c\mu_B)$ (observed)[b]
Cu, Ag, Au	f.c.c. Ni	$1 + \Lambda$	Cu: 1, Au: ~1
	f.c.c. Co	$2 + \Lambda$	
	c.p.h. Co	$2 + \Lambda$	
Zn, Cd	f.c.c. Ni	$2 + \Lambda$	Zn: 2.0
	f.c.c. Co	$3 + \Lambda$	
	c.p.h. Co	$3 + \Lambda$	
Al, Sc, Ga, In	f.c.c. Ni	$3 + \Lambda$	Al: 3.0
	f.c.c. Co	$4 + \Lambda$	
	c.p.h. Co	$4 + \Lambda$	Al: 2.4 (?) ·
Si, Ge, Sn	f.c.c. Ni	$4 + \Lambda$	Si: 4, Sn: 4–4.1
	f.c.c. Co	$5 + \Lambda$	
	c.p.h. Co	$5 + \Lambda$	Si: 5.3
P, As, Sb	f.c.c. Ni	$5 + \Lambda$	Sb: ~5
	f.c.c. Co	$6 + \Lambda$	
	c.p.h. Co	$6 + \Lambda$	

[a] Theory predicts that only solvent atoms carry a magnetic moment.
[b] References (174,412,550).

recent measurements (139) give $\Lambda \approx 0.5$ for Al, Si, and Ge in f.c.c. Ni. The fact that there is no sudden drop in $\bar{\mu}$ at that composition beyond which the simple model calls for $n_g = 4$ indicates that the "extra" electrons contributed by a solute to the d bands of the solvent are constrained by charge-neutrality requirements to remain in the immediate vicinity of the solute. That is, the solvent d states, especially the localized states, are not filled uniformly. This does not invalidate equations 197, 198, which represent averages. However, if $n_g = 4$ at the solute's near-neighbor solvent atoms (as must occur with Al, Si, and Ge solutes), a number of solvent atoms, initially proportional to c, would not have saturated moments. This effect would be reflected in equation 198 by a contribution to $\Lambda > 0$.

If a transition element solute is in a f.c.c. solvent, then any of the cases (a) through (d) discussed below may be anticipated. However, consistency requires that there be a continuous change from (a) to (d) on moving to heavier solute elements in any one long period of the periodic table, or on going down any column. Inspection of Table XX, in which are given atomic moments compatible with observed variations of $\bar{\mu}$ with c according to equation 198, shows that these consistency criteria are everywhere fulfilled, and also that the stability of the solute d levels relative to the solvent Fermi level is consistently greater in f.c.c. Ni alloys than in f.c.c. Co alloys. In binary alloys of case (a), all of the moment is associated, presumably, with the solvent atoms.

Case (b). $0 < n'_d \leq 2$ $(0 < n'_g \leq 2,\, n'_{2g} = 0)$

$$d\bar{n}_B/dc = -(v' + m + \Lambda) + 2n'_d \qquad (200)$$

This case is differentiated from the more general one $n'_d \leq 5$ because of the explicit assumption in Figure 84 that the lower e_g subband lies below the metallic t_{2g} band. The principal relevance of this assumption is that it allows ferromagnetic solute-solute interactions for case (b). Were $0 < n'_{2g} < 2$, near-neighbor solute atoms would form homopolar bonds, in analogy with the Ti–Ti c-axis bonding in Ti_2O_3, to give antiferromagnetic solute-solute interactions.

The measured variations $d\bar{\mu}/dc$ for Ni–Cr and Co–Cr alloys are, respectively (136,412), $-4.4\mu_B$ and $-6.6\mu_B$. With $\Lambda \approx 0$, this corresponds to $n_d^{Cr}(Ni) = 0.8$ and $n_d^{Cr}(Co) = 0.2$. A linear variation of $\bar{\mu}$ with c for the Ni–Cr alloys holds only for the compositional range $0 \leq c \leq 0.07$, the curve deviating to *higher* magnetizations for larger c. Such deviations are consistent with a smaller ionization of a Cr atom given a Cr nearest neighbor: They are not consistent with antiferromagnetic Cr–Cr interactions. This supports the otherwise arbitrary placement of the lower e_g subband below the t_{2g} band in Figure 84.

Case (c). $2 < n'_d \leq 7$ *(dilute alloys having no solute-solute pairs)*

$$d\bar{n}_B/dc = -(v' + m + \Lambda) + 4 + \begin{cases} 2n'_{2g} & \text{if } n'_{2g} \leq 3 \\ 6 & \text{if } n'_{2g} \geq 3 \end{cases} \qquad (201)$$

With at least one t'_{2g} electron or one t'_{2g} hole, homopolar bonding between nearest-neighbor solute-solute pairs introduces antiferromagnetic solute-solute interactions. Therefore the model provides

TABLE XX

Interpretation of Atomic Moments for Disordered f.c.c. Transition-Element Alloys

Case (a): Ferromagnetic. Class (1): $\bar{\mu} = \mu(p) - (v' + m + \Lambda)\mu_B$, $n'_d = 0$. Case (b): Ferromagnetic. Class (1): $\bar{\mu} = \mu(p) - (v' + m + \Lambda - 2n'_o)\mu_B$, $0 \leqslant n'_d \leqslant 2$.
Case (c): Near-neighbor solute-solute pairs antiferromagnetic. If ferromagnetic (no solute-solute pairs),

$$\text{Class (1): } \bar{\mu} = \mu(p) - \left\{ v' + m + \Lambda - \begin{bmatrix} 2n'_o \\ 6 \end{bmatrix} \right\} c\mu_B, \qquad \begin{bmatrix} 0 < n'_{2g} < 3 \\ 3 \leqslant n'_{2g} \leqslant 5 \end{bmatrix}$$

Case (d): Ferromagnetic. Class (1): $\bar{\mu} = \mu(p) - (v' + m + \Lambda - 10)\mu_B$. Class (2): Require sufficient number of ferromagnetic solute-solute pairs to induce ferromagnetism. Symbols: v', v = number of outer electrons of solute, solvent; $m = 10 - v$; $\mu'(p)$ = atomic moment of pure solute, solvent; n'_d = number of solute d electrons; n'_{2g} = number of t_{2g} electrons at solute; $\bar{\mu}$ = average atomic moment, and c = concentration of solute; Λ = measure of relative stability of s bands.

v'	4	5	6	7	8	9	10
Solvent \ Solute	Ti	V	Cr[a]	Mn	Fe	Co	Ni
Ni ($m = 0$) Class (1)	Case (a) $n'_s = 4$ $\dfrac{d\bar{\mu}}{d(c\mu_B)} = \begin{cases} 4\,(\Lambda = 0) \\ 3.8\ (\text{obs.}) \end{cases}$	Case (a) $n'_s = 5$ $\dfrac{d\bar{\mu}}{d(c\mu_B)} = \begin{cases} 5\,(\Lambda = 0) \\ 5.2\ (\text{obs.}) \end{cases}$	Case (b) $n'_s = 5.2$ $\mu_{Cr} \approx 0.9\mu_B$ $\mu_{Ni} \approx \left\{ \dfrac{0.6 - 5.3c}{1 - c} \right\} \mu_B$	Case (c) $n'_s = 2.3$ $\mu_{Mn} \approx 4.7\mu_B$ $\mu_{Ni} \approx \left\{ \dfrac{0.6 - 2.3c}{1 - c} \right\} \mu_B$	Case (d)[b] $n'_s = 0.8$ [c]	Case (d) $n'_s = 0.79$ $\Lambda = -0.19$ [e]	Case (d) $n'_s = 0.6$ $\mu_{Ni} = 0.6\mu_B$
Co (f.c.c.) ($m = 1$) Class (1)	Case (a) $n'_s = 4$ $\dfrac{d\bar{\mu}}{d(c\mu_B)} = 5\,(\Lambda = 0)$	Case (a) $n'_s = 5$ $\dfrac{d\bar{\mu}}{d(c\mu_B)} = 6\,(\Lambda = 0)$	Case (b) $n'_s = 5.8$ $\mu_{Cr} \approx 0.25\mu_B$ $\mu_{Co} \approx \dfrac{0.75 - 6.85c}{1 - c} \mu_B$	Case (c) $n'_s = 4.25$ $\mu_{Mn} \approx 2.8\mu_B$ $\mu_{Co} \approx \dfrac{1.75 - 5.3c}{1 - c} \mu_B$	Probably case (d) Possibly case (c)[d]	Case (d) $n'_s = 0.75$ $\mu_{Co} = 1.75\mu_B$	
Pd Class (2)	Case (a) Paramagnetic	Case (b)	Case (b) or Case (c)	Case (c)	Case (d) $\mu_{Fe} \sim 2.8\mu_B$[f]	Case (d) $\mu_{Co} \sim 1.7\mu_B$[f]	Case (d) $\mu_{Ni} \sim 0.6\mu_B$[f]
Pt Class (2)	Case (a) Paramagnetic	Case (b)	Case (c) Where ferromagnetic $\mu_{Cr} \sim 2.8\mu_B$	Case (c) Where ferromagnetic $\mu_{Mn} \sim 4.7\mu_B$	Case (d) $\mu_{Fe} \sim 2.8\mu_B$[f]	Case (d) $\mu_{Co} \sim 1.7\mu_B$[f]	Case (d) $\mu_{Ni} \sim 0.6\mu_B$[f]

a Mo and W ($v' = 6$) are Case (a) in Ni with $n'_s = 6$, and $d\bar{\mu}/d(c\mu_B) = 6\ (\Lambda = 0)$ is observed.
b Also see Table XXI.
c $\mu_{Fe} = 2.8\mu_B + [(1 - c)/c](0.6\mu_B - \mu_{Ni})$, $c < 0.33$.
d $\mu_{Fe} = 2.5\mu_B + [(1 - c)/c](0.76\mu_B - \mu_{Ni})$, $0.33 < c < 0.6$.
e $\mu_{Co} = 1.79\mu_B + [(1 - c)/c](0.6\mu_B - \mu_{Ni})$.
f Assumes concentration of solute-solute pairs sufficiently great to induce spontaneous polarization of t_{2g} band and therefore ferromagnetism. Anticipate $0\mu_B < \bar{\mu}_{Pd} < 0.6\mu_B$, $0\mu_B < \bar{\mu}_{Pt} < 0.4\mu_B$, the magnitude depending upon the number of solute-solute pairs present.

the sharp prediction that: *Disordered alloys corresponding to case* (*c*), *as determined from measurements on dilute alloys and equation 192, must be ferromagnetic or antiferromagnetic, but without magnetic order, as a result of antiferromagnetic, nearest-neighbor, solute-solute interactions.*

In the compositional range $0 \leq c \leq 0.08$, $d\bar{n}_B/dc \approx +2.4$ for the Ni–Mn alloys (412). With $\Lambda \approx 0$, this gives $n_d^{Mn}(Ni) = 4.7$. Thus Ni–Mn alloys correspond to case (*c*). Evidence for the resulting ferrimagnetism was first observed in Ni_3Mn, which has $\bar{\mu} \sim 0.3\mu_B$ if disordered, but a considerably larger magnetization if ordered (Cu_3Au structure) (340). More recent evidence from magnetization measurements has been reported by Kouvel *et al.* (367,370,371) and from neutron diffraction measurements by Shull and Wilkinson (568). Although the latter workers report $\bar{\mu}_{Mn} = (3.18 \pm 0.25)\mu_B$ in a sample of ordered Ni_3Mn, this is not necessarily in disagreement with $n_c^{Mn} = 4.7$ since only 5% disorder would reduce the observed $\bar{\mu}_{Mn}$ from $4.7\mu_B$ to $3.3\mu_B$. Further, neutron diffraction results (334) for ordered NiMn, which has alternate (001) layers Ni or Mn, give antiferromagnetically coupled Mn atoms within a (001) Mn plane, $\mu_{Mn} = (4.0 \pm 0.1)\mu_B$ and $\mu_{Ni} \approx 0\mu_B$. With a d_{xy} bonding band, the predicted Mn moment for the ordered alloy is $\mu_{Mn} \approx [4.7 - (1 - \delta_{xy})]\mu_B$, where $\delta_{xy} \sim 0.3$ is the induced localization of the bonding electrons. Thus $\mu_{Mn}(\text{theory}) = 4.0\mu_B = \mu_{Mn}(\text{exptl.})$, and $n_d^{Mn} = 4.7$ appears to be correct. From the model it also follows that $\mu_{Ni} \approx 0$ for $c > 0.26$ (refer Table XX).

Crangle (136) reports that f.c.c. Co–Mn alloys have two regions of roughly linear variation of $\bar{\mu}$ with c, one for $c < 0.05$ and one for greater c. From the initial slope $d\bar{\mu}_B/dc = -2.5$ and from equation 201, it follows that $n_d^{Mn}(Co) = 2.75$ and that the change in slope for $c > 0.05$ is due to antiferromagnetic Mn–Mn interactions. Therefore the Co–Mn alloys are predicted to be ferrimagnetic, but without long-range magnetic order, like the Ni–Mn alloys. Displaced hysteresis loops are characteristic of unidirectional anisotropy caused by intimate mixtures of ferromagnetic and antiferromagnetic materials (430). Hysteresis loops for Co–Mn alloys that are asymmetric with respect to the origin give strong evidence for the presence of antiferromagnetic as well as ferromagnetic exchange interactions in f.c.c. Co–Mn alloys (365). The Mn atomic moment of Table XX is for dilute ($c < 0.05$) alloys. Similar measurements (366) for $\sim 25\%$

Mn–Cu and Mn–Ag alloys indicate $n_d^{Mn} \sim 4.6$ with antiferromagnetic near-neighbor interactions and ferromagnetic next-nearest-neighbor (and greater) interactions. Thus Mn acts as a case (c) solute in these solvents also.

Case (d). $7 < n_d' < 10$ $(5 < n_{2g}' < 6)$

$$d\bar{n}_B/dc = -(v' + m + \Lambda) + 10 = n_B(p') - n_B(p) \qquad (202)$$

There can be no solute-solute nearest-neighbor bonding in alloys corresponding to case (d), and therefore all interactions are ferromagnetic. It follows that there can be no sharp discontinuity in $\bar{\mu}$ for ordered versus disordered case (d) alloys. However, changes in Λ can be expected to occur on either side of a critical composition.

From Figure 84 it follows that f.c.c. Co–Ni alloys belong to case (d), which is substantiated by the ferromagnetism of these alloys. Extrapolation to pure Co of the magnetization measurements (657) for f.c.c. Co–Ni alloys gives $\mu(p)_{Co} = 1.79\mu_B$, or $\Lambda = -0.19$, as compared with Crangle's (136) extrapolation from high-temperature measurements on pure Co to $\mu(p)_{Co} = 1.75\mu_B$.

Although it is not possible to determine definitely from Figure 84 whether f.c.c. Fe–Ni alloys correspond to case (c) or case (d), the fact that these alloys are ferromagnetic dictates that $n_d^{Fe} > 7$, or that $\mu_{Fe} < 3\mu_B$ in these alloys. That this condition is fulfilled has been confirmed by neutron diffraction experiments (see Table XXI).

TABLE XXI

Atomic Moments vs. Iron Concentration c for f.c.c. Fe–Ni Alloys

	μ_{Fe}/μ_B		μ_N/μ_B	
c	Observed[a]	Theory	Observed[a]	Theory
0.257	2.91 ± 0.2	2.8	0.62 ± 0.02	0.60
0.399	2.72 ± 0.16	2.65	0.66 ± 0.05	0.66
0.501	2.60 ± 0.1	2.65	0.67 ± 0.1	0.66

[a] See ref. (568).

Predictions for the individual atomic moments can be obtained from magnetization measurements (513), which show two linear regions for $\bar{\mu}$ vs. c in the range of f.c.c. alloys. In the range $0 \leq c \leq 0.33$, the slope is $d\bar{n}_B/dc = 2.2$ corresponding in equation 202 to an effective

$n_B(\text{Fe}) = 2.8$, $n_d^{\text{Fe}} \approx 7.2$, and $\Lambda \approx -0.2$. At FeNi_2 a rearrangement of the band structure seems to occur, and for $0.33 \leq c \leq 0.6$ the effective $n_B(p'')$ and $n_B(p')$ are $2.5\mu_B$ and $0.76\mu_B$, or $d\bar{n}_B/dc = 1.74$, corresponding to $\Lambda \approx +0.26$. In Table XXI the resulting atomic moments are compared with experiment.

There is considerable evidence for low-field antiferromagnetic, but high-field ferromagnetic Fe–Fe interactions in the ordered alloy Ni_3Fe, for ferromagnetic Fe–Fe interactions in the disordered alloy (147,148). In the disordered alloy, near-neighbor Fe–Fe interactions predominate. These are ferromagnetic since there is less than one t_{2g} hole at any atom. In the ordered alloy, the Fe atoms have Ni near neighbors and Fe next-near neighbors. Since $n_g^{\text{Fe}} = 2$, the next-near-neighbor Fe––Fe interactions are antiferromagnetic. The near-neighbor Fe–Ni interactions are ferromagnetic. Since the next-near-neighbor distance is large compared to the near-neighbor distance, it is surprising to find that the Fe––Fe interactions are strong enough to influence the magnetic order even though this represents bonding between *like* atoms whereas the Fe–Ni interactions represent metallic-spin correlations, which are relatively less stable, between *unlike* atoms. That the two effects are of comparable magnitude is indicated by the metamagnetic character of the interaction: In high external fields the near-neighbor spin correlations predominate, and the ordered alloy is ferromagnetic. This example serves to emphasize the stability (at all atomic separations) of antiferromagnetic spin correlations between like atoms that have half filled overlapping orbitals.

Studies (163,234,362,369,502) of the pressure dependence of the Curie temperature and magnetization in Fe–Ni alloys reveal considerable pressure sensitivity for f.c.c. alloys in the compositional interval 30 to 50% nickel. These experiments indicate that pressure is able to induce antiferromagnetic, near-neighbor Fe–Fe interactions in these alloys. This means that Fe may become a class (c) solute at high pressure and high iron concentrations. In view of the fact that n_{2g}^{Fe} appears to be a function of the temperature in f.c.c. iron, it is not surprising that increased pressure is capable of ordering t_{2g} holes at near-neighbor Fe–Fe pairs to induce antiferromagnetic coupling. There must be a threshold number of near-neighbor iron atoms required for this hole-ordering to take place. Hence the sharp increase in pressure sensitivity for less than 40% nickel.

Paladium and platinum are class (2) solvents. As dilute solutes in class (1) solvents, they carry an induced moment and correspond to case (d). [If the next-nearest neighbors of a $4d$ element are all $3d$, $R_{nnn} < R_c$ so that localized e_g electrons result. In the case of Pt, on the other hand, $R_{nnn} \approx R_c$ and localization at a Pt is only induced by the net magnetization of near-neighbor class (1) atoms.] Data (412) for NiPd and NiPt alloys indicate that, for quenched samples, a linear relationship between $\bar{\mu}$ and c holds up to $c \approx 0.4$ for Pd, $c < 0.2$ for Pt, and that $\Lambda < 0.1$ for Ni–Pd ($\bar{\mu}_{Ni-Pd} = \mu(Ni) - \Lambda c$). The Pt atoms contribute noticeably smaller average atomic moments, and in Ni_3Pt there is a small drop in T_c and room-temperature B_s on ordering, presumably because the Pt contribution is reduced if all its next-nearest neighbors are Pt.

More recent measurements (140) (see Table XXII) indicate that Pd and Pt also act like case (d) solutes in f.c.c. Co, but that Ru, Rh, Os and Ir in Ni and f.c.c. Co cause changes in magnetization that are not interpretable from the model for class (1) alloys. With increasing numbers of holes, solutes that are class (2) solvents have an increased tendency to correlate the spin of their d *holes* parallel to the spin of their neighbors.

If Pd or Pt (or Rh, Ir, . . .) form the solvent, the cases (a) through (d) still apply for the definition of solute moments and solute-solute interactions. Magnetization measurements have been made on ordered and disordered Mn–Pt and Cr–Pt alloys (30,195) that indicate antiferromagnetic nearest-neighbor Mn–Mn and Cr–Cr interactions, ferromagnetic Mn–Pt–Mn and Cr–Pt–Cr interactions typical for case (c). For example a maximum magnetization of $4\pi M_s \approx 8000$ gauss was found in an annealed (ordered) sample of Pt_3Mn, and T_c increases monotonically from 20 to 40 atomic per cent Mn even though the magnetization is a maximum at 25 atomic per cent. Similar effects were noticed in Cr–Pt alloys. Ordered Ir_3Cr is also ferromagnetic (538). In Mn_xPd_{1-x} ($0.34 \leq x \leq 0.42$), Wendling (661a) has observed antiferromagnetism and thermoremanent magnetization that appear characteristic of case (c) alloys.

The magnetization of Pd-rich and Pt-rich Fe–Pd, Co–Pd, and Fe–Pt alloys indicate ferromagnetic Co–Co and Fe–Fe interactions typical of case (d), with definite contributions from the solvent atoms, especially from Pd (101,137,138,381). Crangle (138) tentatively concluded that $\mu_{Fe} = 2.8\mu_B$ and for $c > 0.1$, $\mu_{Pd} = 0.4\mu_B$, which is in

TABLE XXII

Rate of Change of Magnetization with Concentration $d\bar{n}_B/dc$, Where Magnetization is Expressed as the Average Number of Bohr Magnetons per Atom, for Dilute ($c < 0.02$) Alloys

I are the theoretical changes corresponding to a case (d) solute in a class (1) solvent. II are the experimental changes as determined by ref. (140). III are the theoretical changes corresponding to solute *hole* spins ordered parallel to the near-neighbor *electron* spins. IV are the changes corresponding to no net average moment on the solute atoms, which could be due to a lack of isolation of the solute atoms. (By isolation is meant no near-neighbor or next-near-neighbor solute atoms.)

Solvent	Solute					
	Ru	Rh	Pd	Os	Ir	Pt
Co: I	$0.25 + n'_s$	$-0.75 + n'_s$	$-1.75 + n'_s$	$0.25 + n'_s$	$-0.75 + n'_s$	$-1.75 + n'_s$
Co: II (obs.)	-4.9 ± 0.1	-1.75 ± 0.1	-0.95 ± 0.05	-9.5 ± 1	-2.95 ± 0.25	-1.26 ± 0.1
Co: III	$-3.75 - n'_s$	$-2.75 - n'_s$		$-3.75 - n'_s$	$-2.75 - n'_s$	
Co: IV	-1.75	-1.75	-1.75	-1.75	-1.75	-1.75
Ni: I	$1.39 + n'_s$	$0.39 + n'_s$	$-0.61 + n'_s$	$1.39 + n'_s$	$0.39 + n'_s$	$-0.61 + n'_s$
Ni: II(obs.)	-3.0 ± 0.1	$+2.0 \pm 0.1$	0 ± 0.1	-2.0 ± 0.1	-0.61 ± 0.1	-0.61 ± 0.1
Ni: III	$-2.61 - n'_s$	$-1.61 - n'_s$		$-2.61 - n'_s$	$-1.61 - n'_s$	
Ni: IV	-0.61	-0.61	-0.61	-0.61	-0.61	-0.61

good agreement with the model.   That Pd is on the verge of being a ferromagnetic metal follows from $R_{nnn} \approx R_c(Pd)$.   Measurements (101) of the saturation moment of Co–Pd alloys, which are ferromagnetic with only 0.1% Co, are compatible with $\mu_{Co} = 1.7\mu_B$ and μ_{Pd}(n.n. to a Co) $= 0.6\mu_B$, but all other $\mu_{Pd} \approx 0\mu_B$.   From the model it is reasonable to expect that a magnetization is induced on those Pd atoms that are near neighbors of a magnetic solute atom.

Surprisingly, ordered Pt_3Fe is antiferromagnetic (137), neutron diffraction suggesting the simultaneous presence of two different antiferromagnetic phases (33).   It appears that the ferromagnetic Fe–Pt–Fe interactions are sufficiently weak that next-nearest-neighbor, antiferromagnetic Fe––Fe interactions are competitive. This situation is analogous to that found in ordered Ni_3Fe at low fields.   The next-nearest-neighbor interactions are antiferromagnetic because the localized e_g states are half filled; they may be relatively strong because they are bonding and between similar atoms whereas the near-neighbor interactions are metallic and between dissimilar atoms.   That similar effects are not found in $MnPt_3$ and $CrPt_3$ may be attributed to stronger metallic correlations of the t_{2g} orbitals if one of the two atoms is half or less filled.

6. Magnetic Properties of Some Special Ordered Alloys

In Table XXIII predictions for several ordered alloys are compared with available experimental data.   Many of these have already been discussed.   Attention is here directed to the Heusler alloys $(Cu_2MnM$, with M = Al, Ga, In, Sn, As, Sb, Bi), some perovskite-type nitrides and carbides, and the Mn–Au alloys.   These examples are discussed because they illustrate how the chemical intuition that has been developed can provide insights into the electron correlations of relatively complex compounds.

(a) Ideally, the Heusler alloys form the ordered structure shown in Figure 85.   It is reasonable to assume that the Cu atoms have a full or nearly filled d shell, and that the strongest electron correlations between unlike neighboring atoms occur with electrons of the same principal and angular-momentum quantum numbers.   Therefore the Mn atoms are expected to have localized electrons that are coupled via the d electrons of the Cu sublattice.   In an ideal structure, the Mn–Mn separation is too great for any competitive Mn––Mn interactions, and the indirect Mn–Cu–Mn interactions predominate. Since the d states are more than half filled, this gives ferromagnetic coupling. (Bonding t_{2g} states on copper sublattice, antibonding states on Mn sublattice.)

However, the possibility of Mn–M–Mn interactions within the Mn–M sublattice must also be considered. These interactions must be distinguished from the indirect cation-anion-cation interactions discussed in Chapter III, Section I. In the latter case the anion is characterized by a *filled* outer p shell; in the former the M atom has

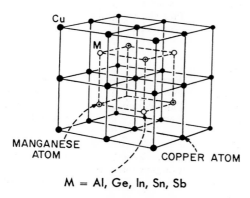

M = Al, Ge, In, Sn, Sb

Fig. 85. Schematic structure of the Heusler alloys.

half or less filled outer p states. Thus whereas a 180° cation-anion-cation interaction is antiferromagnetic if the cation e_g states are half filled (refer equations 164–166), a similar Metal–M–Metal interaction is *ferromagnetic*. That such a ferromagnetic interaction follows from the spin correlations previously considered may be seen in three ways. First, the half filled e_g (or $e_g{}^2s$) states of the metal atoms may be thought of as forming a bonding band with the p states on the M atoms (Metal and M atoms form a two-sublattice structure), in which case the spins of the metal sublattice are correlated parallel. Second, metal- -metal interactions correspond to a three-electron bond since the single M-atom electron forces principal admixing of e_g and p states on each side of the M atom to be via the same (including spin) p state. Third, excitation of one e_g electron onto the M atoms gives the configuration of Case 3, Figure 42. This coupling

TABLE XXIII

Predicted (Given Crystallographic Structure) and Measured Magnetic
Structures and Atomic Moments for Several Ordered Alloys[a]

| Row No. | Alloy | Magnetic sublattice structure | | Ref. |
		Predicted	Observed	
1.	Heusler alloys: Cu_2MnM M = Al, Ge, In, Sn, As	Ferromag., any disordered Mn antiferro. Possibly M = Sb is antiferro.	(As predicted) M = Sb is antiferro.	91 499a 499b
2.	Nitrides and Carbides (a) $M^cNFe_3^f$			
3.	M = Fe	Ferro.	Fig. 88(a)	190
4.	M = Ni, Pt	Ferro.	(As predicted)	653
5.	(b) FeNiN	Pauli paramag.	(As predicted)	224
6.	(c) Mn_4N	Ferri.	Fig. 88(b)	610
7.	(d) $M^cCMn_3^f$			
8.	M^c = Zn	Ferro. (cubic)	(As predicted)	110
9.		Complex ferri. (tet.)	Fig. 88(c)	106
10.	M^c = Al, Ga	Ferro.	(As predicted)	282
11.	Mn–Au alloys			
12.	(a) MnAu (b.c. tet. $c/a < 1$)	S.C. type A (Fig. 18)	(As predicted)	34
13.	(b) $MnAu_2$	Antiferro. spiral possible	Antiferro. spiral, metamag.	269
14.	(c) $MnAu_3$	Mn–Au–Mn ferro.; n.n. Mn–Mn antiferro.	Ferri. with no long- range order if quenched	297, 436,
15.			"Antiferro." if annealed[b]	551
16.	(d) $MnAu_4$	Ferro.	(As predicted)	434
17.	FeV (ordered)	Ferro.	(As predicted)	566
18.	Aluminum and silicon alloys (a) MAl			
19.	M = Fe	S.C. type G (Fig. 18)	Evidence of anti- ferro. 28 to 40 atomic % Al	24,64 3
20.	M = Co	If antiferro., type G		

TABLE XXIII (*continued*)

Atomic Moments			Row
			No.
Predicted	Observed	Ref.	
$\mu_{\text{Mn}} = (4 + \delta_s)\mu_B,\ \delta_s \sim 0.1$	$\mu_{\text{Mn}} = 4.0\mu_B,\ 4.1\mu_B$ for $M = \text{Al, Sn}$	91 499b	1.
if $\text{Mn} = \text{Al, In, Sn}$ $\mu_{\text{Mn}} = (3 + \delta_s)\mu_B,$ $\delta_s \sim 0.1$ if $M = \text{Ge, Sb}$	$\bar{\mu}_{\text{Mn}} = 3.6\mu_B$ for $M = \text{In}$ $\bar{\mu}_{\text{Mn}} = 2.84\mu_B$ for $M = \text{Ge}$		2.
$\mu_{\text{Fe}^c} \approx 3\mu_B,\ \mu_{\text{Fe}^f} \approx 2\mu_B$	$\mu_{\text{Fe}^c} = 3\mu_B,\ \mu_{\text{Fe}^f} = 2\mu_B$	190	3.
$\bar{\mu}(\text{MNFe}_3) = (7 + \delta n_s)\mu_B$	$\bar{\mu} = 7.2\mu_B,\ 7.76\mu_B,$ resp.	653	4.
			5.
$\mu_{\text{Mn}^c} = -(2 + 3\delta_{ij})\mu_B,\ \delta_{ij} \sim 0.5$	$\mu_{\text{Mn}^c} = -3.85\mu_B$	610	6.
$\mu_{\text{Mn}^f} = \nu + \delta'_{ij} \sim 1$	$\mu_{\text{Mn}^f} = +0.90\mu_B$		
			7.
$\mu_{\text{Mn}^f} \approx (1 + \nu)\mu_B,\ \nu \sim 0.5$	$\mu_{\text{Mn}} = 1.57\mu_B$	110	8.
	Fig. 88(c)	106	9.
$\mu_{\text{Mn}^f} \approx (1 + \nu)\mu_B,\ \nu \sim 0.5$	$\mu_{\text{Mn}} = 1.25\ \mu_B,\ 1.42\mu_B,$ resp.	282	10.
			11.
$\mu_{\text{Mn}} = (4 + \delta_s),\ \delta_s \sim 0.1$	$\mu_{\text{Mn}} = 4.2\mu_B$	34, 33a	12.
$\mu_{\text{Mn}} = (4 - \epsilon)\mu_B,\ 0 < \epsilon < 1$	$\mu_{\text{Mn}} = 3.49\mu_B$	438	13.
$\mu_{\text{Mn}} = (4 + \epsilon)\mu_B,$ $\epsilon = (n_s^{\text{Mn}} - 1) \ll 1$	$n_{\text{eff}} = 4.62$ (or $\mu_{\text{Mn}} \approx 3.8\mu_B$)	436a	14.
			15.
$\mu_{\text{Mn}} = (4 + \epsilon)\mu_B,$ $\epsilon = (n_s^{\text{Mn}} - 1) \ll 1$	$\mu_{\text{Mn}} = 4.15\mu_B$	434	16.
$\mu_{\text{V}} = 0\mu_B,\ \mu_{\text{Fe}} \approx 1.14\mu_B$	$\bar{\mu}_{\text{Fe}} = 0.91\mu_B,\ \bar{\mu}_{\text{V}} \approx 0.1\mu_B^c$	566	17.
			18.
$\mu_{\text{Fe}} = n_{sp}^{\text{Fe}}\mu_B$	$\mu_{\text{Fe}} = 0\mu_B$ (?)	522	19.
$\mu_{\text{Co}} = (n_{sp}^{\text{Co}} - 1)\mu_B$			20.

(*continued*)

TABLE XXIII (*continued*)

Row No.	Alloy	Magnetic sublattice structure		Ref.
		Predicted	Observed	
21.	M = Ni	Pauli paramag.		
22.	(b) Fe₃M,	Ferro.	Ferro.	89
	M = Al, Si	(xFe$_{II}$ antiferro., $x \ll 1$)		466
23.	Nickel alloys (a) MNi			
24.	M = Mn (f.c. tet. $c/a < 1$)	Antiferro. within (001) Ferro. along [001]	(As predicted)	334
25.	M = Co (b) MNi₃,	Ferro.	(A predicted)	115a
26.	M = Fe	Ferro. (but antiferro. n.n.n. Fe–Fe interactions may compete)	Ferro., but evidence of complex mag. order near T_c	147, 148
27.	M = Co	Ferro.	(As predicted)	115a
28.	M = Mn	Ferro. (Disordered Mn antiferro.)	(As predicted)	568
29.	Palladium Alloys (a) MPd			
30.	M = Fe, Co (b) MPd₃	Ferro.	(As predicted)	115a
31.	M = Fe, Co	Ferro.	(As predicted)	115a
	M = Mn₃	Like Ni₃Mn	(Antiferro.)[d]	115a′
32.	Platinum alloys			
33.	(a) MPt (f.c. tet. $c/a < 1$)			
34.	M = Cr, Mn	Same as MnNi	Evidence of antiferro.	30, 195
35.	M = Fe, Co, Ni	Ferro. (T_c decreases as order increases) ⎰ Ferro. (001) pos- ⎱ sibly couple antiferro. along [001] for M = Fe, Co	(As predicted)	173, 232, 202, 412

TABLE XXIII (*continued*)

Atomic Moments			
Predicted	Observed	Ref.	Row No.
$\mu_{\mathrm{Ni}} = (n_{sp}^{\mathrm{Ni}} - 2)\mu_B \approx 0\mu_B$			21.
$\mu_{\mathrm{Fe_I}} \approx 2.2\mu_B,\ \mu_{\mathrm{Al}} = \mu_{\mathrm{Si}} = 0\mu_B$	$\mu_{\mathrm{Fe_I}} = 2.14\mu_B,\ \bar\mu_{\mathrm{Fe_{II}}} = 1.46\mu_B$	466	22.
$\mu_{\mathrm{Fe_{II}}} \approx [(2.2 - \delta_{\mathrm{II}})$ $- 4x(5.2 - 2\delta_{\mathrm{II}})]\mu_B$ $x \ll 1$ and $\delta_{\mathrm{II}} \leq 1$	$\bar\mu_{\mathrm{Al}} = 0.12\mu_B,\ \bar\mu_{\mathrm{Fe}}(\mathrm{Fe_3Si}) = 1.5\mu_B$		
			23.
$\mu_{\mathrm{Ni}} = 0\mu_B,\ \mu_{\mathrm{Mn}} \approx (3.7 + \delta_{xy})\mu_B$ and $\delta_{xy} \sim 0.3$	$\mu_{\mathrm{Ni}} = 0\mu_B,\ \mu_{\mathrm{Mn}} = 4.0\mu_B$	334	24.
$\mu_{\mathrm{Ni}} \approx 0.6\mu_B,\ \mu_{\mathrm{Co}} \approx 2.0\mu_B$	$\mu_{\mathrm{Ni}} = 0.6\mu_B,\ \mu_{\mathrm{Co}} = 1.8\mu_B$	115a	25.
$\left.\begin{array}{l}\mu_{\mathrm{Fe}} = (2.8 + 3\Lambda)\mu_B \\ \mu_{\mathrm{Ni}} = (0.6 + \Lambda)\mu_B\end{array}\right\} \Lambda \ll 1$	$\mu_{\mathrm{Fe}} = 2.91\mu_B$ $\mu_{\mathrm{Ni}} = 0.62\mu_B$	568	26.
$\mu_{\mathrm{Ni}} \approx 0.6\mu_B,\ \mu_{\mathrm{Co}} \approx 2.0\mu_B$	$\mu_{\mathrm{Ni}} = 0.6\mu_B,\ \mu_{\mathrm{Co}} = 1.9\mu_B$	115a	27.
$\mu_{\mathrm{Mn}} \approx 4.7\mu_B,\ \bar\mu_{\mathrm{Ni}} = 0.03\mu_B$ 95% *ordered:* $\bar\mu_{\mathrm{Mn}} \approx 3.3\mu_B,$ $\bar\mu_{\mathrm{Ni}} = 0.27\mu_B$	$\bar\mu_{\mathrm{Mn}} = (3.18 \pm 0.25)\mu_B$ $\bar\mu_{\mathrm{Ni}} = (0.30 \pm 0.05)\mu_B$	568	28.
			29.
$\mu_{\mathrm{Pd}} = \frac{\mathrm{Pd}}{2g}\mu_B \approx 0.4\mu_B,\ \mu_{\mathrm{Fe}} \approx 3.0\mu_B$ $\mu_{\mathrm{Co}} \approx 2.0\mu_B$	$\mu_{\mathrm{Pd}} \approx 0.35\mu_B,\ \mu_{\mathrm{Fe}} = 2.9\mu_B$ $\mu_{\mathrm{Co}} = 2.0\mu_B$	115a	30.
$\mu_{\mathrm{Pd}} \approx 0.4\mu_B,\ \mu_{\mathrm{Fe}} \approx 3.0\mu_B$ $\mu_{\mathrm{Co}} \approx 2.0\mu_B,\ \mu_{\mathrm{Mn}} \sim 4.0\mu_B{}^d$	$\mu_{\mathrm{Pd}} = 0.45\mu_B,\ \mu_{\mathrm{Fe}} = 3.0\mu_B$ $\mu_{\mathrm{Co}} = 2.0\mu_B,\ \bar\mu_{\mathrm{Mn}} = 4.0\mu_B{}^d$	115a	31.
			32.
			33.
$\mu_{\mathrm{Pt}} = 0\mu_B,\ \mu_{\mathrm{Mn}} \sim 4\mu_B$ $\mu_{\mathrm{Cr}} \sim 2\mu_B$			34.
$\mu_{\mathrm{Pt}} = \delta_{2g}^{\mathrm{Pt}}\mu_B \lesssim 0.3\mu_B,\ \mu_{\mathrm{Ni}} = 0.4\mu_B$	$\bar\mu(\mathrm{NiPt}) \approx 0.15\mu_B$	412	35.

(*continued*)

TABLE XXIII (continued)

| Row No. | Alloy | Magnetic sublattice structure | | Ref. |
		Predicted	Observed	
	(b) MPt₃,			
36.	M = Cr, Mn	Ferro. (Disordered Cr, Mn antiferro.)	(As predicted)	30, 195
37.	M = Fe	Antiferro. possible, but any n. n. Fe–Fe ferro.	Two antiferro. phases admixed. If disordered, n. n. Fe–Fe ferro.	33, 137
38.	(c) Ni₃Pt	Ferro.	(As predicted)	285

is schematically illustrated in Figure 86.   It is quite general and will be seen to apply particularly to transition metal nitrides and carbides.

Since both the Mn–Cu–Mn and Mn–M–Mn correlations are ferromagnetic, it is not surprising to find that the Heusler alloys are ferromagnetic.   [There must be a critical electronegativity difference above which the Mn–M–Mn couplings of Figure 42 replace those of Figure 86.   Cu₂MnSb is antiferromagnetic with $T_N = 38°$K (499a). Since Sb is the most electronegative of the M atoms, it is probable that three manganese electrons are captured by the antimony to give the antiferromagnetic Mn–Sb³⁻–Mn interaction of Case 2, Figure 42, as was assumed for the compound Mn₂Sb.]   However, an estimate of the manganese atomic moment depends upon the discrepancy δ_b between the number of manganese and M electrons per molecule

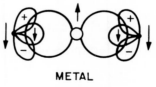

METAL
$(n_p \leq 3)$

Fig. 86.   Ferromagnetic T–M–T superexchange interactions, where T is a transition metal atom with half filled e_g orbitals, M is an interstitial atom with $np \leq 3$.   Excitation of an e_g electron into a p orbital of M atom gives the three-electron configuration of Case 3, Figure 42.   There is collective-electron spin-pairing of the e_g and p electrons so that there is no localized moment on the intermediate metal atom.

TABLE XXIII (*continued*)

Atomic Moments			
Predicted	Observed	Ref.	Row No.
$\mu_{Pt} = 0\mu_B$, $\mu_{Mn} \approx 4.7\mu_B$ $\mu_{Cr} \approx 2.8\mu_B$	$\mu_{Pt} \approx 0.17\mu_B$, $\mu_{Mn} \approx 3.6\mu_B$ $2.2\mu_B < \mu_{Cr} < 2.6\mu_B$	521	36.
$\mu_{Pt} = 0\mu_B$, $\mu_{Fe} \approx 2.8\mu_B$			37.
$\mu_{Pt} = \delta_{2g}^{Pt}\mu_B < 0.3\mu_B$, $\mu_{Ni} = n_s^{Ni}\mu_B$			38.

^a Refer to text for crystallographic structures.

^b Samples annealed below 625°C have antiphase MnAu₃ regions with n. n. Mn–Mn coupling ($R = 2.87$ A) between regions. Samples quenched from 625°C may have considerable MnAu₃ order, but no antiphase character. A spin flip occurs in annealed samples for applied fields $H > 47$ Koe.

^c Sample 80% ordered.

^d MnPd₃ has antiferromagnetic Mn–Pd interactions, but antiphase-domain order with alternate CuAu₃-ordered (001) slabs displaced along [110] to quadruple unit cell along [001] (115a′). This is consistent if there are two kinds of Pd: 2/3Pd_I($4d^9 5s^1$), within CuAu₃ slabs, and 1/3Pd_{II}($4d^{10}$), between slabs, giving Mn–Pd_I bonding, $n_s^{Pd} \approx 0.67$ and $\mu_{Mn} \sim (3.3 + \delta_{ij} + \delta_s)\mu_B$.

in the Mn–M bonding band. Since $n_s^{Cu} = 1$, it is anticipated that $n_s^{Mn} = 1$ and $n_{2g}^{Mn} = 3$, so that for perfect atomic ordering $\mu_{Mn} = (3 + \delta_b + \delta_s)\mu_B$, where $\delta_s \sim 0.1$ and $\delta_b = 1$ for M atoms with two outer p electrons (Al, In, and probably Sn), $\delta_b = 0$ for M atoms with three outer p electrons (Sb). The experimental moments are $\bar{\mu}_{Mn} = 4.1\mu_B$ for M = Al, Sn and $\bar{\mu}_{Mn} = 3.6\mu_B$ for M = In (91,499b). For lighter Group IV elements with greater s–p hybridization, electron-pair bonds may form along a unique [100], one-electron bonds in the (100), to give $\delta_b = 0$ and tetragonal ($c/a < 1$) symmetry. The fact that Cu₂MnGe is tetragonal ($c/a = 0.96$) with $\bar{\mu}_{Mn} = 2.84\mu_B$ (499b) is suggestive of such electron ordering. Experiment also indicates that if perfect order on the Mn–M sublattice is destroyed, the wrongly placed Mn atoms couple antiferromagnetically to the Mn sublattice. Such an antiferromagnetic interaction is also anticipated by the model since $R_{nnn} < R_c(3d)$ in b.c.c. structures, so that hole ordering into the e_g orbitals permits bond stabilization. (As in FeRh, bonding between like next-near-neighbors is stronger than electron correlation between *unlike* near neighbors on one of which are located nearly all of the bonding states).

(*b*) In the perovskite oxides and fluorides, the f.c.c. AX_3 sublattice of Figure 56 is composed of nonmagnetic ions (unless the *A* cation is a rare earth), and the magnetic properties are due to the *B* cations. In the metallic perovskites, on the other hand, the *B*-cation site is occupied by interstitial, nonmagnetic N or C and the AX_3 sites are occupied by metal atoms that may be magnetic. Whereas only indirect cation-anion-cation interactions are present in the oxides and fluorides (if *A* is not a rare earth), both metal- -metal and metal-(N or C)-metal interactions are present in the metallic perovskites.

Chemical stability indicates that in the cubic, metallic perovskites the interstitial C and N are probably neutral. They represent, therefore, an M atom with half filled *p* or *s–p* orbitals, and in the cubic structure the metal-M-metal interaction is defined by Figure 86. [This is to be contrasted with low-temperature CrN, which has considerable ionic character and an ordering of its covalent character along a given axis.] In contrast to the M atoms of the Heusler alloys, the *p* electrons of C and N correlate with, and therefore spin pair, the near-neighbor e_g electrons. The metal- -metal interactions are determined by the t_{2g} electron-spin correlations since $R_{tt} \approx 2.76$ A $< R_c$.

(*i*) The ferromagnetic nitrides $Fe^cNFe_3^f$ (or Fe_4N), $NiNFe_3^f$, and $PtNFe_3^f$ are readily interpreted. The qualitative features of Figure 84 apply, except that for the face-centered iron atoms Fe^f the *e* levels are split in two by the half filled *p* states of the interstitial N atoms, so that an antibonding $N–Fe^f$ band lies above the *d* bands. The bonding $N–Fe^f$ level is spin-paired, so that one e_g state per Fe^f atom can no longer contribute to the atomic moment. The $Fe^f–N–Fe^f$ interactions are all strongly ferromagnetic (Fig. 86), and this coupling serves to differentiate the iron atoms into two sublattices, the Fe^f atoms occupying the face-centered positions and the Fe^c atoms the corner positions. Therefore it is only necessary to ask whether the intersublattice Fe^c- -Fe^f coupling is ferromagnetic or antiferromagnetic. From equation 195, $n_s^{Fe} \approx 1$ is anticipated. This allows one t_{2g} hole per iron atom, and ordering of all of the holes into the Fe^c- -Fe^f states still requires some antibonding states to be occupied. Therefore the Fe^c- -Fe^f interactions are ferromagnetic. With $n_s^{Fe} = 1$ and one e_g electron per Fe^f spin paired, the predicted ferromagnetic moments are

$$\mu_{Fe^f} = 2\mu_B \qquad \mu_{Fe^c} = 3\mu_B \qquad (203)$$

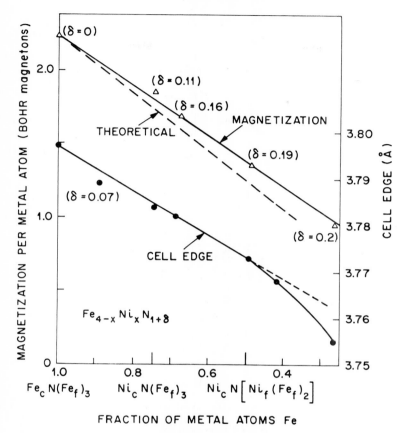

Fig. 87. Magnetization and cell edge for $Fe_{1-x}Ni_xN_{1+\delta}$. Theory assumes $\delta = 0$ and $n_B^{Fe_c} = 2$, $n_B^{Ni_e} = 1$, $n_B^{Ni_f} = 0$. (After Goodenough, Wold and Arnott (224).)

These are precisely the moments that were determined by neutron diffraction (190) (see Fig. 88(a)).

Substitution of iron by nickel can be expected to order the Ni atoms at the corner positions since placement of a nickel atom ($t_{2g}^6 e_g^3 s^1$) at a face requires the e_g orbital perpendicular to the N—Ni^f bond to be filled, thus preventing N atoms from occupying adjacent octahedral sites. (Occupancy would require antibonding Ni^f states to be populated.) Such an effect hinders N diffusion. In fact it was found

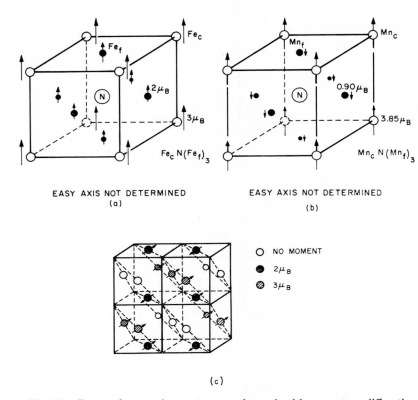

Fig. 88. Proposed magnetic structures, as determined from neutron diffraction data, for (a) Fe₄N (after Frazer (190)), (b) Mn₄N (after Takei, Shirane and Frazer (610)), and (c) ZnCMn₃ (after Brockhouse and Myers (106)).

(23) impossible to make Ni_4N by the usual procedure, which involves diffusion of N atoms from the surface, and this was attributed (224) to the inability of the nitrogen to diffuse past neighboring atoms that order the nickel e_g orbitals. However, some Ni^f atoms may be present, and it was possible to prepare $Fe_{4-x}Ni_xN_{1+\delta}$ up to $x = 3$. Given δn_s is the same whether a Ni replaces Fe^f or Fe^c, it follows that the variation of the average ferromagnetic moment per molecule is

$$d\bar{n}_B/dx = -(2 - \delta n_s)\mu_B \qquad (204)$$

Whereas $\bar{n}_B(Fe_4N) = 9\mu_B$, $\bar{n}_B(NiNFe_3) = 7.2\mu_B$ and $\bar{n}_B(PtNFe_3) = 7.76\mu_B$ (653). This gives $\delta n_s = +0.2x$ for Ni additions, but a rather high $\delta n_s = +0.76x$ for Pt additions. A small change in $d\bar{n}_B/dx$ may occur at $x = 1$ in the nickel system, which is shown in Figure 87, but it is within the errors introduced by $\delta \neq 0$.

As an aside, it is interesting to note that the tetragonal compound FeNiN can be prepared. From the model, it was predicted that the compound should be ordered into alternate Fe and Ni layers perpendicular to the c axis with the N atoms filling all the octahedral interstices of the Fe layers. (The filled $d_{x^2-y^2}$ orbitals at the Ni atoms prevent occupation of the octahedral sites in a Ni layer.) This atomic ordering was indeed found. Further, with all localized electrons spin-paired, the compound is paramagnetic (224).

(ii) Magnetic order in the compound Mn$_4$N is complicated by the fact that there are a sufficient number of t_{2g} holes available to leave the antibonding Mn^c--Mn^f states empty, or to induce *antiferromagnetic* coupling between the two Mn sublattices. Since the two remaining d_{ij} states per Mn^f are forced to have parallel-spin correlations, they are more unstable than localized, nonbonding e_g electrons that are not spin-paired (and thus stabilized by intraatomic exchange), but probably overlap spin-paired e_g states. Since one e_g electron per Mn^f participates in Mn^f—N bonding, intraatomic-exchange splitting is smaller at the Mn^f atoms and spin-paired e_g electrons are more probable. Therefore if antiparallel coupling between the two manganese sublattices occurs, this means that the corner and face-center manganese contribute, respectively, $n_d^c = 5$ and $n_d^f = n_g^f + n_{2g}^f = 3 + (1 + \nu)$, where $\nu = 3 - n_{sp}^f$ is the number of electrons per Mn^f atom in the antibonding d_{ij} states. Extrapolation of equation 162 to collective-electron spin correlations suggests $\nu \leq 1$, which means that antiferromagnetic coupling requires $\bar{n}_{sp} \geq 2$, a marked increase over $\bar{n}_{sp} \sim 1.15$ for γ-Mn (see eq. 195). Nevertheless antiferromagnetic coupling does occur, and polarized neutron data (610) give experimental moments at 77°K of $\mu_{Mn^c} = +3.85\mu_B$ and $\mu_{Mn^f} = -0.90\mu_B$ (see Fig. 88(b)). From the above discussion, the predicted moments are

$$\mu_{Mn^c} = (2 + \delta_{xy} + \delta_{yz} + \delta_{zx})\mu_B \qquad \mu_{Mn^f} = -(\nu + \delta'_{ij})\mu_B \qquad (205)$$

This would mean $\delta_{ij} \approx 0.6$ and $(\nu + \delta'_{ij}) \approx 0.9$, which are the type of values anticipated by the model. Thus an $n_{sp}^f \approx 2.5$ is estimated for Mn$_4$N. (Some stabilization, relative to the f.c.c. metals, of the s-p band is anticipated by the Mn^c–Mn^f bonding correlations.)

These conclusions are reinforced by studies on the systems $Mn_3^t Mn_{1-x}^c M_x N$, where M = In or Sn. Since the M atoms substitute for a Mn^c, which has five d electrons, it follows that

$$d\mu_s/dx = d(\mu_c + \mu_f)/dx = -(5 + d\nu/dx)\mu_B$$
$$= -(5 - dn_{sp}^t/dx)\mu_B \qquad (206)$$

M atoms that stabilize s–p states increase n_{sp}^t. Since $n_{sp}^t \approx 2.5$ in Mn_4N, it is not surprising that Mekata (431) found a

$$d\mu_s/dx \approx -4.8\mu_B$$

for the indium-substituted alloys. The

$$d\mu_s/dx \approx -3.25\mu_B$$

that he reported for the tin-substituted alloys would suggest that either the tin atoms have a much stronger influence on the stability of neighboring s–p states or, which is more probable, that some of the Sn atoms substitute for Mn^f.

(*iii*) Several manganese carbides, $ACMn_3$ with A = Zn, Al, Ga, have been reported to be magnetic perovskites (110,282). $ZnCMn_3$ is cubic and ferromagnetic ($T_c = 353°K$) at high temperatures ($T > 231°K$), ferrimagnetic and tetragonal ($c/a < 1$) if $T < 231°K$. $AlCMn_3$ and $GaCMn_3$ are cubic and ferromagnetic at all temperatures. In the ferromagnetic samples, $\mu_{Mn} = 1.57\mu_B$ (extrapolated from 231°K), $1.25\mu_B$, and $1.42\mu_B$, respectively. The spin configuration in antiferromagnetic, tetragonal $ZnCMn_3$ is complex, a possible (but not unique) solution of the neutron data being that of Figure 88(c) (106).

Since there is only one magnetic sublattice, the ferromagnetism of the cubic phases, with disordered t_{2g} hole, follows immediately from the model. Since the corner atoms are nonmagnetic, the atomic moment of equation 205 becomes

$$\mu_{Mn^f} = (1 + \nu)\mu_B \qquad (207)$$

where now $\nu = 2.67 - n_{sp}^t$ since 0.33 electrons per Mn^f are contributed to the C–Mn^f bonding band. (Carbon has four holes, nitrogen three, in its outer s^2p^6 shell.) This means that $2.1 < n_{sp}^{Mn^f} < 2.4$, which is in excellent agreement with the conclusion for Mn_4N.

Extrapolated magnetizations for the cubic phases in the system $(Z_{1-n}{}^x Mn_x^c)CMn_3^t$ give $d\bar{\mu}_B/dx = -4.2\mu_B$, where $\bar{\mu}_B$ is the number of

Bohr magnetons per molecule (see Fig. 89(a)). As in Mn_4N, the Mn^c should have five d electrons and couple antiparallel to the Mn^f atoms. This gives an atomic moment and a rate of change of magnetization of

$$\mu_{Mn^c} = (2 + \delta_{xy} + \delta_{yz} + \delta_{zx})\mu_B \sim 3.8\mu_B$$
$$d\bar{n}_B/dx = -(5 + d\nu/dx) \tag{208}$$

where $d\nu/dx < 0$ if the A atom is electropositive. (See the analogous equations 205 and 206.) Again the model is in reasonable agreement with the observations.

In the above discussion, it has been assumed that the M-Mn^f bonding band (M is N or C) is sufficiently stable that it is always full. This would imply that in systems of the type $AMn_3^fN_{1-x}C_x$, the number of electrons per Mn^f atom in antibonding d_{ij} states is $\nu < 1$, where

$$\nu = 3 - 0.33x - n_{sp}^t \tag{209}$$

However, it is quite possible that for smaller values of x holes are trapped at the C atoms, which act as acceptors relative to the N–Mn^f bonding band. If this happens, the holes will *add* an average moment of $0.33x\mu_B$ to each Mn^f and there is no depletion of the antibonding electrons to fill the holes. This gives an effective ν for equations 205, 207 of

$$\nu' = 3 + 0.33x - n_{sp}^t \tag{210}$$

A neutron-diffraction study (610a) of $Mn_4N_{0.75}C_{0.25}$ gave the room-temperature moments $\mu_{Mnc} = 3.53\mu_B$ and $\mu_{Mnf} = 0.98\mu_B$, which represents the anticipated no change in μ_{Mnc} and an *increase* with x in μ_{Mnf}. This result supports equation 210 in preference to 209 for $x \leq 0.25$.

(*iv*) A low-temperature phase of lower symmetry in $ZnCMn_3$ is not surprising in view of the possibilities for metal- -metal homopolar bonding due to many t_{2g} holes and for electronic ordering of the s–p hybrid (or p hole) of carbon. Also, the hole ordering associated with bonding Mn^c atoms would suppress the low-temperature phase. However, the magnetic order of Figure 88(c) does not follow readily from simple, qualitative arguments.

(*v*) Magnetization measurements (25) for the perovskite system $Mn_{4-x}Sn_xC$ through the range $0.15 \leq x \leq 0.50$ give an extrapolated

$\mu_{\mathrm{Mn}^f} = 0.7\mu_B$, or $n_B \approx 2.1$, for $\mathrm{SnCMn_3^f}$ and a $d\bar{n}_B/dx \approx 0.85$. If the tin orders on the corner sites, a $\mu_{\mathrm{Mn}^f} > 1\mu_B$ and a $d\bar{n}_B/dx \sim 4$ is anticipated from equations 207 and 208. On the other hand, if the tin orders on the face centers, then an $\bar{n}_B \approx 3 - 2\nu \sim 2$ is anticipated for $\mathrm{Mn_3SnC}$ and a $d\bar{n}_B/dx \approx 1 + \nu - dn_{sp}^f/dx$. This suggests that the tin is preferentially ordered on the face-center positions in this system.

(*vi*) Finally, attention is called to the series of compounds $\mathrm{BC}_x\mathrm{T}_3$,

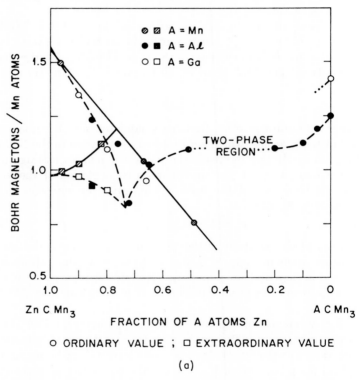

(a)

Fig. 89. Magnetic data for the mixed system $(\mathrm{Zn}_{1-x}\mathrm{A}_x)\mathrm{CMn_3}$, where A = Al, Ga, Mn. (a) Variation of Bohr magnetons per Mn atom with composition. (Ordinary values obtained by extrapolation from cubic phase; extraordinary value corresponds to low-temperature tetragonal phase.) (b) (facing page) Variation of Curie and phase-transition temperatures with composition. (After Howe and Myers (282).)

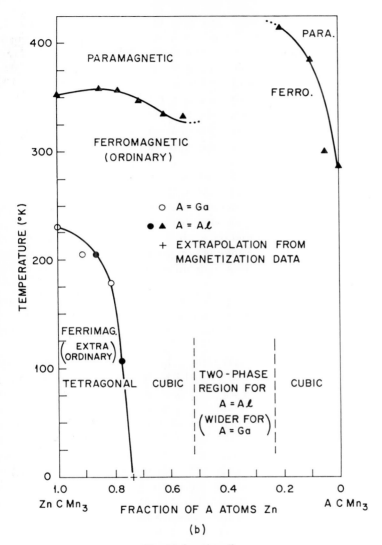

(b)

Fig. 89 (*continued*)

$0.25 \leq x \leq 1$, where B = Mn, Zn, Al, Ga, In, Ge, Sn and T = Mn, Fe, Co, Ni (284). The iron and manganese compounds are reported to be ferromagnetic, the nickel compounds were all "non-magnetic," and some cobalt compounds were ferromagnetic, others were not. This is in accord with the above discussions. Also from the model, compounds with a given T (and $x = 1$) are expected to have a smaller net moment the larger the valence on the B atom. Detailed magnetic measurements have not been made, but no new principles beyond those already illustrated should be required for their interpretation.

(c) There appear to be four stable, intermediate compounds in the Mn–Au system (108,209,380,434,539): Mn_3Au, $MnAu_2$, $MnAu_3$, and $MnAu_4$. These are all ordered compounds. $MnAu_3$ and $MnAu_4$ are transformed at high temperatures to a disordered, f.c.c. phase; $MnAu_2$ and Mn_3Au to a disordered b.c.c. phase. In the vicinity of 50 atomic per cent Au, there is a range of compositions with a CsCl structure. However, whether there is a definite MnAu compound is not yet established.

Since nothing definite can be said about the expected magnetic order and atomic moments without a knowledge of the structure, comments are confined to those cases where the structure has been established.

(i) Bacon and Street (34) report that b.c.tet. $(c/a < 1)$ MnAu is antiferromagnetic below $T_N = 515°K$ with simple-cubic type A ordering (Fig. 18) and a $\mu_{Mn} = 4.2\mu_B$ (see Table VIII). Since the d shell of Au is full, only the Mn atoms carry an atomic moment. Further, with two atoms per unit cell, the s band is separated into a bonding and antibonding portion and there is little overlap of the bonding s states by bonding p states (in CsAu the bonding s states are completely split apart, and the compound is a semiconductor), so that there is probably one s electron per atom. This gives an outer-d-electron configuration at a Mn atom $t_{2g}^3 d_{x^2-y^2}^2 d_{z^2}^1$, where the bonding d_{z^2} electrons along the c axis are localized (R_{MnMn} (c axis) = 3.1 A $> R_c(Mn)$ in metals, equations 183 and 174) and the localized t_{2g}^3 electrons are coupled parallel through an intermediary Au atom (as through a Cu atom in the Heusler alloys). Since the Mn––Mn interactions are stronger than the Mn–Au–Mn interactions, this gives ferromagnetic (001) sheets coupled antiparallel along [001] and $\mu_{Mn} = (4 + \delta_s)\mu_B$. Since the electrons are already ordered by the

Jahn-Teller effect above T_N, there is no large exchange striction at T_N. Note that the sign of the distortions ($c/a < 1$ vs. $c/a > 1$) to be associated with Jahn-Teller ordering of e_g electrons depends upon second-order effects, which may explain why MnAu sometimes has $c/a > 1$.

(*ii*) The compound $MnAu_2$ is crystallized from a peritectic at 730°C. Its structure may be visualized as the product of ordering within a disordered, b.c.tet. ($c/a < 1$) phase: There are two Au (001) planes followed by one Mn (001) plane to give a unit cell with three times the number of atomic layers along the c axis as along the a axes (271,438,592). The Mn–Mn distance within an (001) plane is 3.37 A $> R_c(Mn)$. This gives a Mn outer-electron configuration $d^2_{x^2-y^2}d^1_{z^2}t^{3-\epsilon}_{2g}n^{1+\epsilon}_{sp}$, or a $\mu_{Mn} = (4 - \epsilon)\mu_B$. The magnetic interactions are 180° Mn–Au–Au–Mn, ∼140° Mn–Au–Mn, and <90° Mn–Au–Mn. The significance of the angles is somewhat different here than in the case of an anion intermediary because electron correlations in the intermediary orbitals are complex. Nevertheless, the significant point is that the Mn-sublattice symmetry is b.c.tet. ($c/a > 1$) with competitive interactions between nearest, next-nearest, and next-next-nearest neighbors. The mathematics of the molecular field calculations is therefore just that used in the case of MnO_2 (see Fig. 29(a) and Chapter II, Section III-B), and a spiral spin configuration is possible.

Experimentally $MnAu_2$ is found to be metamagnetic: In fields less than 10,000 oe, it contains an antiferromagnetic spiral (269) with $T_N = 90°C$ and **k** vector parallel to the c axis; and in fields greater than 20,000 oe it becomes ferromagnetic with $\mu_{Mn} = 3.49\mu_B$ (438). An $n^{Mn}_{sp} \approx 1.5$ is reasonable for this compound. The basal-plane component of strong external fields destroys the spiral to orient all the spins toward that direction. This type of metamagnetization has also been found in oxide systems that contain antiferromagnetic spirals at low temperatures (169).

(*iii*) With f.c.c. symmetry, the two-sublattice criterion does not hold, and the t_{2g} electrons form a metallic band, which is always stabilized by a ferromagnetic correlation. It follows that any Mn–Au–Mn or Mn–Au–Au–Mn interactions are ferromagnetic. (However, any near-neighbor Mn–Mn interactions are antiferromagnetic since Mn acts like a case (*c*) solute.)

The compound $MnAu_4$ is ordered f.c.tet. ($c/a = 0.988$) below 420°C and ferromagnetic below 100°C (646). The unit cell is **2.5** times larger than the high-temperature, f.c.c. unit cell. It contains 2 Mn and 8 Au atoms, the Mn atoms having a b.c.tet. arrangement. Each Mn atom has 12 Au near neighbors, 2 Mn next-near neighbors at 4.03 A $> R_c$(Mn), and 8 Mn next-next-near neighbors. The Mn--Mn interactions must be quite weak at 4.03 A, so that the ferromagnetic interactions via the Au sublattice may dominate, as is observed. Further, with f.c.c. symmetry $n_s^{Mn} \sim 1$ is anticipated (see eq. 198), or a $\mu_{Mn} \sim 4\mu_B$. Meyer (434) reports a $\bar{\mu}_{Mn} = 4.15\mu_B$.

The compound MnAu₃ is disordered and f.c.c. if quenched from above 625°C. This disordered phase is "ferromagnetic" below 120°K (436). Since the Mn atoms have more than one t_{2g} hole, near-neighbor Mn--Mn interactions must be antiferromagnetic. However, f.c.c. MnAu₃ with CuAu₃-type order would be ferromagnetic, as in MnPt₃. Therefore it is probable that the quenched, f.c.c. MnAu₃ was partially ordered and that it was ferrimagnetic (but without long-range ferrimagnetic order) below 120°K. Subsequent measurements (297) indicate that specimens quenched from 900°C are *not* ferromagnetic, but are similar to disordered Cu₃Mn alloys, showing the displaced hysteresis loop indicative of intimately mixed ferromagnetic and antiferromagnetic regions.

If the compound is annealed below 625°C, it has a different type of magnetic order. Ogawa and Watanabe (487) report a two-dimensional antiphase-domain structure whose unit cell consists of a f.c. orthorhombic cell with an atomic arrangement similar to Cu₃Au, but in which there are two kinds of Mn–Mn distance: 2.87 A and 4.5 A. The first distance is $< R_c$(Mn), so that it must introduce strong, antiferromagnetic Mn--Mn coupling. This calls for ferromagnetic Cu₃Au-type regions coupled antiferromagnetically across the antiphase boundaries. This is compatible with an observed "antiferromagnetism" with $T_N = 145°K$ and with a spin-flipping in external fields $H > 47$ Koe (297).

IV. Concluding Remarks

The present paper has been confined to a consideration of the origin of the atomic moments and of the interactions between them. It has been argued that the outer electrons in a solid may be described either as collective electrons that belong to the lattice as a whole or as atomic-like electrons that are localized at a given lattice site.

The first description is valid at interatomic distances that are short relative to the radial extension of the atomic wave functions, the second, at distances that are large. The MO description is good up to about the equilibrium separation for the electrons in question, but must be modified by the inclusion of many configuration-interaction terms at larger separations. The MO description gives the conventional band model for a solid. It fails, however, to provide adequate insight into the electron-spin correlations among the collective electrons. For separations greater than about twice the equilibrium separation, a Heitler-London-Heisenberg description of the electrons is applicable, and empirical relationships for the critical atomic separation about which there is a transition from collective to localized-electron behavior has been given. Calculation of the localized-electron energies requires account be taken of the ligand fields. The various contributions to the spin-correlation problem can be calculated. These are the contributions to the Heisenberg exchange integral. By extrapolation to the collective-electron case of the spin correlations calculated for the localized-electron case, it has been possible to derive a general set of rules for the sign of the coupling between neighboring spins. (The s–d interactions in dilute alloys and the s–f interactions of the rare earth metals have not been discussed.) Further, from a knowledge of the signs and relative strengths of these couplings, it is possible to calculate the ordered spin configurations to be anticipated at low temperatures. (The molecular field approximation has been shown capable of surprising detail (329). In the single case of dysprosium it appears that spin wave theory and the molecular field approximation require, to describe the observed magnetic order, different assumptions about the crystalline anisotropy (708). The fact that such an example exists, however, provides a warning against the general applicability of the approximation.) Conversely, it is possible to draw conclusions about the nature of the outer electrons and of the spin correlations within a band from a measure of the atomic moments and the magnetic order. These ideas have been illustrated by application to a wide variety of materials: ionic insulators and semiconductors, ionic metals, metallic elements, and metal alloys. Although a rich variety of situations is illustrated, the basic criteria upon which their interpretation is based are lattice symmetry, the distance between magnetic atoms, the fixed rules for spin correlations, and the number of outer electrons with given principal and angular-momentum quantum numbers.

However, it would be inappropriate to conclude without some reference to recent form-factor calculations for $3d$ electrons that have relaxed the requirement that electrons of opposite spin have the same radial extension. These calculations use a conventional Hartree-Fock formalism, which has been discussed with and without restrictions by Watson and Freeman (651).* These calculations show that if the net spin on an atom is positive, then the spin-density function $(\rho \uparrow - \rho \downarrow)$ for all the paired electrons, which integrates to zero over all space, is negative at the nucleus and at large separations, but is positive in the radial region where there is appreciable density of the unpaired electrons. (The $3d$ and $4f$ electrons have a node at the nucleus, Figure 1, and the antibonding electrons have a smaller radial extension than the bonding electrons.) These intraatomic spin correlations for the core electrons reflect the fact that the quantum mechanical exclusion of parallel electrons from the same region in space (see Chapter I, Section I) introduces a different electron-electron interaction contribution to the potential function for core and collective electrons of different spin should a net unpaired spin be present at the atom. This effect has three consequences: (1) the core s electrons contribute a *negative* effective field at the nucleus of a

* There are three restrictions that are normally incorporated into Hartree-Fock calculations, and a fourth often appears when the Hartree-Fock formalism is used to parametrize the experimental results. (1) The spacial part of a one-electron wave function ψ_i is assumed to be separable into a radial and an angular part, so that $\psi_i(r,\theta,\phi,\sigma) = r^{-1}u_i(r)S_i(\theta,\phi)S_i(\sigma)$ where $S_i(\sigma)$ is a spin function with spin quantum number $m_s = \pm 1/2$ and, in practice, $S_i(\theta,\phi)$ is normally *chosen* to be a spherical harmonic $Y_l^m(\theta,\phi)$. (2) The radial part, $u_i(r)$, is constrained to be independent of the m_l value associated with ψ_i, which is not a restriction only for the case of a spherical atom. (3) Similarly $u_i(r)$ is constrained to be independent of m_s, which is not a restriction only for the case where the total spin quantum number S is a good quantum number and $S = 0$. It is this restriction that is relaxed by the Watson-Freeman Calculations. (4) Examples of the added restriction that appears in analysis of experimental data are the following: In the case of a many-electron state that is ionized by removal of an electron associated with a particular ψ_i, it is assumed that the other ψ_i's are unperturbed by the removal of electron j, which leads to *Koopmans' theorem* (363). The Racah parametrization (535) of atomic multiplet spectra in terms of a limited number of Slater F^k and G^k integrals is based on the assumption that the $u_i(r)$ for any shell is the same for all states of a single configuration (assignment of n and l values to the ψ_i's).

ferromagnet (192,226). Nuclear magnetic resonance (NMR) in the field at the nucleus gives rise to a hyperfine splitting that directly demonstrates that the molecular field at the nucleus is *opposite* to that which aligns the unpaired electron spins (249). This surprising experimental fact is accounted for if the field at the nucleus is predominantly from core s electrons. (Core electrons of higher orbital momentum have a node at the nucleus, so that they do not contribute.) (*2*) The electron spin density of the "paired" electrons, $\rho\uparrow - \rho\downarrow$, contributes measurably to the neutron form factor (11). (*3*) NMR studies (572) in magnetic crystals have revealed large, internal magnetic fields at the anion nuclei. Since this anion is normally diamagnetic, these fields provide a measure of the covalent character of the anion-cation bonds and of the anion-electron spin that is delocalized by the bonding. For a rare earth ion, the core $5s$ and $5p$ electrons have a greater radial extension than the $4f$ electrons. Therefore at large distances from the nucleus, the negative $\rho\uparrow - \rho\downarrow$ from the $5s$, $5p$ electrons is appreciably greater than the positive $\rho\uparrow$ from the $4f$ electrons (652). This means that in its interactions with neighboring anions or metal atoms *the Gd^{3+} ion appears (from NMR experiments) to have a spin which is antiparallel to the actual Gd^{3+} spin.* Jaccarino et al. (304) have observed with NMR a negative Knight shift in $GdAl_2$, that is fields at the Al^{27} nuclei that are opposite to those of the $4f$ electrons. The $4f$–$6s$ interactions were found to dominate over $(\rho\uparrow - \rho\downarrow)$–$6s$ interactions, in agreement with Hund's rule, so that the postulate (304) of a negative $4f$–$6s$ exchange interaction does not seem tenable. However, the negative $\rho\uparrow - \rho\downarrow$ in regions of greatest overlap makes a postulate unnecessary.

References

1. Abragam, A., and M. H. L. Pryce, *Proc. Roy. Soc. (London)* **205A,** 135 (1951); **206A,** 164, 173 (1951).
2. Abrahams, S. C. (private communication).
2a. Abrahams, S. C., L. Guttman, and J. S. Kasper, *Phys. Rev.* **127,** 2052 (1962).
3. Adachi, K., *J. Phys. Soc. Japan* **16,** 2187 (1961).
4. Akimoto, S., and T. Katsura, *Nature (London)* **179,** 37 (1957).
5. Aléonard, R., *J. Phys. Chem. Solids* **15,** 167 (1960).
6. Aléonard, R., and R. Pauthenet, *Compt. rend.* **251,** 1730 (1960).
7. Aléonard, R., J. C. Barbier, and R. Pauthenet, *Compt. rend.* **242,** 2531 (1956).
8. Alikhanov, R. A., *J. Exptl. Theoret. Phys. (USSR)* **36,** 1690 (1959); *Soviet Phys. JETP* **9,** 1204 (1959).
9. Alikhanov, R. A., *J. Exptl. Theoret. Phys. (USSR)* **37,** 1145 (1959); *Soviet Phys. JETP* **10,** 814 (1960).
10. Alikanov, R. A., *J. Exptl. Theoret. Phys. (USSR)* **39,** 1481 (1960); *Soviet Phys. JETP* **12,** 1029 (1961).
11. Alperin, H. A., *Phys. Rev. Letters* **6,** 55 (1961).
12. Alperin, H. A., and S. J. Pickart, *Bull. Am. Phys. Soc.* [II] **5,** 458 (1960).
13. Alperin, H. A., and S. J. Pickart, *Antiferromagnetic Compounds,* Landolt-Bornstein Tabellen Vol. II/9 Springer-Verlag, Berlin-Göttingen-Heidelberg 1962, pp. 3–143.
14. Anderson, C. T., *J. Am. Chem. Soc.* **58,** 564 (1936).
15. Anderson, E. E., *J. Appl. Phys. Supp.* **30,** 299S (1959).
16. Anderson, P. W., *Phys. Rev.* **79,** 350 (1950).
17. Anderson, P. W., *Phys. Rev.* **79,** 705 (1950).
18. Anderson, P. W., *Phys. Rev.* **86,** 694 (1952).
19. Anderson, P. W., *Phys. Rev.* **102,** 1008 (1956).
20. Anderson, P. W., *Phys. Rev.* **115,** 2 (1959).
20a. Andersson, S., *Acta Chem. Scand.* **14,** 1161 (1960).
21. Andresen, A. F., *Acta Chem. Scand.* **14,** 919 (1960).
22. Appel, J., and S. W. Kurnick, *J. Appl. Phys.* **32,** 2206 (1961).
23. Arnott, R. J., and A. Wold, *J. Phys. Chem. Solids* **15,** 152 (1960).
24. Arrott, A., and H. Sato, *Phys. Rev.* **114,** 1420 (1959).
25. Asanuma, M., *J. Phys. Soc. Japan* **15,** 1136 (1960).
26. Asanuma, M., *J. Phys. Soc. Japan* **15,** 1343 (1960).
27. Asanuma, M., *J. Phys. Soc. Japan* **16,** 1265 (1961).
28. Askham, F., I. Fankuchen, and R. Ward, *J. Am. Chem. Soc.* **72,** 3799 (1950).

29. Austin, A. E., E. Adelson, and W. H. Cloud, *J. Appl. Phys. Supp.* **33**, 1356 (1962).
30. Auwärter, M., and A. Kussmann, *Ann. Physik* **7**, 169 (1950).
31. Bacher, R. F., and S. Goudsmit, *Atomic Energy States*, McGraw-Hill, New York, 1932.
32. Bacon, G. E., *Neutron Diffraction*, Oxford Univ. Press, London, 1955 gives an introductory discussion of these techniques.
33. Bacon, G. E., *Bull. Am. Phys. Soc.* [II] **5**, 455 (1960).
33a. Bacon, G. E., *Proc. Phys. Soc.* **79**, 938 (1962).
34. Bacon, G. E., and R. Street, *Proc. Phys. Soc.* (*London*) **72**, 470 (1958).
35. Bacon, G. E., I. W. Dunmur, J. H. Smith, and R. Street, *Proc. Roy. Soc.* (*London*) **A241**, 223 (1957).
36. Bain, E. C., *Trans. Am. Inst. Mining, Met., Petrol. Engrs.* **70**, 25 (1924).
37. Baltzer, P. K., *J. Phys. Soc. Japan* **17**, Suppl. B-I, (1962).
38. Baltzer, P. K., and J. G. White, *J. Appl. Phys.* **29**, 445 (1958) and private communication.
38a. Balz, D. and K. Plieth, *Z Electrochem.* **59**, 545 (1955).
39. Banewicz, J. J., and R. F. Heidelberg, *Phys. Rev.* **117**, 736 (1960).
40. Barnett, S. J., and L. J. H. Barnett, *Phys. Rev.* **17**, 404 (1921); **20**, 90 (1922); *Physik. Z.* **24**, 14 (1923).
41. Bates, L. F., *Phil. Mag.* **8**, 714 (1929).
42. Batterman, B. W., *Phys. Rev.* **115**, 81 (1959).
43. Batterman, B. W., D. R. Chipman and J. J. DeMarco, *Phys. Rev.* **122**, 68 (1961).
44. Bean, C. P., and D. S. Rodbell, *Phys. Rev.* **126**, 104 (1962).
45. Beckman, O., and K. Knox, *Phys. Rev.* **121**, 376 (1961).
46. Becquerel, J., and W. Opechowski, *Physica* **6**, 1039 (1939).
46a. Belov, K. P., and A. V. Pedko, *J. Exptl. Theoret. Phys.* (*USSR*) **42**, 87 (1962); *Soviet Phys. JETP* **15**, 62 (1962).
47. Belov, K. P., M. A. Zaitseva, and A. V. Ped'ko, *J. Exptl. Theoret. Phys.* (*USSR*) **36**, 1672 (1959), *Soviet Phys. JETP* **9**, 1191 (1959).
48. Belov, K. P., R. Z. Levitin, S. A. Nikitin, and A. V. Ped'ko, *J. Exptl. Theoret. Phys.* (*USSR*) **40**, 1562 (1961); *Soviet Phys. JETP* **13**, 1096 (1961) and private communication.
49. Benoit, R., *Compt. rend.* **234**, 2174 (1952); Thesis, University of Grenoble, 1954.
50. Benoit, R., *J. chim. phys.* **52**, 119 (1955).
51. Bents, U. H., *Phys. Rev.* **106**, 225 (1957).
52. Bertaut, E. F., *J. phys. radium* **12**, 252 (1951).
53. Bertaut, E. F., *Acta Cryst.* **6**, 557 (1953).
54. Bertaut, E. F., *Bull. soc. franç. mineral. et crist.* **79**, 276 (1956).
55. Bertaut, E. F., *Compt. rend.* **252**, 252 (1961).
56. Bertaut, E. F., and C. Delorme, *Compt. rend.* **238**, 1829 (1954).
57. Bertaut, E. F., and C. Delorme, *Compt. rend.* **239**, 504 (1954).
58. Bertaut, E. F., and F. Forrat, *Compt. rend.* **242**, 382 (1956).
59. Bertaut, E. F., and F. Forrat, *J. Appl. Phys.* **29**, 247 (1958).
60. Bertaut, E. F., and R. Pauthenet, *Proc. Inst. Elec. Engrs. Supp.* **B104**, 261 (1957).

61. Bertaut, E. F., L. M. Corliss, and F. Forrat, *Compt. rend.* **251**, 1733 (1960).
62. Bertaut, E. F., F. Forrat and J. Dulac, *Compt. rend.* **249**, 726 (1959).
63. Bertaut, E. F., A. Deschamps, R. Pauthenet, and S. J. Pickart, *J. phys. radium* **20**, 404 (1959).
64. Bertaut, E. F., F. Forrat, A. Herpin, and P. Mériel, *Compt. rend.* **243**, 898 (1956).
65. Bertaut, E. F., A. Delapalme, F. Forrat, G. Roult, F. de Bergevin, and R. Pauthenet, *J. Appl. Phys. Supp.* **33**, 1123 (1962).
66. Bethe, H. A., *Ann. Physik* [5] **3**, 133 (1929).
67. Bethe, H. A., *Z. Physik* **71**, 205 (1931).
68. Bhatnagar, S. S., and K. N. Mathur, *Physical Principles and Applications of Magnetochemistry*, Macmillan, London, 1935.
69. Bhatnagar, S. S., A. Cameron, E. H. Harbard, P. L. Kapur, A. King, and B. Prakash, *J. Chem. Soc.* **1939**, 1433.
70. Bierstedt, P. E., F. J. Darnell, W. H. Cloud, R. B. Flippen, and H. S. Jarrett, *Phys. Rev. Letters* **8**, 15 (1962).
70a. Billy, C. and H. M. Haendler, *J. Am. Chem. Soc.* **79**, 1049 (1957).
71. Bizette, H., *Ann. phys.* **1**, 306 (1946).
72. Bizette, H., *J. phys. radium* **12**, 161 (1951).
73. Bizette, H., and B. Tsai, *Compt. rend.* **211**, 252 (1940).
74. Bizette, H., and B. Tsai, *Compt. rend.* **234**, 2124 (1956).
75. Bizette, H., R. Chevallier, and B. Tsai, *Compt. rend.* **236**, 2043 (1953).
76. Bizette, H., C. Terrier, and B. Tsai, *Compt. rend.* **245**, 507 (1957).
77. Bizette, H., C. Terrier, and B. Tsai, *Compt. rend.* **246**, 250 (1958).
78. Blasse, G., and E. W. Gorter, *J. Phys. Soc. Japan* **17**, Suppl. B-I, 176 (1962).
79. Bloch, F., *Z. Physik* **52**, 555 (1928).
80. Bloch, F., *Z. Physik* **61**, 206 (1930).
81. Bloembergen, N., and T. J. Rowland, *Phys. Rev.* **97**, 1679 (1955).
82. Bongers, P. F., Thesis, University of Leiden, July 4, 1957, unpublished.
83. Bongers, P. F. (private communication).
84. Born, M., and R. J. Oppenheimer, *Ann. Physik* **84**, 457 (1927).
85. Borovik, E. S., *Izvest. Akad. Nauk. SSSR Ser. Fiz.* **19**, 429 (1955) [translation: *Bull. Acad. Sci. USSR* (Columbia Technical Translations, White Plains, New York) **19**, 383 (1955)], for example.
86. Borovik-Romanov, A. S., *J. Exptl. Theoret. Phys. (USSR)* **31**, 579 (1956); *Soviet Phys. JETP* **4**, 531 (1957).
87. Borovik-Romanov, A. S., *J. Exptl. Theoret. Phys. (USSR)* **36**, 1954 (1959); *Soviet Phys. JETP* **9**, 1390 (1959).
87a. Borovik-Romanov, A. S., V. R. Karasik, and N. M. Kreines, *J. Exptl. Theoret. Phys. (USSR)* **31**, 18 (1956); *Soviet Phys. JETP* **4**, 109 (1957).
88. Boucher, B., *Compt. rend.* **249**, 514 (1959).
89. Bozorth, R. M., *Ferromagnetism*, D. Van Nostrand, New York, 1951.
90. Bozorth, R. M., *Ferromagnetism*, D. Van Nostrand, New York, 1951, pp. 74, 79.
91. Bozorth, R. M., *Ferromagnetism*, D. Van Nostrand, New York, 1951, p. 328.
92. Bozorth, R. M., *Ferromagnetism*, D. Van Nostrand, New York, 1951, p. 431.
93. Bozorth, R. M., *American Institute of Physics Handbook*, Vol. V, McGraw-Hill, New York, 1957, p. 208.

94. Bozorth, R. M., *Phys. Rev. Letters* **1**, 362 (1958).
95. Bozorth, R. M., and S. Geller, *J. Phys. Chem. Solids* **11**, 263 (1959).
96. Bozorth, R. M., and V. Kramer, *J. phys. radium* **20**, 393 (1959).
97. Bozorth, R. M., and D. E. Walsh, *J. Phys. Chem. Solids* **5**, 299 (1958).
98. Bozorth, R. M., V. Kramer, and J. P. Remeika, *Phys. Rev. Letters* **1**, 3 (1958).
99. Bozorth, R. M., D. E. Walsh, and H. J. Williams, *Phys. Rev.* **108**, 157 (1957).
100. Bozorth, R. M., H. J. Williams, and D. E. Walsh, *Phys. Rev.* **103**, 572 (1956).
101. Bozorth, R. M., P. A. Wolff, D. D. Davis, V. B. Compton, and J. H. Wernick, *Phys. Rev.* **122**, 1157 (1961).
102. Braun, P. B., *Philips Research Rpts.* **12**, 491 (1957) gives a complete description of the structures.
103. Brillouin, L., *Die Quantenstatistik und ihre Anwendung auf die Elektronentheorie der Metalle*, translated from French to German by E. Rabinowitsch, Julius Springer, Berlin, 1931.
104. Brockhouse, B. N., *J. Chem. Phys.* **21**, 961 (1953).
105. Brockhouse, B. N., *Phys. Rev.* **94**, 781 (1954).
106. Brockhouse, B. N., and H. P. Myers, *Can. J. Phys.* **35**, 313 (1957).
107. Brown, H. A., and J. M. Luttinger, *Phys. Rev.* **100**, 685 (1955).
108. Bumm, H., and U. Dehlinger, *Metallwirtschaft* **13**, 23 (1934).
108a. Burger, J. P., and M. A. Taylor, *Phys. Rev. Letters* **6**, 185 (1961).
109. Busch, G., and J. Muller, *Physica Supp.* **24**, S152 (1958).
110. Butters, R. G., and H. P. Myers, *Phil. Mag.* **46**, 132 and 895 (1955).
111. Bykov, V. N., V. S. Galovkin, N. V. Ageev, V. A. Levdik, and S. I. Vinogradov, *Doklady Akad. Nauk SSSR* **128**, 1153 (1959); *Soviet Phys. Doklady* **4**, 1070 (1960).
112. Cable, J. W., M. K. Wilkinson, and E. O. Wollan, *Phys. Rev.* **118**, 950 (1960).
113. Cable, J. W., M. K. Wilkinson, and E. O. Wollan, *Bull. Am. Phys. Soc.* [II] **5**, 458 (1960).
114. Cable, J. W., M. K. Wilkinson, E. O. Wollan, and W. C. Koehler, *Phys. Rev.* **125**, 1860 (1962).
115. Cable, J. W., E. O. Wollan, W. C. Koehler, and M. K. Wilkinson, *J. Appl. Phys. Supp.* **32**, 49S (1961).
115a. Cable, J. W., E. O. Wollan, W. C. Koehler, and M. K. Wilkinson, *J. Appl. Phys. Supp.* **33**, 1340 (1962).
115a'. Cable, J. W., E. O. Wollan, W. C. Koehler, and H. R. Child, *Phys. Rev.* **128**, 2118 (1962).
115b. Cadeville, M–C, and A. J. P. Meyer, *Compt. rend.* **251**, 1621 (1960); **252**, 1124 (1961).
116. Carr, P. H., and S. Foner, *J. Appl. Phys. Supp.* **31**, 344S (1960).
116a. Castelliz, L., *Z. Metallkunde* **46**, 199 (1955).
117. Červinka, L., S. Krupička, and V. Syneček, *J. Phys. Chem. Solids* **20**, 167 (1961).
117a. Cheng, C. H., C. T. Wei, and P. A. Beck, *Phys. Rev.* **120**, 426 (1960).
117a'. Chandross, R. J. and D. P. Shoemaker, *J. Phys. Soc. Japan* **17**, Suppl. B-III, 16 (1962).
118. Clark, C. A., and W. Sucksmith, *Proc. Roy. Soc. (London)* **A225**, 147 (1954).

119. Cloud, W. H., *Phys. Rev.* **111,** 1046 (1958).
120. Cloud, W. H., T. A. Bither, and T. J. Swoboda, *J. Appl. Phys. Supp.* **32,** 55S (1961).
121. Cloud, W. H., H. S. Jarrett, and M. S. Sadler, *Bull. Am. Phys. Soc.* [II] **5,** 188 (1960).
121a. Cloud, W. H., D. S. Schreiber, and K. R. Babcock, *J. Appl. Phys. Supp.* **33,** 1193 (1962).
122. Cloud, W. H., H. S. Jarrett, A. E. Austin, and E. Adelson, *Phys. Rev.* **120,** 1969 (1960).
123. Condon, E. U., and G. H. Shortley, *The Theory of Atomic Spectra*, Cambridge Univ. Press, London, 1935, gives a proof of this rule.
124. Corliss, L. M., and J. M. Hastings, *American Institute of Physics Handbook*, McCraw-Hill, New York, 1957, Vol. V, p. 228.
125. Corliss, L. M., and J. M. Hastings, *J. Appl. Phys. Supp.* **33,** 1138 (1962); *Phys. Rev.* **126,** 556 (1962).
126. Corliss, L. M., N. Elliott, and J. M. Hastings, *Phys. Rev.* **104,** 924 (1956).
127. Corliss, L. M., N. Elliott, and J. M. Hastings, *Phys. Rev.* **117,** 929 (1960).
128. Corliss, L. M., J. M. Hastings, and F. G. Brockman, *Phys. Rev.* **90,** 1013 (1953).
129. Corliss, L. M., J. M. Hastings, and J. E. Goldman, *Phys. Rev.* **93,** 893 (1954).
130. Corliss, L. M., J. M. Hastings, and R. J. Weiss, *Phys. Rev. Letters* **3,** 211 (1959).
131. Corliss, L. M., N. Elliott, J. M. Hastings, and R. L. Sass, *Phys. Rev.* **122,** 1402 (1961).
132. Cossee, P., *Rec. trav. chim. Pays-Bas* **75,** 1089 (1956); *J. Inorg. & Nuclear Chem.* **8,** 483 (1958).
133. Cossee, P., and A. E. Van Arkel, *J. Phys. Chem. Solids* **15,** 1 (1960).
134. Coulson, C. A., and I. Fischer, *Phil. Mag.* [7] **40,** 386 (1949).
135. Cox, D. E., W. J. Takei, and G. Shirane, *J. Phys. Chem. Solids* **23,** 863 (1962).
136. Crangle, J., *Phil. Mag.* [8] **2,** 659 (1957).
137. Crangle, J., *J. phys. radium* **20,** 435 (1959).
138. Crangle, J., *Phil. Mag.* [8] **5,** 335 (1960).
139. Crangle, J., and M. J. C. Martin, *Phil. Mag.* [8] **4,** 1006 (1959).
140. Crangle, J., and D. Parsons, *Proc. Roy. Soc. (London)* **A255,** 509 (1960).
140a. Crangle, J., and T. F. Smith, *Phys. Rev. Letters* **9,** 86 (1962).
141. Date, M., *Phys. Rev.* **104,** 623 (1956).
141a. Davis, D. D., and R. M. Bozorth, *Phys. Rev.* **118,** 1543 (1960).
142. Dayhoff, E. S., *Phys. Rev.* **107,** 84 (1957).
143. de Bergevin, F., and L. Muldawer, *Bull. Am. Phys. Soc.* [II] **6,** 159 (1961).
144. De Boer, F., J. H. Van Santen, and E. J. W. Verwey, *J. Chem. Phys.* **18,** 1032 (1950).
145. Debye, P., *Physik. Z.* **13,** 97 (1912).
145a. de Gennes, P-G, *Phys. Rev.* **118,** 141 (1960).
146. de Haas, W. J., B. H. Schultz, and J. Koolhaas, *Physica* **7,** 57 (1940).

147. Dekhtiar, M. V., *J. Exptl. Theoret. Phys.* (*USSR*) **34**, 772 (1958); *Soviet Phys. JETP* **7**, 531 (1958). *Fiz. Metal. i Metalloved.* **9**, 345 (1960); *Phys. Metal. Metallog.* **9**, No. 3, 23 (1960).

148. Dekhtiar, M. V., and N. M. Kazantseva, *Fiz. Metal. i Metalloved.* **7**, 453 (1959); *Phys. Metal. Metallog.* **7**, No. 3, 129 (1959).

149. Delorme, C., *Compt. rend.* **241**, 1588 (1955).

150. Delorme, C., Thesis, University of Grenoble, 27 October 1956.

151. Derbyshire, W. D., and H. J. Yearian, *Phys. Rev.* **112**, 1603 (1958).

152. De Vries, G., *J. phys. radium* **20**, 438 (1959).

153. Dexter, R. N., B. Lax, A. F. Kip, and G. Dresselhaus, *Phys. Rev.* **96**, 222 (1954).

154. See Ref. 293a.

155. Donnay, G., L. M. Corliss, J. D. H. Donnay, N. Elliott, and J. M. Hastings, *Phys. Rev.* **112**, 1917 (1958).

156. Dunitz, J. D., and L. E. Orgel, *J. Phys. Chem. Solids* **3**, 20 (1957).

157. Dwight, K., and N. Menyuk, *Phys. Rev.* **119**, 1470 (1960).

158. Dwight, K., R. W. Germann, A. Wold, and N. Menyuk, *J. Appl. Phys. Supp.* **33**, 1341 (1962).

159. Dyer, L. D., B. S. Borie, Jr., and G. P. Smith, *J. Am. Chem. Soc.* **76**, 1499 (1954).

160. Dyson, F. J., *Phys. Rev.* **102**, 1217 (1956).

161. Dzialoshinsky, I. E., *J. Exptl. Theoret. Phys.* (*USSR*) **33**, 807 (1957); *Soviet Phys. JETP* **6**, 621 (1958).

162. Dzialoshinsky, I. E., *J. Phys. Chem. Solids* **4**, 241 (1958).

163. Ebert, H., and A. Kussmann, *Physik. Z.* **38**, 437 (1937).

164. Einstein, A., and W. J. de Haas, *Verhandl. deut. physik. Ges.* **17**, 152 (1915).

165. Elliott, N., J. M. Hastings, and R. L. Sass (unpublished data).

166. Elliott, R. J., *Phys. Rev.* **124**, 346 (1961); *J. Phys. Soc. Japan* **17**, Suppl. B-I, 1 (1962).

167. Elliott, R. J., and K. W. H. Stevens, *Proc. Roy. Soc.* (*London*) **A218**, 553 (1953).

168. Endô, K., *Sci. Repts. Tôhoku Univ.* **25**, 879 (1937).

169. Enz, U., *J. Appl. Phys. Supp.* **32**, 22S (1961).

170. Erickson, R. A., *Phys. Rev.* **85**, 745 (1952).

171. Erickson, R. A., *Phys. Rev.* **90**, 779 (1953).

172. Fakidov, I. G., and V. P. Krasovskii, *J. Exptl. Theoret. Phys.* (*USSR*) **36**, 1063 (1959); *Soviet Phys. JETP* **9**, 755 (1959).

172a. Fakidov, L. G., and Yu.N. Tsiovkin, *Fiz. metal. metalloved.* **7**, 685 (1959); *Phys. Metal. Metallog.* **7**, No. 5, 47 (1959).

173. Fallot, M., *Ann. phys.* **10**, 291 (1938).

174. Farcas, T., *Ann. phys.* **8**, 146 (1937).

174a. Feinlieb, J. (private communication).

175. Fermi, E., *Z. Physik* **60**, 320 (1930).

176. Finch, G. I., A. P. B. Sinha, and K. P. Sinha, *Proc. Roy. Soc.* (*London*) **A242**, 28 (1957).

177. Finkelnburg, W., and W. Humbach, *Naturwiss.* **42**, 35 (1955).

178. Finlayson, D. M., J. P. Llewellyn, and T. Smith, *Proc. Phys. Soc. (London)* **74**, 75 (1959).

179. Foëx, M., *Compt. rend.* **223**, 1126 (1946).

180. Foëx, M., *Compt. rend.* **227**, 193 (1948).

181. Foëx, M., and J. Loriers, *Compt. rend.* **226**, 901 (1948).

182. Foëx, M., and J. Wucher, *Compt. rend.* **229**, 882 (1949).

183. Foëx, M., and J. Wucher, *Compt. rend.* **241**, 184 (1955).

184. Foëx, M., J. Jaffray, S. Goldsztaub, R. Lyand, R. Wey, and J. Wucher, *J. recherches centre natl. recherche sci., Labs. Bellevue (Paris)* **4**, 237 (1952).

185. Foner, S., *Phys. Rev.* **107**, 1513 (1957).

186. Foner, S., *Phys. Rev.* **107**, 683 (1957); *J. phys. radium* **20**, 336 (1959).

187. Foner, S., *Bull. Am. Phys. Soc.* [II] **3**, 42 (1958).

188. Foner, S., *J. Appl. Phys. Supp.* **32**, 63S (1961).

188a. Fontaine, R., and R. Pauthenet, *Compt. rend.* **254**, 650 (1962).

189. Francombe, M. H., *J. Phys. Chem. Solids* **3**, 37 (1957).

190. Frazer, B. C., *Phys. Rev.* **112**, 751 (1958).

191. Frazer, B. C., and P. J. Brown, *Phys. Rev.* **125**, 1283 (1962).

192. Freeman, A. J., and R. E. Watson, *Phys. Rev. Letters* **5**, 498 (1960).

193. Freeman, A. J., and R. E. Watson, *Phys. Rev.* **124**, 1439 (1961).

194. Frenkel, J., *Wave Mechanics*, 2nd ed., Oxford Univ. Press, London, 1936; or any other text on quantum mechanics.

195. Friederich, E., and A. Kussmann, *Physik. Z.* **36**, 185 (1935).

196. Fröhlich, H., in *Advances in Physics*, Vol. 3, N. F. Mott, ed., Taylor and Francis, Ltd., London, 1954, p. 325.

197. Fröhlich, H., and G. L. Sewell, *Proc. Phys. Soc. (London)* **74**, 643 (1959).

198. Fujimi, S., M. Murakami, and E. Hirahara, *J. Phys. Soc. Japan* **16**, 183 (1961).

199. Furukawa, G. T., and T. B. Douglas, *American Institute of Physics Handbook*, McGraw-Hill, New York, 1957, Vol. IV, p. 48.

200. Galitsky, V. M., and A. B. Migdal, *J. Exptl. Theoret. Phys. (USSR)* **34**, 139 (1958); *Soviet Phys. JETP* **7**, 96 (1958). Implied by (206), (285), (286), (385)

201. Galt, J. K., W. A. Yager, F. R. Merritt, B. B. Catlin, and A. D. Brailsford, *Phys. Rev.* **114**, 1396 (1959).

202. Gebhardt, E., and W. Köster, *Z. Metallk.* **32**, 253 (1940).

203. Geller, S., *J. Chem. Phys.* **24**, 1236 (1956).

204. Geller, S., *J. Appl. Phys. Supp.* **31**, 30S (1960).

205. Geller, S., and M. A. Gilleo, *Acta Cryst.* **10**, 239 (1957).

205a. Geller, S., H. J. Williams, R. C. Sherwood, and G. P. Espinosa, *J. Appl. Phys. Supp.* **33**, 1195 (1962).

206. Gell-Mann, M., *Phys. Rev.* **106**, 369 (1957).

207. Gerritsen, H. J., Thesis, University of Leiden, 1955: *Physica* **21**, 189, 197, 213, 629, 639 (1955).

208. Giansoldati, A., *J. phys. radium* **16**, 342 (1955).

209. Giansoldati, A., J. O. Linde, and G. Borelius, *J. Phys. Chem. Solids* **11**, 46 (1959).

210. Goldring, G., M. Schieber, and V. Vager, *J. Appl. Phys.* **31**, 2057 (1960).
211. Goldstein, H., *Classical Mechanics*, Addison Wesley, Cambridge, Mass., 1950, p. 176.
212. Goodenough, J. B., *Phys. Rev.* **89**, 282 (1953).
213. Goodenough, J. B., *Phys. Rev.* **100**, 564 (1955).
214. Goodenough, J. B., *J. Phys. Chem. Solids* **6**, 287 (1958).
215. Goodenough, J. B., *J. phys. radium* **20**, 155 (1959).
216. Goodenough, J. B., *Phys. Rev.* **117**, 1442 (1960).
217. Goodenough, J. B., *Phys. Rev.* **120**, 67 (1960).
218. Goodenough, J. B., *Quart. Progr. Rept., Solid State Research*, Lincoln Laboratory, MIT, Cambridge, Mass., 15 Jan. 1961, p. 71.
219. Goodenough, J. B., *Magnetic Properties of Perovskites*, Landolt-Bornstein Tabellen Vol. II/9 Springer-Verlag, Berlin-Göttingen-Heidelberg, p. 2–187.
220. Goodenough, J. B., *J. Appl. Phys. Supp.* **33**, 1197 (1962).
221. Goodenough, J. B., *J. Phys. Soc. Japan* **17**, Suppl. B-I, 185 (1962).
222. Goodenough, J. B., and A. L. Loeb, *Phys. Rev.* **98**, 391 (1955).
223. Goodenough, J. B., D. G. Wickham, and W. J. Croft, *J. Phys. Chem. Solids* **5**, 107 (1958).
224. Goodenough, J. B., A. Wold, R. J. Arnott, *J. Appl. Phys. Supp.* **31**, 342S (1960).
225. Goodenough, J. B., A. Wold, R. J. Arnott, and N. Menyuk, *Phys. Rev.* **124**, 373 (1961).
226. Goodings, D. A., and V. Heine, *Phys. Rev. Letters* **5**, 370 (1960).
227. Gorter, C. J., and J. Haantjes, *Physica* **18**, 285 (1952).
228. Gorter, E. W., *Compt. rend.* **230**, 192 (1950); Nature, **165**, 798 (1950).
229. Gorter, E. W., *Philips Research Repts.* **9**, 295, 321, 403 (1954).
230. Gorter, E. W., and J. A. Schulkes, *Phys. Rev.* **90**, 487 (1953).
231. Goudsmit, S., *Phys. Rev.* **31**, 946 (1928).
232. Graf, L., and A. Kussmann, *Physik. Z.* **36**, 544 (1935).
233. Griffel, M., and J. W. Stout, *J. Am. Chem. Soc.* **72**, 4351 (1950).
233a. Griffith, J. S., *The Theory of Transition-Metal Ions*, Cambridge Univ. Press, London, 1961.
234. Gugan, D., *Proc. Phys. Soc. (London)* **72**, 1013 (1958).
235. Guillaud, C., Thesis, University of Strasbourg, 1943.
236. Guillaud, C., *J. phys. radium* **12**, 223 (1951).
237. Guillaud, C., *J. phys. radium* **12**, 489 (1951).
238. Guillaud, C., *Compt. rend.* **235**, 468 (1952).
239. Guillaud, C., *Revs. Modern Phys.* **25**, 119 (1953).
240. Guillaud, C., and H. Créveaux, *Compt. rend.* **224**, 266 (1947).
241. Guillaud, C., R. Bertrand, and R. Vautier, *Compt. rend.* **228**, 1403 (1949).
242. Guillaud, C., A. Michel, J. Bernard, and M. Fallot, *Compt. rend.* **219**, 58 (1944).
243. Guillaud, C., *et al.*, *J. phys. radium* **12**, 239 (1951); *Compt. rend.* **229**, 1133 (1949); **230**, 1256, 1458 (1950); **232**, 944 (1951).
244. Guiot-Guillain, G., *Compt. rend.* **237**, 1654 (1953).
245. Guiot-Guillain, G., R. Pauthenet, and H. Forestier, *Compt. rend.* **239**, 155 (1954).

246. Haken, H., "Halbleiterproblem II," W. Schottky, ed., Friedr. Vieweg und Sohn, Braunschweig, Germany, 1955, p. 1.

247. Halpern, O., and M. H. Johnson, *Phys. Rev.* **55**, 898 (1939).

248. Hamilton, W. C., *Phys. Rev.* **110**, 1050 (1958).

249. Hanna, S. S., J. Heberle, G. J. Perlow, R. S. Preston, and D. H. Vincent, *Phys. Rev. Letters* **4**, 513 (1960).

250. Hansen, M., *Constitution of Binary Alloys*, McGraw-Hill, New York, 1958.

250a. Hansen, W. N., *J. Appl. Phys. Supp.* **30**, 304S (1959).

251. Hansen, W. N., and M. Griffel, *J. Chem. Phys.* **30**, 913 (1959).

251a. Haraldsen, H., *Z. anorg. u. allgem. Chem.* **224**, 85 (1935).

252. Haraldsen, H., *Z. anorg. u. allgem. Chem.* **231**, 78 (1937); **246**, 169, 195 (1941).

253. Haraldsen, H., and A. Neuber, *Z. anorg. u. allgem. Chem.* **234**, 337, 372, (1937).

254. Hartree, D. R., *Proc. Camb. Phil. Soc.* **24**, 89 (1928).

255. Hastings, J. M., *Bull. Am. Phys. Soc.* [II] **5**, 455 (1960).

256. Hastings, J. M., and L. M. Corliss, *Revs. Modern Phys.* **25**, 114 (1953).

257. Hastings, J. M., and L. M. Corliss, *Phys. Rev.* **102**, 1460 (1956).

258. Hastings, J. M., and L. M. Corliss, *Phys. Rev.* **104**, 328 (1956).

259. Hastings, J. M., and L. M. Corliss (private communication).

260. Hastings, J. M., N. Elliott, and L. M. Corliss, *Phys. Rev.* **115**, 13 (1959).

261. Hebborn, J. E., and E. S. Sondheimer, *J. Phys. Chem. Solids* **13**, 105 (1960).

261a. Heeger, A. H., O. Beckman, and A. M. Portis, *Phys. Rev.* **123**, 1652 (1961).

262. Heikes, R. R., *Phys. Rev.* **99**, 446 (1955).

263. Heikes, R. R., and W. D. Johnston, *J. Chem. Phys.* **26**, 582 (1957).

264. Heikes, R. R., T. R. McGuire, and R. J. Happel, Jr., *Phys. Rev.* **121**, 703 (1961).

265. Heisenberg, W., *Z. Physik.* **49**, 619 (1928).

266. Heitler, W., and F. London, *Z. Physik.* **44**, 455 (1927).

267. Heller, G. S., J. J. Stickler, and J. B. Thaxter, *J. Appl. Phys. Supp.* **32S**, 307S (1961).

267a. Heller, G. S., J. J. Stickler, A. Wold, and S. Kern, *J. Appl. Phys. Supp.* **34S** (to be published 1963).

267b. Henry, W. E., *J. Appl. Phys. Supp.* **31**, 323S (1960).

268. Hepworth, M. A., and K. H. Jack, *Acta Cryst.* **10**, 345 (1957).

269. Herpin, A., and P. Mériel, *Bull. Am. Phys. Soc.* [II] **5**, 457 (1960).

270. Herpin, A., W. C. Koehler, and P. Mériel, *Bull. Am. Phys. Soc.* [II] **5**, 457 (1960).

271. Herpin, A., P. Mériel, and A. J. P. Meyer, *Compt. rend.* **246**, 3170 (1958).

271a. Herring, C., *Revs. Mod. Phys.* **34**, 631 (1962).

272. Herzberg, G., *Atomic Spectra and Atomic Structure*, 2nd ed., translated by J. W. T. Spinks, Dover, New York, 1944.

273. Hirahara, E., (private communication).

274. Hirahara, E., and M. Murakami, *J. Phys. Chem. Solids* **7**, 281 (1958).

275. Hirakawa, K., K. Hirakawa, and T. Hashimoto, *J. Phys. Soc. Japan* **15**, 2063 (1960).

275a. Hirone, T., and S. Chiba, *J. Phys. Soc. Japan* **15**, 1991 (1960).

276. Hirone, T., S. Maeda, S. Chiba and N. Tsuya, *J. Phys. Soc. Japan* **9**, 500, 503 (1954).

277. Hirone, T., S. Maeda, I. Tsubokawa, and N. Tsuya, *J. Phys. Soc. Japan* **11**, 1083 (1956).

277a. Hofer, L. J. E., and E. M. Cohn, *J. Am. Chem. Soc.* **81**, 1576 (1959).

278. Hollander, L. E., Jr., and P. L. Castro, *Phys. Rev.* **119**, 1882 (1960).

279. Holstein, T., *Ann. Phys.* (*N.Y.*) **8**, 325, 343 (1959).

280. Horowitz, M., and J. G. Daunt, *Phys. Rev.* **91**, 1099 (1953).

281. Hoschek, E., and W. Klemm, *Z. anorg. u. allgem. Chem.* **242**, 63 (1939).

282. Howe, L., and H. P. Myers, *Phil. Mag.* [8] **2**, 554 (1957).

283. Huber, E., and D. Ridgley, *J. Appl. Phys. Supp.* **34S**, (to be published 1963).

284. Huetter, L. J., and H. H. Stadelmaier, *Acta Met.* **6**, 367 (1958); **7**, 415 (1959); *Z. Metallk.* **50**, 199 (1959); **51**, 41 (1960).

285. Hugenholtz, N. M., *Physica* **23**, 481, 533 (1957).

286. Hugenholtz, N. M., and L. Van Hove, *Physica* **24**, 363 (1958).

287. Hulthèn, L., *Koninkl. Akad. Wetenschap. Amsterdam* **39**, 190 (1936).

288. Hume-Rothery, W., and B. R. Coles, *Advances in Physics*, Vol. 3, *Phil. Mag. Supp.*, N. F. Mott, ed., Taylor and Francis, Ltd., London, 1954, p. 149.

289. Hund, F., *Linienspektren und Periodisches System der Elemente*, Julius Springer, Berlin, 1927, Chap. V.

290. Hund, F., *Z. Physik* **51**, 759 (1928); **63**, 719 (1930).

291. Irani, K. S., A. P. B. Sinha, and A. B. Biswas, *J. Phys. Chem. Solids* **17**, 101 (1960).

291a. Irani, K. S., A. P. B. Sinha, and A. B. Biswas, *J. Phys. Chem. Solids* **23**, 711 (1962).

292. Ishikawa, Y., and S. Akimoto, *J. Phys. Soc. Japan* **13**, 1298 (1958).

293. Ishikawa, Y., et al., *J. Phys. Soc. Japan* **11**, 496 (1956); **12**, 834, 1083, 1165 (1957); **13**, 37, 828 (1958).

293a. Iyenger, P. K., B. A. Dasannacharya, P. R. Vijayaraghavan, and A. P. Roy, *J. Phys. Soc Japan* **17**, Suppl. B-III, 41 (1962).

294. Jack, K. H., and R. Maitland, *Proc. Chem. Soc.* (*London*) **1957**, 232.

295. Jacobs, I. S., *J. Phys. Chem. Solids* **15**, 54 (1960).

296. Jacobs, I. S., and J. S. Kouvel, *Phys. Rev.* **122**, 412 (1961).

297. Jacobs, I. S., J. S. Kouvel, and P. E. Lawrence, *J. Phys. Soc. Japan* **17**, Suppl. B-I, 157 (1962).

297a. Jacobs, I. S., D. S. Rodbell, and W. L. Roth, Aeronautical Systems Division, AF Syst. Command, Wright-Patterson AF Base, Ohio, *Technical Report* 61-630 (Feb. 1962).

298. Jaffray, J., and A. Dumas, *J. recherches centre natl. recherche sci.*, *Labs. Bellevue* (*Paris*) **5**, 360 (1953–1954).

299. Jaffray, J., and R. Lyand, *J. recherches centre natl. recherche sci.*, *Labs. Bellevue* (*Paris*) **4**, 249 (1952).

300. Jaffray, J., and J. Viloteau, *Compt. rend.* **226**, 1701 (1948).

301. Jahn, H. A., *Proc. Roy. Soc.* (*London*) **A164**, 117 (1938).

302. Jahn, H. A., and E. Teller, *Proc. Roy. Soc.* (*London*) **A161**, 220 (1937).

302a. Jarrett, H. S. (private communication).

302a . James, W., R. Lemaire, and F. Bertaut, *Compt. rend.* **255**, 896 (1962).

303. Jarrett, H. S., and R. K. Waring, *Phys. Rev.* **111**, 1223 (1958).

304. Jaccarino, V., B. T. Matthias, M. Peter, H. Suhl, and J. H. Wernick, *Phys. Rev. Letters* **5**, 251 (1960).

305. Jellinek, F., *Acta Cryst.* **10**, 620 (1957).

306. Johnson, F. M., and A. H. Nethercot, Jr., *Phys. Rev.* **104**, 847 (1956); **114**, 705 (1959).

307. Jones, H., *Proc. Roy. Soc. (London)* **A147**, 396 (1934).

308. Jonker, G. H., *Physica* **22**, 707 (1956).

309. Jonker, G. H., and S. van Houten, *Semiconducting Properties of Transition Metal Oxides*, in *Halbleiterprobleme VI*, F. Sauter, ed., Friedr. Vieweg und Sohn, Braunschweig, 1961, p. 118.

310. Jonker, G. H., and J. H. Van Santen, *Physica* **16**, 337 (1950).

311. Jonker, G. H., and J. H. Van Santen, *Physica* **19**, 120 (1953).

312. Jonker, G. H., H. P. J. Wijn, and P. B. Braun, *Philips Tech. Rev.* **18**, 145 (1956–1957).

313. Judd, B. R., *Proc. Roy. Soc. (London)* **A227**, 552 (1955).

314. Judd, B. R., *Proc. Phys. Soc. (London)* **70B**, 880 (1957).

315. Juza, R., and W. Blitz, *Z. anorg. u. allgem. Chem.* **205**, 273 (1932).

316. Kamigaichi, T., *J. Sci. Hiroshima Univ.* **A19**, 499 (1956).

317. Kamigaichi, T., K. Masumoto and T. Hihara, *J. Phys. Soc. Japan* **15**, 1355 (1960).

318. Kanamori, J., *Progr. Theoret. Phys. (Kyoto)* **17**, 177 (1957).

319. Kanamori, J., *Progr. Theoret. Phys. (Kyoto)* **17**, 197 (1957).

320. Kanamori, J., *Progr. Theoret. Phys. (Kyoto)* **20**, 890 (1958).

321. Kanamori, J., *J. Chem. Phys. Solids* **10**, 87 (1959).

322. Kanamori, J., *J. Appl. Phys. Supp.* **31**, 14S (1960).

323. Kanematsu, K., K. Yasukochi, and T. Ohoyama, *J. Phys. Soc. Japan* **15**, 2358 (1961).

323a. Kanematsu, K. and K. Yasukochi, *J. Phys. Soc. Japan* **17**, 932 (1962).

324. Kaplan, H., *Phys. Rev.* **85**, 1038 (1952).

325. Kaplan, H., *Phys. Rev.* **86**, 121 (1952).

326. Kaplan, T. A., *Phys. Rev.* **109**, 782 (1958).

327. Kaplan, T. A., *Phys. Rev.* **116**, 888 (1959).

328. Kaplan, T. A., *Phys. Rev.* **119**, 1460 (1960).

329. Kaplan, T. A., *Phys. Rev.* **124**, 329 (1961); *J. Phys. Soc. Japan* **17**, Suppl. B-I, 3 (1962).

330. Kaplan, T. A., *J. Appl. Phys. Supp.* **34S**, (to be published (1963).

331. Kaplan, T. A., K. Dwight, D. H. Lyons, N. Menyuk, *J. Appl. Phys. Supp.* **32**, 13S (1961).

332. Kasper, J. S., *Bull. Am. Phys. Soc.* [II] **4**, 178 (1959).

333. Kasper, J. S., (private communication).

334. Kasper, J. S., and J. S. Kouvel, *J. Phys. Chem. Solids* **11**, 231 (1959).

335. Kasper, J. S., and R. M. Waterstrat, *Phys. Rev.* **109**, 1551 (1958).

336. Kasper, J. S., and R. H. Wilson, as quoted in reference 44.

337. Kasteleijn, P. W., and J. Van Kranendonk, *Physica* **22**, 367 (1956).

338. Kaufmann, L., and S. Foner (private communication).

339. Kawakubo, T., T. Yanagi, and S. Nomura, *J. Phys. Soc. Japan* **15**, 2102 (1960).

340. Kaya, S., and A. Kussmann, *Z. Physik* **72**, 293 (1931).

341. Keffer, F., *Phys. Rev.* **87**, 608 (1952).

341a. Keffer, F., *Phys. Rev.* **126**, 896 (1962).

342. Keffer, F., and C. Kittel, *Phys. Rev.* **85**, 329 (1952).

343. Keffer, F., and T. Oguchi, *Phys. Rev.* **115**, 1428 (1959).

344. Keffer, F., and W. O'Sullivan, *Phys. Rev.* **108**, 637 (1957).

345. Keffer, F., A. J. Sievers III, and M. Tinkham, *J. Appl. Phys. Supp.* **32**, 65S (1961).

346. Kittel, C., *Phys. Rev.* **71**, 270 (1947); **73**, 155 (1948).

347. Kittel, C., *Phys. Rev.* **76**, 743 (1949).

348. Kittel, C., *Phys. Rev.* **82**, 565 (1951).

349. Kittel, C., *Phys. Rev.* **120**, 335 (1960).

350. Kittel, C., and A. H. Mitchell, *Phys. Rev.* **101**, 1611 (1956).

351. Kleiner, W. H., *J. Chem. Phys.* **20**, 1784 (1952).

352. Knox, K., *J. Chem. Phys.* **30**, 991 (1959).

352a. Kocher, C. W., and P. J. Brown, *J. Appl. Phys. Supp.* **33**, 1091 (1962).

353. Koehler, W. C., *J. Appl. Phys. Supp.* **32**, 20S (1961).

354. Koehler, W. C., and E. O. Wollan, *J. Phys. Chem. Solids* **2**, 100 (1957).

355. Koehler, W. C., E. O. Wollan, and M. K. Wilkinson, *Phys. Rev.* **118**, 58 (1960).

355a. Koehler, W. C., J. W. Cable, E. O. Wollan, and M. K. Wilkinson, *Phys. Rev.* **126**, 1672 (1962).

356. Kohn, W., *Phys. Rev.* **105**, 509 (1957); **110**, 857 (1958).

357. Kojima, H., R. S. Tebble, and D. E. G. Williams, *Proc. Roy. Soc. (London)* **A260**, 237 (1961).

357a. Komura, S., *et al.*, *J. Phys. Soc. Japan* **16**, 1479, 1486 (1961).

358. Komura, Y., Y. Tomiie, and R. Nathans, *Phys. Rev. Letters* **3**, 268 (1959).

359. Komura, Y., Y. Tomiie, and R. Nathans, *J. Phys. Soc. Japan* **15**, 1434 (1960).

360. Kondo, J., *Prog. Theoret. Phys. (Kyoto)* **22**, 41 (1959).

361. Kondoh, H., *J. Phys. Soc. Japan* **15**, 1970 (1960).

362. Kondorsky, E. I., and V. L. Sedov, *J. phys. radium* **20**, 185 (1959); *J. Appl. Phys. Supp.* **31**, 331S (1960).

363. Koopmans, T., *Physica* **1**, 104 (1933).

363a. Kornelsen, R. O., *Can. J. Phys.* **39**, 1728 (1961).

364. Kouvel, J. S., *J. Appl. Phys. Supp.* **30**, 313S (1959).

365. Kouvel, J. S., *J. Phys. Chem. Solids* **16**, 107 (1960).

366. Kouvel, J. S., *J. Appl. Phys. Supp.* **31**, 142S (1960); *J. Phys. Chem. Solids* **21**, 57 (1961).

367. Kouvel, J. S., and C. D. Graham, Jr., *J. Phys. Chem. Solids* **11**, 220 (1959); *J. Appl. Phys. Supp.* **30**, 312S (1959).

368. Kouvel, J. S., and C. C. Hartelius, *J. Appl. Phys. Supp.* **33**, 1343 (1962).

368a. Kouvel, J. S., and C. C. Hartelius, *Phys. Rev.* **123**, 124 (1961).

369. Kouvel, J. S., and R. H. Wilson, *J. Appl. Phys.* **32**, 435 (1961).

370. Kouvel, J. S., C. D. Graham, Jr., and J. J. Becker, *J. Appl. Phys.* **29**, 518 (1958).

371. Kouvel, J. S., C. D. Graham, Jr., and I. S. Jacobs, *J. phys. radium* **20**, 198 (1959).
372. Kramers, H. A., *Koninkl. Akad. Wetenschap. Amsterdam* **33**, 959 (1930).
373. Kramers, H. A., *Physica* **1**, 182 (1934).
374. Kriessman, C. J., and H. B. Callen, *Phys. Rev.* **94**, 837 (1954).
375. Krutter, H. M., *Phys. Rev.* **48**, 664 (1935).
376. Kubo, R., *Phys. Rev.* **87**, 568 (1952); *Revs. Modern Phys.* **25**, 344 (1953).
377. Kubota, B., and E. Hirota, *J. Phys. Soc. Japan* **16**, 345 (1960).
378. Kurlina, E. V., V. G. Prokhvatilov, and I. T. Sheftel, *Doklady Akad. Nauk USSR* **86**, 305 (1952).
379. Kurnick, S. W., M. F. Merriam, and R. L. Fitzpatrick, *Advanced Energy Conversion* **1**, 157 (1962).
380. Kussmann, A., and E. Raub, *Z. Metallk.* **47**, 9 (1956).
381. Kussmann, A., and G. G. von Rittberg, *Z. Metallk.* **41**, 470 (1950).
382. LaBlanchetais, C. H., *J. phys. radium* **12**, 765 (1951).
383. Landau, L. D., *Z. Physik* **64**, 629 (1930).
384. Landau, L. D., *Physik. Z. Sowjetunion* **3**, 664 (1933).
385. Landau, L. D., *J. Exptl. Theoret. Phys.* **30**, 1058 (1956); *Soviet Phys. JETP* **3**, 920 (1957).
386. Landé, A., *Z. Physik* **15**, 189 (1923).
387. Landolt, H. H., and R. Börnstein, *Zahlenwerte und Funktionen aus Physik Chemie Astronomie Geophysik und Technik*, Springer-Verlag., Berlin, 1955.
388. Langevin, P., *J. Physique* **4**, 678 (1905); *Ann. chim. et phys.* **5**, 70 (1905).
389. Larmor, J., *Aether and Matter*, Cambridge, London, 1900, p. 341. For a discussion of the Larmor theorem, see ref. (211).
389a. Lavine, J. M., *Phys. Rev.* **114**, 482 (1959).
390. Lax, B., H. J. Zeiger, R. N. Dexter, and E. S. Rosenblum, *Phys. Rev.* **93**, 1418 (1945).
391. Le Clerc, G., and A. Michel, *Compt. rend.* **208**, 1583 (1939).
392. Leech, J. W., and A. J. Manuel, *Proc. Phys. Soc. (London)* **69B**, 220 (1956).
392a. Legrand, E., and R. Plumier, *Physica Status Solidi* **2**, 317 (1962).
393. Lidiard, A. B., *Repts. Prog. in Phys.* **17**, 201 (1954).
394. Liehr, A. D., and C. H. Ballhausen, *Ann. Phys. (N. Y.)* **3**, 304 (1958).
395. Liehr, A. D., and W. Moffitt, *J. Chem. Phys.* **25**, 1074 (1956).
395a. Lin, S. T., and A. R. Kaufmann, *Phys. Rev.* **108**, 1171 (1957).
396. Lindsay, R., *Phys. Rev.* **84**, 569 (1951).
397. Llewellyn, J. P., and T. Smith, *Proc. Phys. Soc. (London)* **74**, 65 (1959).
398. Loeb, A. L., and J. B. Goodenough, *Conference on Magnetism and Magnetic Materials*, Boston, Mass., Oct. 16–18, 1956, *Published by AIEE*, Feb. **(1957)**.
399. Löwdin, P. O., *Advances in Physics*, Vol. 5, *Phil. Mag. Supp.*, N. F. Mott, ed., Taylor and Francis, Ltd., London, 1 (1956), p. 9.
400. Löwdin, P. O., *Advances in Chemical Physics*, Vol. II, I. Prigogine, ed., Interscience, New York, 1959, p. 207.
401. Longuet,Higgins, H. C., U. Öpik, M. H. L. Pryce, and R. A. Sack, *Proc. Roy. Soc. (London)* **A244**, 1 (1958).
402. Lotgering, F. K., *Philips Research Repts.* **11**, 190 (1956).

403. Lotgering, F. K., and E. W. Gorter, *J. Phys. Chem. Solids* **3**, 238 (1957)
404. Low, W., *Paramagnetic Resonance in Solids*, Supplement 2 of *Solid State Physics*, F. Seitz and D. Turnbull, eds., Academic, New York, 1960.
405. Lowde, R. D., *Revs. Modern Phys.* **30**, 69 (1958).
405a. Lundquist, N., and H. P. Myers, *Arkiv för Fysik* **20**, 463 (1961).
406. Luttinger, J. M., *Phys. Rev.* **119**, 1153 (1960).
407. Luttinger, J. M., and L. Tisza, *Phys. Rev.* **70**, 954 (1946); J. M. Luttinger, *Phys. Rev.* **81**, 1015 (1952).
408. Lyons, D. H., and T. A. Kaplan, *Phys. Rev.* **120**, 1580 (1960).
409. Lyons, D. H., T. A. Kaplan, K. Dwight, and N. Menyuk, *Phys. Rev.* **126**, 540 (1962).
410. Magnéli, A., and G. Andersson, *Acta Chem. Scand.* **9**, 1378 (1955).
411. Malevskaya, L. A., and G. M. Nurmukhamedov, *J. Exptl. Theoret. Phys. (USSR)* **36**, 1600 (1959); *Soviet Phys. JETP* **9**, 1137 (1959).
412. Marian, V., *Ann. phys.* **7**, 459 (1937).
413. Mashiyama, Y., E. Uchida, H. Kondoh, *Busseiron Kenkyu* (Researches on Chemical Physics) **71**, 9 (1954).
414. Mason, B., *Amer. Min.* **32**, 426 (1947); *Geol. Fören i Stockholm Förh.* **65**, 97 (1943).
415. Mattheiss, L. F. (see also J. C. Slater 1961) *Phys. Rev.* **123**, 1209, 1219 (1961).
416. Matthias, B. T., and E. Corenzwit, *Phys. Rev.* **100**, 626 (1955).
417. Matthias, B. T., V. B. Compton, H. Suhl, and E. Corenzwit, *Phys. Rev.* **115**, 1597 (1959).
418. Matthias, B. T., M. Peter, H. J. Williams, A. M. Clogston, E. Corenzwit, and R. C. Sherwood, *Phys. Rev. Letters* **5**, 542 (1960).
418a. Maxwell, L. R., J. S. Smart, and S. Brunauer, *J. Chem. Phys.* **19**, 303 (1951).
419. Mayer, J. E., and M. G. Mayer, *Statistical Mechanics*, Wiley, New York, 1940, p. 378 ff., or any other text on statistical mechanics.
420. McCarroll, W. H., L. Katz, and R. Ward, *J. Am. Chem. Soc.* **79**, 5410 (1957).
421. McClure, D. S., *J. Phys. Chem. Solids* **3**, 311 (1957).
422. McClure, J. W., *Phys. Rev.* **108**, 612 (1957) gives, for example, an application of the de Haas–Van Alphen oscillations to graphite.
423. McGuire, T. R., *Phys. Rev.* **93**, 682 (1954).
424. McGuire, T. R., *Bull. Am. Phys. Soc.* [II] **5**, 456 (1960).
425. McGuire, T. R., and S. W. Greenwald, *Phys. Rev.* **90**, 373 (1953).
426. McGuire, T. R., and S. W. Greenwald, *Solid State Physics in Electronics and Telecommunications*, Vol. 3, *Magnetic and Optical Properties*, Part I, M. Désirant and J. L. Michiels, eds., Academic, London and N.Y., 1960, p. 50.
427. McGuire, T. R., E. J. Scott, and F. H. Grannis, *Phys. Rev.* **102**, 1000 (1956).
428. McMurdie, H. F., and E. Golovato, *J. Research Natl. Bur. Standards* **41**, 589 (1948).
429. McQuillan, A. D., and M. K. McQuillan, *Metallurgy of Rare Metals*, Butterworths Scientific Publications, Ltd., London, 1956.
430. Meiklejohn, W. H., and C. P. Bean, *Phys. Rev.* **102**, 1413 (1956); **105**, 904 (1957).

431. Mekata, M., *J. Phys. Soc. Japan* **17**, 796 (1962).
432. Meneghetti, D., and S. S. Sidhu, *Phys. Rev.* **105**, 130 (1957).
433. Menyuk, N., *Solid State Quart. Progr. Rept.*, Lincoln Laboratory, MIT, Cambridge, Mass., July 15, 1961.
434. Meyer, A. J. P., *Compt. rend.* **242**, 2315 (1956); **244**, 2028 (1957).
435. Meyer, A. J. P., *Compt. rend.* **246**, 1517 (1958).
436. Meyer, A. J. P., *J. phys. radium* **20**, 430 (1959).
436a. Meyer, A. J. P., and M–J Besnus, *Compt. rend.* **253**, 2651 (1961).
437. Meyer, A. J. P., and M. C. Cadeville, *J. Phys. Soc. Japan* **17**, Suppl. B-I, 223 (1962).
438. Meyer, A. J. P., and P. Taglang, *J. phys. radium* **17**, 457 (1956).
439. Miller, A., *J. Appl. Phys. Supp.* **30**, 24S (1959).
440. Miller, A., *Phys. Rev.* **116**, 1481 (1959).
441. Miyahara, S., *Proc. Phys. Math. Soc. Japan* **22**, 358 (1940).
442. Miyahara, S., and H. Ohnishi, *J. Phys. Soc. Japan* **11**, 1296 (1956).
443. Miyahara, S., and T. Tsushima, *J. Phys. Soc. Japan* **13**, 758 (1958).
444. Moffitt, W., and A. D. Liehr, *Phys. Rev.* **106**, 1195 (1957).
445. Moffitt, W., and W. Thorson, *Phys. Rev.* **108**, 1251 (1957).
446. Morin, F. J., *Phys. Rev.* **78**, 819 (1950).
447. Morin, F. J., *Bell System Tech. J.* **37**, 1047 (1958).
448. Morin, F. J., *Phys. Rev. Letters* **3**, 34 (1959).
449. Moriya, T., *J. Phys. Chem. Solids* **11**, 73 (1959).
450. Moriya, T., *Phys. Rev.* **117**, 635 (1960).
451. Moriya, T., *Phys. Rev.* **120**, 91 (1960).
452. Moriya, T., K. Motizuki, J. Kanamori, and T. Nagamiya, *J. Phys. Soc. Japan* **11**, 211 (1956).
453. Mott, N. F., *Can. J. Phys.* **34**, 1356 (1956).
454. Mott, N. F., *Nuovo cimento* [10] **7**, Suppl., 312 (1958).
455. Mott, N. F., and P. W. Gurney, *Electronic Process in Ionic Crystals*, Oxford Univ. Press, London, 1940, p. 86.
455a. Mott, N. F., and H. Jones, *The Theory of the Properties of Metals and Alloys*, Clarendon Press, Oxford, 1936, p. 310.
456. Mueller, C. R., and H. Eyring, *J. Chem. Phys.* **19**, 1495 (1951).
457. Mulliken, R. S., *Phys. Rev.* **32**, 186, 761 (1928); **33**, 730 (1928).
457a. Mulliken, R. S., *J. Chem. Phys.* **3**, 375 (1935).
458. Murakami, M., and E. Hirahara, *J. Phys. Soc. Japan* **13**, 1407 (1958).
459. Muramori, K., and S. Miyahara, *J. Phys. Soc. Japan* **15**, 1906 (1960).
459a. Murray, R. B., *Phys. Rev.* **128**, 1570 (1962).
460. Murray, R. B., and L. D. Roberts, *Phys. Rev.* **100**, 1067 (1955).
461. Nagamiya, T., *Prog. Theoret. Phys.* (*Kyoto*) **6**, 342 (1951).
462. Nagamiya, T., K. Yosida, and R. Kubo, *Advances in Physics*, Vol. 4, *Phil. Mag. Supp.*, N. F. Mott, ed., Taylor and Francis, Ltd., London, 1955, p. 1.
463. Nakamura, T., *Prog. Theoret. Phys.* (*Kyoto*) **7**, 539 (1952).
463a. Nassau, K., L. V. Cherry, and W. E. Wallace, *J. Phys. Chem. Solids* **16**, 123, 131 (1960).
464. Nathans, R., and A. Paoletti, *Phys. Rev. Letters* **2**, 254 (1959).
465. Nathans, R., S. J. Pickart, and A. Miller, *Bull. Am. Phys. Soc.* [II] **6**, 54 (1961).

466. Nathans, R., M. T. Pigott, and C. G. Shull, *J. Phys. Chem. Solids* **6**, 38 (1958).
467. Nathans, R., S. J. Pickart, S. E. Harrison, and C. J. Kriessman, *Proc. IEE Supp.* **104B**, 217 (1957).
468. Naylor, B. F., *J. Am. Chem. Soc.* **68**, 1077 (1946).
469. Néel, L., *Ann. phys.* [10] **18**, 5 (1932); *J. phys. radium* [7] **3**, 160 (1932).
470. Néel, L., *Ann. phys.* [11] **5**, 232 (1936); *Compt. rend.* **203**, 304 (1936).
471. Néel, L., *Ann. phys.* [12] **3**, 137 (1948).
472. Néel, L., *J. phys. radium* **12**, 258 (1951).
473. Néel, L., *Revs. Modern Phys.* **25**, 293 (1953).
474. Néel, L., *Bull. soc. franç. minéral. et crist.* **77**, 257 (1954).
475. Néel, L., and P. Brochet, *Compt. rend.* **230**, 280 (1950).
476. Néel, L., and R. Pauthenet, *Compt. rend.* **234**, 2172 (1952).
476a. Nereson, N. G., C. E. Olsen, and G. P. Arnold, *Phys. Rev.* **127**, 2101 (1962).
477. Nesbet, R. K., *Ann. Phys.* (*N.Y.*) **4**, 87 (1958).   See also ref. (373) and the discussion in ref. (530).
478. Nesbet, R. K., *Phys. Rev.* **119**, 658 (1960).
479. Nesbet, R. K., *Phys. Rev.* **122**, 1497 (1961).
480. Nesbet, R. K. (private communication).
480a. Nevitt, M. V., *J. Appl. Phys.* **31**, 155 (1960).
480a'. Nesbitt, E. A., H. J. Williams, J. H. Wernick, and R. C. Sherwood, *J. Appl. Phys. Supp.* **32**, 342S (1961); *J. Appl. Phys.* **33**, 1674 (1962).
480b. Newkirk, J. B., *Trans. AIME* **209**, 1214 (1957).
481. Newnham, R. E., and Y. M. de Haan, *Quart. Progr. Rept.* No. XXVI, Laboratory for Insulation Research, MIT, Cambridge, Mass., January, 1960, p. 10; *Z. Krist.* **117**, 235 (1962).
482. Nomura, S., T. Kawakubo, and T. Yanagi, *J. Phys. Soc. Japan* **16**, 706 (1961).
483. Nyholm, R., and A. G. Sharpe, *J. Chem. Soc.* 3579 (**1952**).
484. Öpik, U., and M. H. L. Pryce, *Proc. Roy. Soc.* (*London*) **A238**, 425 (1957).
485. Ogawa, S., *J. Phys. Soc. Japan* **14**, 1115 (1959).
486. Ogawa, S., *J. Phys. Soc. Japan* **15**, 1901 (1960).
487. Ogawa, S., and D. Watanabe, *Acta Cryst.* **10**, 860 (1957).
488. Ohnishi, H., and T. Teranishi, *J. Phys. Soc. Japan* **16**, 35 (1961).
489. Ohnishi, H., T. Teranishi, and S. Miyahara, *J. Phys. Soc. Japan* **14**, 106 (1959).
490. Okazaki, A., and K. Hirakawa, *J. Phys. Soc. Japan* **11**, 930 (1956).
491. Okazaki, A., and K. Hirakawa, presented at the annual meeting of the Physical Society of Japan, October, 1959.
492. Okazaki, A., Y. Suemene, and T. Fuchikami, *J. Phys. Soc. Japan* **14**, 1823 (1959).
493. O'Keeffe, M., *J. Phys. Chem. Solids* **21**, 172 (1961).
493a. Olsen, C. E., N. G. Nereson, and G. P. Arnold, *J. Appl. Phys. Supp.* **33**, 1135 (1962).
494. O'ohata, K., *J. Phys. Soc. Japan* **15**, 1449 (1960).
495. Opechowski, W., *Physica* **4**, 715 (1937).
496. Opechowski, W., *Physica* **4**, 181 (1937); **6**, 1112 (1939).

496a. Osmond, W. P., *Proc. Phys. Soc.* **79**, 394 (1962).

497. Overhauser, A. W., and A. Arrott, *Phys. Rev. Letters* **4**, 226 (1960); Overhauser, A. W., *J. Phys. Chem. Solids* **13**, 71 (1960); *Bull. Am. Phys. Soc.* [II] **7**, 219 (1962).

498. Owen, J., *Proc. Roy. Soc. (London)* **A227**, 183 (1954).

499. Owen, J., M. R. Brown, B. A. Coles, and R. W. H. Stevenson, *J. Phys. Soc. Japan* **17**, Suppl. B-I, 428 (1962).

499a. Oxley, D. P., R. S. Tebble, C. T. Slack, and K. C. Williams, *Nature* **197**, 465 (1962).

499b. Oxley, D. P., R. S. Tebble, and K. C. Williams (unpublished research).

500. Paoletti, A., and S. J. Pickart, *J. Chem. Phys.* **32**, 308 (1960).

501. Pascal, P., *Ann. chim. et phys.* [8] **19**, 5 (1910); **25**, 289 (1912); **29**, 218 (1913); *Compt. rend.* **156**, 323 (1913); **158**, 377 (1914); **173**, 144 (1921); **176**, 1887 (1923); **177**, 765 (1923); **180**, 1596 (1925).

502. Patrick, L., *Phys. Rev.* **93**, 384 (1954).

503. Pauli, W., *Z. Physik* **31**, 765 (1925).

504. Pauli, W., *Z. Physik* **41**, 81 (1927).

505. Pauling, L., *The Nature of the Chemical Bond*, 3rd ed., Cornell Univ. Press, Ithaca, N. Y., 1960.

506. Pauthenet, R., *Compt. rend.* **234**, 2261 (1952).

507. Pauthenet, R., *Ann. phys.* **3**, 424 (1958).

508. Pauthenet, R., and P. Blum, *Compt. rend.* **239**, 33 (1954).

509. Pauthenet, R., *et al.*, *Compt. rend.* **230**, 1842 (1950); *J. phys. radium.* **12**, 249 (1951); *Ann. phys.* **7**, 710 (1952).

510. Pearson, A. D., *J. Phys. Chem. Solids* **5**, 316 (1958).

510a. Pearson, J. J., *Phys. Rev.* **126**, 901 (1962).

511. Perakis, N., *J. phys. radium* **8**, 473 (1927).

512. Perakis, N. (private communication).

512a. Perakis, N., J. Wucher, and G. Parravano, *Compt. rend.* **248**, 2306 (1959).

513. Peschard, M., *Compt. rend.* **180**, 1836 (1925).

514. Phillips, J. C., *J. Phys. Chem. Solids* **11**, 226 (1959).

515. Pickart, S. J., *Bull. Am. Phys. Soc.* [II] **5**, 59 (1960).

516. Pickart, S. J., *Bull. Am. Phys. Soc.* [II] **5**, 357 (1960).

517. Pickart, S. J., and R. Nathans, *Bull. Am. Phys. Soc.* [II] **3**, 231 (1958).

518. Pickart, S. J., and R. Nathans, *Phys. Rev.* **116**, 317 (1959).

519. Pickart, S. J., and R. Nathans, *J. Appl. Phys. Supp.* **30**, 280S (1959).

520. Pickart, S. J., and R. Nathans, *J. Appl. Phys. Supp.* **31**, 372S (1960).

521. Pickart, S. J., and R. Nathans, *J. Appl. Phys. Supp.* **33**, 1336 (1962).

522. Pickart, S. J., and R. Nathans (private communication).

523. Pickart, S. J., R. Nathans, and G. Shirane, *Phys. Rev.* **121**, 707 (1961).

524. Pines, D., *Solid State Physics*, F. Seitz and D. Turnbull, eds., Vol. 1, Academic, New York, 1955, p. 367 gives a summary.

525. Pippard, A. B., *Trans. Roy. Soc. (London)* **250**, 325 (1957) gives, for example, the application to copper.

526. Polder, D., *Phys. Rev.* **73**, 1120 (1948).

527. Pratt, G. W., Jr., *Phys. Rev.* **106**, 53 (1957).

528. Pratt, G. W., Jr., *Phys. Rev.* **122**, 489 (1961).

529. Pratt, G. W., Jr. (private communication).

530. Pratt, G. W., Jr., and H. J. Zeiger, *Quantum Theory of Magnetism*, McGraw-Hill, New York, to be published.

531. Prince, E., *Acta Cryst.* **10**, 554 (1957).

532. Prince, E., *Acta Cryst.* **10**, 787 (1957).

533. Prince, E., *J. Appl. Phys. Supp.* **32**, 68S (1961).

534. Prince, E., and R. G. Treuting, *Acta Cryst.* **9**, 1025 (1956).

535. Racah, G., *Phys. Rev.* **61**, 186 (1942); **62**, 438 (1942); **63**, 369 (1943).

536. Rado, G. T., and V. J. Folen, *J. Appl. Phys.* **31**, 62 (1960).

537. Ramsey, N. F., *Phys. Rev.* **91**, 303 (1953).

538. Raub, E., and W. Mahler, *Z. Metallk.* **46**, 210 (1955).

539. Raub, E., V. Zwicker, and H. Bauer, *Z. Metallk.* **44**, 312 (1953).

540. Roberts, B. W., *J. Metals* **8**, 1407 (1956); *Phys. Rev.* **104**, 607 (1956).

541. Rodbell, D. S., and P. E. Lawrence, *J. Appl. Phys. Supp.* **31**, 275S (1960).

542. Rogers, D., *Solid State Quart. Progr. Repts.*, Lincoln Laboratory, MIT, Cambridge, Mass., July 15, 1961.

543. Roth, W. L., *Phys. Rev.* **110**, 1333 (1958); **111**, 772 (1958).

543a. Roth, W. L., *Acta Cryst.* **13**, 140 (1960).

544. Roth, W. L., and G. A. Slack, *Bull. Am. Phys. Soc.* [II] **5**, 457 (1960).

545. Rubens, H., and H. Hollnagel, *Phil. Mag.* [6] **19**, 761 (1910).

546. Ruderman, M. A., and C. Kittel, *Phys. Rev.* **96**, 99 (1954).

547. Rüdorff, W., G. Walter, and J. Stadler, *Z. anorg. u. allgem. Chem.* **297**, 1 (1958).

548. Rundle, R. E., *Acta Cryst.* **1**, 180 (1948).

549. Russell, H. N., and F. A. Saunders, *Astrophys. J.* **61**, 38 (1925). For complete details on approved spectroscopic nomenclature, see the report of an informal committee on notation in *Phys. Rev.* **33**, 900 (1929).

550. Sadron, C., *Ann. phys.* **17**, 371 (1932).

550a. Salikhov, S. G., *J. Exptl. Theoret. Phys.* (*USSR*) **34**, 39 (1958); *Soviet Phys. JETP* **7**, 27 (1958).

551. Sato, K., T. Hirone, H. Watanabe, S. Maeda, and K. Adachi, *J. Phys. Soc. Japan* **17**, Suppl. B-I, 160 (1962).

552. Satomi, K., *J. Phys. Soc. Japan* **16**, 258 (1961).

553. Scatturin, V., L. M. Corliss, N. Elliott, and J. M. Hastings, *Acta Cryst.* **14**, 19 (1961).

554. Seavey, M. H. Jr., and P. E. Tannewald, *Phys. Rev. Letters* **1**, 168 (1958); *J. Appl. Phys. Supp.* **30**, 227S (1959).

555. Seitz, F., *Modern Theory of Solids*, McGraw-Hill, New York, 1940, pp. 339–342.

556. Seitz, F., *Modern Theory of Solids*, McGraw-Hill, New York, 1940, p. 151.

557. Serres, A., *J. phys. radium* **8**, 146 (1947).

558. Sewell, G. L., *Phil. Mag.* [8] **3**, 1361 (1958).

558a. Sheftel, I. T., A. I. Zaslavskii, and E. V. Kurvlina, *Fiz. Tverdogo Tela* **3**, 2712 (1961); *Soviet Phys. Solid State* **3**, 1979 (1962).

559. Sheldon, E. A., and A. J. King, *Acta Cryst.* **6**, 100 (1953).

560. Sherwood, R. C., J. P. Remeika, and H. J. Williams, *J. Appl. Phys.* **30**, 217 (1959).

561. Shimomura, Y., and I. Tsubokawa, *J. Phys. Soc. Japan* **9**, 19 (1954).

562. Shirane, G., and W. J. Takei, *J. Phys. Soc. Japan* **17**, Suppl. B-III, 35 (1962).

563. Shirane, G., S. J. Pickart, Y. Ishikawa, *J. Phys. Soc. Japan* **14**, 1352 (1959).

564. Shirane, G., S. J. Pickart, and R. Newnham, *J. Phys. Chem. Solids* **13**, 167 (1960).

565. Shirane, G., S. J. Pickart, R. Nathans, and Y. Ishikawa, *J. Phys. Chem. Solids* **10**, 35 (1959).

566. See Ref. 117a'.

566a. Shull, C. G. (private communication).

567. Shull, C. G., and M. K. Wilkinson, *Revs. Modern Phys.* **25**, 100 (1953).

568. Shull, C. G., and M. K. Wilkinson, *Phys. Rev.* **97**, 304 (1955).

569. Shull, C. G., and Y. Yamada, *J. Phys. Soc. Japan* **17**, Suppl. B-III, 1 (1962).

570. Shull, C. G., W. A. Strauser, and E. O. Wollan, *Phys. Rev.* **83**, 333 (1951).

571. Shull, C. G., E. O. Wollan, and W. C. Koehler, *Phys. Rev.* **84**, 912 (1951).

572. Shulman, R. G., and V. Jaccarino, *Phys. Rev.* **103**, 1126 (1956); **108**, 1219 (1957), for example.

573. Shulman, R. G., and K. Knox, *Phys. Rev. Letters* **4**, 603 (1960).

574. Sidhu, S. S., and D. Meneghetti, *Phys. Rev.* **91**, 435 (1953).

575. Sidhu, S. S., L. Heaton, and M. H. Mueller, *J. Appl. Phys.* **30**, 1323 (1959).

576. Singer, J. R., *Phys. Rev.* **104**, 929 (1956).

577. Sinha, A. P. B., N. R. Sanjana, and A. B. Biswas, *Acta Cryst.* **10**, 439 (1957).

578. Siratori, K., and S. Iida, *J. Phys. Soc. Japan* **15**, 210, 2362 (1960).

579. Slater, J. C., *Revs. Modern Phys.* **6**, 209 (1934).

580. Slater, J. C., *Phys. Rev.* **49**, 537 (1936).

581. Slater, J. C., *J. Appl. Phys.* **8**, 385 (1937).

582. Slater, J. C., *Phys. Rev.* **82**, 538 (1951).

583. Slater, J. C., *Quart. Progr. Rept.*, Res. Lab. Electronics, MIT, July 15, p. 1; Oct. 15, p. 1, 1953.

584. Slater, J. C., *Revs. Modern Phys.* **25**, 199 (1953).

585. Slater, J. C., *Solid State and Molecular Theory Group*, MIT, Cambridge, Mass., July 15, 1961.

586. Slater, J. C., and G. F. Koster, *Phys. Rev.* **94**, 1498 (1954).

587. Slonczewski, J. C., *J. Appl. Phys.* **29**, 448 (1958); *Phys. Rev.* **110**, 1341 (1958); *J. Phys. Chem. Solids* **15**, 335 (1960).

588. Smart, J. S., *Phys. Rev.* **101**, 585 (1956).

589. Smart, J. S., *J. Phys. Chem. Solids* **20**, 41 (1961).

590. Smit, J., and H. P. J. Wijn, *Ferrites*, Wiley, New York, 1959.

591. Smit, J., F. K. Lotgering, and R. P. van Stapele, *J. Phys. Soc. Japan* **17**, Suppl. B-I, 268 (1962).

592. Smith, J. H., and R. Street, *Proc. Phys. Soc. (London)* **B70**, 1089 (1957).

593. Snow, A. I., *Revs. Modern Phys.* **25**, 127 (1953).

594. Sommerfeld, A., *Atomic Structure and Spectral Lines*, Methuen Co., Ltd., London, 1934.

595. Sommerfeld, A., and H. A. Bethe, *Ferromagnetism*, in *Handbuch der Physik*,

Vol. 24, Part II, S. Flügge, ed., Verlag Julius Springer, Berlin, 1933, p. 595.

596. Sparks, J. T., W. Mead, and T. Komato, *J. Phys. Soc. Japan* **17**, Suppl. B-I, 249 (1962).

597. Sparks, J. T., W. Mead, A. J. Kirschbaum, and W. Marshall, *J. Appl. Phys. Supp.* **31**, 356S (1960).

598. Spence, R. D., and R. D. Ewing, *Phys. Rev.* **112**, 1544 (1958).

598a. Starke, E. A. Jr., C. H. Cheng, and P. A. Beck, *Phys. Rev.* **126**, 1746 (1962).

599. Starr, C., F. Bitter, and A. R. Kaufmann, *Phys. Rev.* **58**, 977 (1940).

600. Stevens, K. W. H., *Proc. Phys. Soc. (London)* **A65**, 209 (1952).

600a. Stickler, J. J., and G. S. Heller, *J. Appl. Phys. Supp.* **33**, 1302 (1962).

601. Stoner, E. C., *Phil. Mag.* **15**, 1018 (1933).

602. Stoner, E. C., *Magnetism and Matter*, Methuen Co., Ltd., London, 1934, gives a discussion of the Pascal rule.

603. Stoner, E. C., *Proc. Roy. Soc. (London)* **A165**, 372 (1938); **A169**, 339 (1939).

604. Stout, J. W., and R. C. Chisholm, *J. Phys. Soc. Japan* **17**, Suppl. B-I, 522 (1962).

605. Stuart, R., and W. Marshall, *Phys. Rev.* **120**, 353 (1960).

606. Stull, D. R., and G. C. Sinke, *Thermodynamic Properties of the Elements*, *Advan. Chem. Ser.* **18** (1956).

607. Swanson, J. A., *Phys. Rev.* **99**, 1799 (1955).

608. Swoboda, T. J., R. C. Toole, and J. D. Vaughan, *J. Phys. Chem. Solids* **5**, 293 (1958).

609. Swoboda, T. J., W. H. Cloud, T. A. Bither, M. S. Sadler, and H. S. Jarrett, *Phys. Rev. Letters* **4**, 509 (1960).

610. Takei, W. J., G. Shirane, and B. C. Frazer, *Phys. Rev.* **119**, 122 (1960).

610a. Takei, W. J., R. R. Heikes, and G. Shirane, *Phys. Rev.* **125**, 1893 (1962).

611. Tanabe, Y., and S. Sugano, *J. Phys. Soc. Japan* **11**, 864 (1956).

611a. Taniguchi, S., R. S. Tebble, and D. E. G. Williams, *Proc. Roy. Soc. (London)* **265A**, 502 (1962).

612. Tannenwald, P. E., and R. Weber, *Phys. Rev.* **121**, 715 (1960).

613. Tauer, K. J., and R. J. Weiss, *Bull. Am. Phys. Soc.* [II] **6**, 125 (1961).

614. Teodorescu, I., and A. Glodeanu, *Phys. Rev. Letters* **4**, 231 (1960).

615. Teranishi, T., *J. Phys. Soc. Japan* **16**, 1881 (1961).

616. Tessman, J. R., *Phys. Rev.* **88**, 1132 (1952).

616a. Thilo, E., J. Jander, and H. Seeman, *Z. anorg u. algem. Chem.* **279**, 2 (1955).

617. Tinkham, M., (quoted in reference 361).

618. Tsubokawa, I., *J. Phys. Soc. Japan* **11**, 662 (1956); **15**, 2243 (1960).

619. Tsubokawa, I., *J. Phys. Soc. Japan* **14**, 196 (1959).

620. Tsubokawa, I., *J. Phys. Soc. Japan* **15**, 1664 (1960).

621. Tsubokawa, I., *J. Phys. Soc. Japan* **15**, 2109 (1960).

622. Tsubokawa, I., and S. Chiba, *J. Phys. Soc. Japan* **14**, 1120 (1959).

623. Ubbink, J., *et al.*, *Physica* **18**, 361 (1952); **19**, 928 (1953).

623a. Ueda, R., and K. Hasegawa, *J. Phys. Soc. Japan* **17**, Suppl. B-II, 391 (1962).

624. Ueda, R., T. Ichinokawa, and T. Mitsui, *Eusseiron Kenkyu* (Researches on Chemical Physics) **33**, 55 (1950).

625. Uhlenbeck, G. E., and S. Goudsmit, *Naturwiss.* **13**, 953 (1925); *Nature* **117**, 264 (1926).

626. van Houten, S., *J. Phys. Chem. Solids* **17**, 7 (1960).

626a. Van Santen, J. H., *Philips Research Repts.* **5**, 282 (1950).

626a′. van Houten, S., *Physics Letters* **2**, 215 (1962).

627. Van Santen, J. H., and J. S. van Wieringen, *Rec. trav. chim.* (Pays-Bas) **71**, 420 (1952).

628. Van Vleck, J. H., *The Theory of Electric and Magnetic Susceptibilities*, Oxford Univ. Press, London, 1932.

629. Van Vleck, J. H., *J. Chem. Phys.* **7**, 72 (1939).

630. Van Vleck, J. H., *J. Chem. Phys.* **9**, 85 (1941).

631. Van Vleck, J. H., *Revs. Modern Phys.* **17**, 27 (1945).

632. Van Vleck, J. H., *Phys. Rev.* **78**, 266 (1950).

633. Van Vleck, J. H., *J. phys. radium* **12**, 262 (1951).

634. Van Vleck, J. H., *Revs. Modern Phys.* **25**, 220 (1953).

635. van Wieringen, J. S., *Phys. Rev.* **90**, 488 (1953).

636. Verwey, E. J. W., and J. H. De Boer, *Rec. trav. chim.* (Pays-Bas) **55**, 531 (1936).

637. Verwey, E. J. W., and P. W. Haayman, *Physica* **8**, 979 (1941).

638. Verwey, E. J. W., and E. L. Heilmann, Jr., *J. Chem. Phys.* **15**, 174 (1947).

639. Verwey, E. J. W., P. W. Haayman, and F. C. Romeijn, *J. Chem. Phys.* **15**, 181 (1947).

640. Villain, J., *J. Phys. Chem. Solids* **11**, 303 (1959).

641. Villers, G., J. Loriers, and R. Pauthenet, *Compt. rend.* **247**, 587 (1958).

642. Von Hippel, A., J. Kalnajs, and W. B. Westphal, *J. Phys. Chem. Solids* **23**, 779 (1962).

643. Waddington, T. C., *Advances Inorg. Chem. and Radiochem.*, **1**, 157 (1959).

643a. Walmsley, R. A., *Phys. Rev. Letters* **8**, 242 (1962).

644. Wangsness, R. K., *Phys. Rev.* **91**, 1085 (1953).

645. Warekois, E. P., *J. Appl. Phys. Supp.* **31**, 346S (1960).

646. Watanabe, D., *Acta Cryst.* **10**, 483 (1957).

647. Watanabe, H., *J. Phys. Soc. Japan* **12**, 515 (1957).

648. Watanabe, H., *Sci. Repts. Research Insts. Tohoku Univ.* **A8**, 14 (1956); *J. Phys. Soc. Japan* **14**, 511 (1959).

649. Watanabe, H., *J. Phys. Soc. Japan* **16**, 433 (1961).

650. Watanabe, H., and N. Tsuya, *Sci. Repts. Research Insts., Tohoku Univ.* **A2**, 503, 764 (1950).

651. Watson, R. E., and A. J. Freeman, *Phys. Rev.* **120**, 1125 (1960).

652. Watson, R. E., and A. J. Freeman, *Phys. Rev. Letters* **6**, 277 (1961).

653. Weiner, G. W., and J. A. Berger, *J. Metals* **7**, 360 (1955).

654. Weiss, P., *J. Physique* [4] **4**, 469 (1905).

655. Weiss, P., *J. Physique* [4] **6**, 661 (1907).

656. Weiss, P., and R. Forrer, *Ann. phys.* [10] **12**, 279 (1929).

657. Weiss, P., R. Forrer, and F. Birch, *Compt. rend.* **189**, 789 (1929).

658. Weiss, P. R., *Phys. Rev.* **74**, 1493 (1948).

659. Weiss, R. J., and J. J. DeMarco, *Revs. Modern Phys.* **30**, 59 (1958).

659a. Weiss, R. J., and A. Marotta, *J. Phys. Chem. Solids* **9**, 302 (1959).

660. Weiss, R. J., and K. J. Tauer, *J. Phys. Chem. Solids* **4**, 135 (1958).

661. Welling, J. C., and P. B. Bunn, *Proc. Phys. Soc.* (*London*) **74**, 417 (1959).

661a. Wendling, R., *Compt. rend.* **250,** 2173 (1960); **252,** 3207 (1961); **253,** 408 (1961).
662. Wendling, R., and J. Wucher, *Compt. rend.* **250,** 2691 (1960).
663. Went, J. J., G. W. Rathenau, E. W. Gorter, and G. W. van Oosterhout, *Philips Tech. Rev.* **13,** 194 (1951–1952).
663a. Wertheim, G. K., and J. H. Wernick, *Phys. Rev.* **125,** 1937 (1962).
664. Whipple, E. R., and A. Wold, *J. Inorg. & Nuclear Chem.* **24,** 23 (1962).
665. Whipple, E. R., A. Wold, and R. J. Arnott, *Solid State Quart. Progr. Rept.,* Lincoln Laboratory, MIT, Cambridge, Mass., April 15, 1961.
666. White, R. L., *J. Appl. Phys.* **32,** 1178 (1961).
667. Wickham, D. G., and R. J. Arnott (private communication).
668. Wickham, D. G., and W. J. Croft, *J. Phys. Chem. Solids* **7,** 351 (1958).
669. Wickham, D. G., and W. J. Croft (private communication).
670. Wickham, D. G., and J. B. Goodenough, *Phys. Rev.* **115,** 1156 (1959).
671. Wickham, D. G., N. Menyuk, and K. Dwight, *J. Phys. Chem. Solids* **20,** 316 (1961).
672. Wickham, D. G., E. R. Whipple, and E. G. Larson, *J. Inorg. Nuclear Chem.* **14,** 217 (1960).
673. Wickham, D. G., N. Menyuk, K. Dwight, and R. J. Arnott, *Solid State Quart. Progr. Rept.,* Lincoln Laboratory, MIT, Cambridge, Mass., Jan. 15, 1960 and April 15, 1960.
674. Wilhelmi, K. A., and O. Jonsson, *Acta Chem. Scand.* **12,** 1532 (1958).
675. Wilkinson, M. K., and C. G. Shull, *Phys. Rev.* **103,** 516 (1956).
676. Wilkinson, M. K., N. S. Gingrich, and C. G. Shull, *J. Phys. Chem. Solids* **2,** 289 (1957).
677. Wilkinson, M. K., E. O. Wollan, W. C. Koehler, and J. W. Cable, *Phys. Rev.* **127,** 2080 (1962).
678. Wilkinson, M. K., J. W. Cable, E. O. Wollan, and W. C. Koehler, *Phys. Rev.* **113,** 497 (1959).
679. Wilkinson, M. K., J. W. Cable, E. O. Wollan, and W. C. Koehler, *Oak Ridge National Laboratory Report* ORNL-2501, 1958 (unpublished), p. 37; and ORNL-2430, 1958 (unpublished), p. 65.
680. Wilkinson, M. K., W. C. Koehler, E. O. Wollan, and J. W. Cable, *J. Appl. Phys. Supp.* **32,** 48S (1961).
681. Wilkinson, M. K., E. O. Wollan, H. R. Child, and J. W. Cable, *Phys. Rev.* **121,** 74 (1961).
682. Wilkinson, M. K., H. R. Child, J. W. Cable, W. C. Koehler, and E. O. Wollan, *J. Phys. Soc. Japan* **17,** Suppl. B-III, 27 (1962).
683. Wilkinson, M. K., H. R. Child, J. W. Cable, E. O. Wollan, and W. C. Koehler, *J. Appl. Phys. Supp.* **31,** 358S (1960).
684. Williams, E. J., *Proc. Roy. Soc. (London)* **A152,** 231 (1935).
684a. Williams, H. J., and E. A. Nesbitt, quoted by reference 663a.
685. Wilson, A. H., *Proc. Roy. Soc. (London)* **A133,** 458 (1931).
686. Wilson, V. C., and J. S. Kasper, *Phys. Rev.* **95,** 1408 (1954).
687. Wohlfarth, E. P., *Nature* **163,** 57 (1949).
688. Wohlfarth, E. P., *Proc. Roy. Soc. (London)* **A195,** 434 (1949).
689. Wojtowicz, P. J., *J. Appl. Phys. Supp.* **30,** 30S (1959); *Phys. Rev.* **116,** 32 (1959).

690. Wold, A., and R. J. Arnott, *J. Phys. Chem. Solids* **9**, 176 (1959).
691. Wold, A., and N. Menyuk, *Solid State Quart. Progr. Rept.*, Lincoln Laboratory, MIT, Cambridge, Mass., April 15, 1961.
692. Wold, A., R. J. Arnott, and J. B. Goodenough, *J. Appl. Phys.* **29**, 387 (1958).
692a. Wold, A., R. J. Arnott, and J. B. Goodenough, unpublished research.
693. Wolf, W. P., *Proc. Phys. Soc. (London)* **74**, 665 (1959).
694. Wollan, E. O., and W. C. Koehler, *Phys. Rev.* **100**, 545 (1955).
695. Wollan, E. O., W. C. Koehler, and M. K. Wilkinson, *Phys. Rev.* **110**, 638 (1958).
696. Wollan, E. O., H. R. Child, W. C. Koehler, and M. K. Wilkinson, *Phys. Rev.* **112**, 1132 (1959).
697. Woyci, J., V. Hicks, and S. S. Sidhu, *Bull. Am. Phys. Soc.* [II] **5**, 458 (1960).
698. Yafet, Y., and C. Kittel, *Phys. Rev.* **87**, 290 (1952).
699. Yakel, H., and R. Steele, quoted by reference 112.
700. Yamashita, J., and K. Kondo, *Phys. Rev.* **109**, 730 (1958).
701. Yamashita, J., and T. Kurosawa, *J. Phys. Chem. Solids* **5**, 34 (1958).
702. Yamashita, J., and T. Kurosawa, *J. Phys. Soc. Japan* **15**, 802 (1960).
703. Yasukochi, K., K. Kanematsu, and T. Ohoyama, *J. Phys. Soc. Japan* **16**, 429 (1961).
704. Yasukochi, K., K. Kanematsu, and T. Ohoyama, *J. Phys. Soc. Japan* **16**, 1123 (1961).
705. Yasukochi, K., K. Kanematsu, and T. Ohoyama, *J. Phys. Soc. Japan* **17**, Suppl. B-I, 165 (1962). See also ref. 323a.
706. Yoshimori, A., *J. Phys. Soc. Japan* **14**, 807 (1959).
707. Yosida, K., *Phys. Rev.* **106**, 893 (1957).
708. Yosida, K., and H. Miwa, *J. Appl. Phys. Supp.* **32**, 8S (1961).
709. Yosida, K., and H. Miwa, *J. Phys. Soc. Japan* **17**, Suppl. B-I, 5 (1962).
710. Yuzuri, M., *J. Phys. Soc. Japan* **15**, 2007 (1960).
711. Yuzuri, M., and M. Yamada, *J. Phys. Soc. Japan* **15**, 1845 (1960).
712. Yuzuri, M., Y. Kang, and Y. Goto, *J. Phys. Soc. Japan* **17**, Suppl. B-I, 253 (1962).
713. Yuzuri, M., T. Hirone, H. Watanabe, S. Nagasaki, and S. Maeda, *J. Phys. Soc. Japan* **12**, 385 (1957).
714. Zachariasen, W., *Strukturbericht* **1**, 213 (1931).
715. Zehler, V., *Z. Naturforsch.* **5A**, 344 (1950).
716. Zener, C., *Phys. Rev.* **81**, 440 (1951); **82**, 403 (1951); **83**, 299 (1951).
717. Ziegler, M., Thesis, University of Zürich, 1915.
718. Ziman, J. M., *Proc. Phys. Soc. (London)* **65**, 540, 548 (1952).
719. Zotov, T. D. (private communication).
720. For a discussion of the Fermi or exchange hole, see for example references 399, 555, and 579.
721. See, for example, the application to Ge by reference 390, to Si by reference 153, and to Bi by reference 201.
722. Uniform polarization of the conduction electrons was first suggested by reference 716. This proposal has been modified by the addition of higher order terms in reference 707.

CHEMICAL FORMULA INDEX

379

SUBJECT INDEX

A

Alternant molecular orbital. *See* Collective electrons
Anisotropic resistivity, 271, 272
Anisotropic superexchange. *See* Exchange, Heisenberg, anisotropic
Anisotropy, elastic, 211, 225
  magnetic, crystalline, 73, 97, 112, 137, 154, 216, 237, 247, 248, 264, 286, 351
    exchange, 239, 327
    of exchange forces, 154, 213
  magnetoelastic, 225
Antibonding band. *See* Collective electrons
Anti-Curie temperature, 288
Antiferromagnetism. *See* Order, magnetic *and* Configuration, spin

B

Band model for collective electrons, 28–48
  assumptions, major, of, 28, 29
  band overlap from, 33
  band splittings in, 31–34, 46, 157–159
  bandwidth of, 34
  criterion for insulator or semiconductor *vs.* metal in, 35, 46, 157
  effective mass of charge carriers for, 30, 32, 34, 312
  energies of one-electron states in, 30, 32, 34, 36
  energy gap in, 31–34, 46, 157–159, 249, 266
  Fermi energy in, 36, 37. *See also* Fermi surface
  lattice periodicity, consequences of, for, 29–36

  periodic boundary condition of, 29
  wave numbers of one-electron states in, 29, 30
Band structure, for b.c.c. transition metals, 298, 305, 306
  for f.c.c. transition metals, 307, 310
  for f.c.tet transition metals, 308
Bloch $T^{3/2}$ law, 85, 116
Body-centered-cubic metals and alloys, 297–306
  magnetic properties of, 144, 145, 314–319, 332–339, 348, 349
Bohr magneton, 7
Boltzmann statistics, 39, 40
Bonding band. *See* Collective electrons
Borides, 146
Bragg reflection, 31
Bravais lattice, 30, 35
  magnetic order in, 134–137, 244, 246
Brillouin function, 15, 16, 81–83, 110–113, 264, 265
Brillouin zone, 30–35, 132, 133, 312
Bronzes, 272

C

Calcite, 98
Carbides, 146, 340, 344–348
Cartesian reference frame, 297, 306, 307
Cesium-chloride compounds, 100, 144, 145, 315–318, 334–336, 339, 348, 349
Chalcopyrite, 106, 248
Character table of irreducible representations, 53–55, 64
Collective electrons, alternant molecular-orbital description of, 44
  antibonding band of, 46, 47, 251, 282, 288, 291, 297–299, 316–318
  band model for, 28–48